ELEMENTARY EXCITATIONS IN SOLIDS

LECTURE NOTES AND SUPPLEMENTS IN PHYSICS

John David Jackson and David Pines, *Editors*

Mathematics for Quantum Mechanics	*John David Jackson (Illinois)*
Elementary Excitations in Solids	*David Pines (Illinois)*
Fundamental Particles	*K. Nishijima (Illinois)*
Matrix Methods in Optical Instrument Design	*Willem Brouwer (Diffraction Limited)*
Relativistic Kinematics of Scattering and Spin	*R. Hagedorn (CERN)*

ELEMENTARY EXCITATIONS IN SOLIDS

DAVID PINES
University of Illinois

W. A. BENJAMIN, INC.
new york amsterdam 1963

ELEMENTARY EXCITATIONS IN SOLIDS

Library of Congress Catalog Card
Number 63-19982
Manufactured in the United States of America

The final manuscript copy was received on February 25, 1963; this volume was published July 30, 1963

The publisher is pleased to acknowledge the assistance of Cecilia Duray-Bito, who produced the illustrations, and William Prokos, who designed the cover and dust jacket

W. A. BENJAMIN, INC.
2465 Broadway, New York 25, New York

EDITORS' FOREWORD

Everyone concerned with the teaching of physics at the advanced undergraduate or graduate level is aware of the continuing need for a modernization and reorganization of the basic course material. Despite the existence today of many good textbooks in these areas, there is always an appreciable time-lag in the incorporation of new viewpoints and techniques which result from the most recent developments in physics research. Typically these changes in concepts and material take place first in the personal lecture notes of some of those who teach graduate courses. Eventually, printed notes may appear, and some fraction of such notes evolve into textbooks or monographs. But much of this fresh material remains available only to a very limited audience, to the detriment of all. Our series aims at filling this gap in the literature of physics by presenting occasional volumes with a contemporary approach to the classical topics of physics at the advanced undergraduate and graduate level. Clarity and soundness of treatment will, we hope, mark these volumes, as well as the freshness of the approach.

Another area in which the series hopes to make a contribution is by presenting useful supplementing material of well-defined scope. This may take the form of a survey of relevant mathematical principles, or a collection of reprints of basic papers in a field. Here the aim is to provide the instructor with added flexibility through the use of supplements at relatively low cost.

The scope of both the lecture notes and supplements is somewhat different from the "Frontiers in Physics" series. In spite of wide variations from institution to institution as to what comprises the basic graduate course program, there is a widely accepted group of "bread and butter" courses that deal with the classic topics in physics. These include: Mathematical methods of physics, electromagnetic theory, advanced dynamics, quantum mechanics, statistical mechanics, and frequently nuclear physics and/or solid-state physics. It is chiefly these areas that will be covered by the present series. The listing is perhaps best described as including all advanced undergraduate and graduate courses which are at a level below seminar courses dealing entirely with current research topics.

The publishing format for the series is in keeping with its intentions. Photo-offset printing is used throughout, and the books are paperbound in order to speed publication and reduce costs. It is hoped that books will thereby be within the financial reach of graduate students in this country and abroad.

Finally, because the series represents something of an experiment on the part of the editors and the publisher, suggestions from interested readers as to format, contributors, and contributions will be most welcome.

J. David Jackson
David Pines

PREFACE

This book has grown from lectures given in an advanced course in the theory of solids at the University of Illinois during the fall semester 1961-1962. It was assumed that the student possessed a knowledge of quantum mechanics equivalent to a year's course in that topic; no prior knowledge of field theory was assumed. The course was designed to follow one in the one-electron or band theory of solids. However, in the view of the wide applicability (to plasma physics, nuclear physics, low-temperature physics) of many of the physical ideas and techniques developed in the course, a prior knowledge of solid-state physics was not regarded as a sine qua non. For this reason, both Chapter 2 on phonons and Chapter 3 on electrons contain a certain amount of material which is usually included in an introductory solid-state physics course.

The course was a new one. It was prompted by the need to communicate to the graduate student at an early stage in his career our present view of a solid as a system of interacting particles which, under suitable circumstances, behaves like a collection of nearly independent elementary excitations. Such a view has emerged from the work of many people during the past decade; its development has been greatly influenced by the many exciting discoveries in the closely related field of the many-body problem. Just as the "one-electron" problem in solid-state physics has long served as a proving ground for the ideas of elementary quantum mechanics, so now the theory of elementary excitations in solids serves as a proving ground for the application of general quantum mechanical techniques developed for the study of many-particle systems.

Many of these techniques and concepts are essentially field-theoretic in nature, and there is little doubt that the present-day solid-state physicist will have need of them. However, a detailed exposition of the Green's function approach to many-particle systems is essentially a matter for a course in itself. It would seem that until the appropriate field-theoretic techniques become part of a standard course in quantum mechanics it is not likely to prove easy to draw upon them extensively for an exposition of solid-state physics. The writer has attempted an uneasy compromise in this respect. Two of the most important developments on the many-body side have been the solution of certain model problems (problems for which the solution is valid in a certain range of densities, temperature, etc., . . .) and the formal but exact theory of the response of a system to a weakly coupled external probe. Examples of both developments are considered in Chapter 3, which deals with the interacting electron gas; the random phase approximation is described in detail, as is the response of an electron system to an external longitudinal probe. In addition, the equation-of-motion is introduced and applied to both the Hartree-Fock approximation and the random phase approximation. On the other hand, Feynman diagrams are introduced for essentially pictorial purposes only (no rules for calculations being given) and Green's functions are mentioned only very briefly. The interested reader may find an elementary introduction to these techniques in the following books: L. P. Kadanoff and G. Baym, *Quantum Statistical Mechanics,* W. A. Benjamin, Inc., 1962; P. Nozières, *Theory of Interacting Fermi Systems,* Dunod-Benjamin, 1963; D. Pines, *The Many-Body Problem,* W. A. Benjamin, Inc., 1962.

In addition to introducing a certain number of basic concepts, the writer has endeavored to refer to experiment as frequently as possible. For the most part, both the basic theory and the applications discussed deal with the behavior of "simple" metals, such as the alkali metals, in contrast to "complicated" metals, such as the transition metals and the rare earths. Insulators are scarcely discussed; there is some consideration of the consequences of electron interaction in semiconductors in Chapter 4.

There are a number of different elementary excitations of importance in solids; these are described briefly in Chapter 1. Of these only three are discussed in any detail in this book. The choice was a deliberate one; the writer felt it was better to discuss a few examples in some detail, rather than giving a broader, but less detailed survey of the field. The general methods and points of view developed for the excitations described herein may be applied equally well to the other excitations of interest; it is the writer's hope to return to this question at a subsequent date. For the excitations not considered in detail, an attempt has been made to provide the reader with a list of some recent relevent references. To these should be added the following lecture-note volume which is, in many respects, a companion volume to this one: P. W. Anderson, *Concepts in Solids,* W. A. Benjamin, Inc., 1963.

Chapter 3, which deals with the interacting electron gas, omits one major development of importance, the application of the Landau Fermi liquid theory to this system. The Landau theory represents a powerful tool for the discussion of the behavior of an almost-free-electron-like system in the limit of long wavelengths and low excitation frequencies. For example, it tells one which properties of the system are unaffected by electron-electron interaction; where it is applicable it also specifies the minimum number of parameters required to describe a given system property. On the other hand, it offers no explicit method for the calculation of the quasi-particle properties of interest. Methods, approximate though they may be, do exist for calculating various properties of an electron gas at metallic densities. It therefore seemed better to concentrate on the microscopic, albeit approximate, approach to quantities like the specific heat and spin susceptibility in lieu of the exact, but phenomenological application of the Landau theory. It may be added that the Landau theory applies not at all to many of the problems discussed in this book (e.g., the correlation energy of an electron gas, plasmons, optical properties of solids, etc., . . .).

The introduction of a frequency and wave-vector-dependent dielectric constant offers a way to discuss a number of properties of an electron gas in simple compact fashion. The method is described and applied to the discussion of the random phase approximation in Chapter 3. Nevertheless, it seemed useful from a pedagogical point of view to present first a historical survey of the earlier methods for treating the electron gas. It is hoped that the survey will enable the reader to place the more recent developments in their proper perspective, as well as to indicate some of the existing interrelationships between the many apparently different approaches developed for this problem.

In Chapter 5, which deals with electron-phonon interactions, considerable emphasis is placed on the development of a unified theory in which both electron-electron *and* electron-phonon interactions are considered at the outset. Particular attention is paid to phonon frequencies, the effective electron-electron interaction, and the effective electron-phonon interaction in simple metals. Calculations of the conductivity of the alkali metals are presented, but no detailed derivation of transport properties is given. This restricted view of the field has been adopted for two reasons: First, it is now possible to give an elementary discussion of the combined effects of electron-electron and electron-phonon interactions; second, there now exist a number of good discussions of transport properties in the scientific literature.

Problems have been included with all chapters but the first. It is hoped that the problems will enable the reader to fill in some of the missing steps in derivations quoted in the book, and serve as well to assist him in applying some of the concepts he has learned to physical situations not discussed explicitly herein.

I should like to thank Dr. Setsuo Ichimaru for his very considerable assistance in the preparation of this book. Dr. Ichimaru's notes on the lectures were of great value in the writing of the present manuscript. He is, in addition, in large part responsible for the preparation of the Appendixes. I am greatly indebted to Dr. Henry Ehrenreich, who read carefully the entire manuscript, and made a number of extremely useful suggestions. It is a pleasure to acknowledge helpful comments and discussions with my colleagues, Professors John Bardeen and Philippe Nozières on the matters discussed herein. I should like also to thank the John Simon Guggenheim Memorial Foundation for their support during the preparation of the book, and to thank Mrs. Ann Wells, Mme R. Chadan, and Mme O. Jancovici for their assistance with the typing of the manuscript.

DAVID PINES

Paris, France
February 25, 1963

CONTENTS

Chapter 1

INTRODUCTORY SURVEY

1-1 GENERAL CONSIDERATIONS

Whenever we deal with solids we are dealing with a many-body problem. Thus we ask what happens when we bring together some 10^{23} atoms/per cubic centimeter to make a crystal. This has certain important consequences. For instance, it means that we cannot expect exact solutions—that instead we must be continually developing approximate models to fit the situation at hand. Thus in making a theory it is usually essential that we be aware of the experimental work on the phenomenon under consideration and vice versa. Many of the important present-day developments arise out of such a close collaboration between the theoretical and the experimental physicist.

It is this use of approximate models which lends solid-state physics much of its fascination. Indeed, we may regard it as a marvelous proving ground for quantum mechanics and the ingenuity of the theoretical and experimental physicist. For unlike the nuclear or elementary particle physicist, we know what our particles are, and what are the forces between them, but we must use all our intelligence and insight to understand the consequences of this interaction. Thanks to the work of many people, particularly during the last decade, it is now possible to view much of solid-state physics in terms of certain *elementary excitations* which interact only weakly with one another.

The use of an elementary excitation to describe the complicated interrelated motion of many particles has turned out to be an extraordinarily useful device in contemporary physics, and it is this view of a solid which we wish to adopt in this book.

Under what circumstances is it useful to regard a solid as a collection of essentially independent elementary excitations? First of all, it is necessary that the excitations possess a well-defined energy. Let us suppose that the excitations are labeled by their momenta, which will be the case for a translationally invariant system. We shall see that the energy of a given excitation of momentum p will be of the form

$$\tilde{\xi}_p = \xi_p - i\gamma_p \tag{1-1}$$

where γ_p, the imaginary part of the energy, is inversely proportional to the lifetime of the excitation. In order that the excitation be well defined, it must be long-lived. This means that one must have

$$\gamma_p << \xi_p \tag{1-2}$$

the real part of the energy of the excitation.

One may well ask how it is possible that in a system, which, like a solid, is composed of strongly interacting particles, it is possible to find elementary excitations which satisfy the requirement (1-2). To answer this question let us consider the ways in which an excitation may decay. There are essentially two: (1) scattering against another excitation, and (2) scattering against the "ground-state particles."

The first mode of decay is negligible if one confines one's attention to temperatures sufficiently low that only a comparatively small number of excitations are present. The second mode of decay is less easily inhibited; it turns out for the various systems of interest there exist *coherence* factors which limit the phase space available for the decay of an excitation of low momentum or long wavelength. (An obvious example is the limit placed by the Pauli principle on the scattering of an electron in the immediate vicinity of Fermi surface.)

The requirement, (1-2), usually limits one to comparatively low temperatures and often, as well, to phenomena that involve comparatively low frequencies and long wavelengths. Where it is not satisfied, it may still be useful to describe a given physical process in terms of the excitations involved, but it becomes essential to take into account the fact that the excitations possess a finite lifetime.

Where (1-2) is satisfied, in thermal equilibrium one may characterize the excitation by a distribution function,

$$f_p(T) = \frac{1}{e^{\beta\xi_p} \pm 1} \tag{1-3}$$

where $\beta = 1/\kappa T$; the plus sign applies if the excitation obeys Fermi-Dirac statistics, the minus sign for Bose-Einstein statistics. $f_p(T)$ gives the probability of finding an excitation of momentum p, energy ξ_p, at the temperature T; from a knowledge of all the $f_p(T)$, one can determine in straightforward fashion the various thermodynamic properties of the system.

These remarks are quite general; to see what they mean, it is necessary that one consider some specific examples. But before doing that let us specify clearly the basic model we shall take to describe a solid throughout this book.

1-2 BASIC HAMILTONIAN

The basic Hamiltonian which describes our model of the solid is of the form

$$H = H_{ion} + H_{electron} + H_{electron\text{-}ion} \tag{1-4}$$

where

$$H_{ion} = \sum_i \frac{P_i^2}{2M} + 1/2 \sum_{i \neq j} V(R_i - R_j) \tag{1-5}$$

$$H_{electron} = \sum_i \frac{p_i^2}{2m} + 1/2 \sum_{i \neq j} \frac{e^2}{|r_i - r_j|} \tag{1-6}$$

$$H_{electron\text{-}ion} = \sum_{i,j} v(r_i - R_j) \tag{1-7}$$

H_{ion} describes a collection of ions (of a single species) which interact through a potential $V(R_i - R_j)$ which depends only on the distance between the ions. By ion we mean a nucleus plus the closed-shell, or core, electrons, that is, those electrons which are essentially unchanged when the atoms are brought together to make a solid. $H_{electron}$ describes the valence electrons (the electrons outside the last closed shell), which are assumed to interact via a Coulomb interaction. Finally, $H_{electron\text{-}ion}$ describes the interaction between the electrons and the ions, which is again assumed to be represented by a suitably chosen potential.

In adopting (1-4) as our basic Hamiltonian, we have already made a number of approximations in our treatment of a solid. Thus, in general the interaction between ions is not well-represented by a potential, V(R), when the coupling between the closed-shell electrons on different ions begins to play an important role. Again, in using a potential to represent electron-ion interaction, we have neglected the fact that the ions possess a structure (the core electrons); again, where the Pauli principle plays an important role in the interaction between the valence electrons and the core electrons, that interaction may no longer be represented by a simple potential. It is desirable to consider the validity of these approximations in detail, but such a study lies beyond the scope of this book; we shall therefore simply regard them as valid for the problems we study here. (It may be added that compared to the approximations which of necessity we shall have to make later, the present approximations look very good indeed.)

In general one studies only selected parts of the Hamiltonian, (1-4). Thus, for example, the band theory of solids is based upon the model Hamiltonian,

$$H_B = \sum_i \frac{p_i^2}{2m} + \sum_{i,j} v(\mathbf{r}_i - \mathbf{R}_{jo}) + V_H(\mathbf{r}_i) \tag{1-8}$$

where the R_{jo} represents the fixed equilibrium positions of the ions and the potential V_H represents the (periodic) Hartree potential of the electrons. One studies the motion of a single electron in the periodic field of the ions and the Hartree potential, and takes the Pauli principle into account in the assignment of one-electron states. In so doing one neglects aspects other than the Hartree potential of the interaction between the electrons. On the other hand, where one is primarily interested in understanding the interaction between electrons in metals, it is useful to consider only H_{electron}, (1-5), replacing the effect of the ion cores by a uniform distribution of positive charge. In this way one can approximate the role that electron interaction plays without having present the additional complications introduced by the periodic ion potential. Of course one wants finally to keep both the periodic ion potential and the electron interactions, and to include as well the effects associated with the departure of the ions from the equilibrium positions, since only in this way does one arrive at a generally adequate description of the solid.

1-3 ELEMENTARY EXCITATIONS

We have built up our knowledge about the elementary excitations in solids by first considering various different parts of the Hamiltonian (1-4), and then taking into account the remaining terms which act to couple different excitations together. Let us adopt this approach in carrying out a preliminary survey of some of the excitations of importance in solids.

Phonons

It is well known that the motions of a crystal lattice, in which each atom vibrates about an equilibrium point, may be resolved into normal modes, each mode generally representing a wave moving through the lattice. The system, from this viewpoint, is simply a collection of harmonic oscillators, with one oscillator for each of the lattice waves;

if we impose the quantum commutation rules on the canonical momenta, the familiar harmonic-oscillator energy spectrum is obtained. These elementary units of lattice excitation are given the name *phonon*; phonons are bosons, and represent perhaps the simplest elementary excitation in a solid.

One arrives at a description in terms of completely independent phonons if one takes the ion Hamiltonian as (1-5) and keeps only the terms which are quadratic in the displacement of the ions from their equilibrium positions. If, however, one includes as well the third-order, or anharmonic, terms in the expansion of the potential energy, one finds a *phonon-phonon interaction*; this interaction gives rise to a scattering between phonons of different wavevectors which acts to limit the lifetime of a given phonon; it acts also to shift the phonon energy.

Another term which influences phonon motion is the *electron-phonon interaction*, which one obtains on keeping the first-order term (in the displacement of the ions from their equilibrium positions) in the expansion of the electron-ion Hamiltonian, (1-7). In metals this term acts to change the phonon frequencies markedly from those obtained using only H_{ion}, (1-5); it also offers an additional mechanism by which the phonons may be damped.

Despite the phonon-phonon and phonon-electron interactions, both long-wavelength and short-wavelength phonons turn out to be well-defined excitations up to the melting point of a solid; in the liquid state, only the comparatively long-wavelength longitudinal phonons continue to represent a well-defined excitation.

Quasi-Particles

In the absence of electron-electron or electron-ion interaction, it is well known that we can describe the excitations of an electron system in terms of single-particle excitations, of energy

$$\varepsilon_p = \frac{p^2}{2m} - \mu_o \tag{1-9}$$

measured relative to the chemical potential, μ_o, for the noninteracting system. At $T = 0$, all the momentum states $p \leq p_o$ are occupied, while those for $p \geq p_o$ are empty; p_o, the radius of the filled Fermi sphere, is simply related to the electron density. At finite temperatures, the distribution function for an excitation of momentum p is

$$f_p^o(T) = \frac{1}{e^{\beta \epsilon_p} + 1} \tag{1-10}$$

Suppose one now considers the electron-electron interaction, that is, assumes that the system Hamiltonian is given by (1-6). It is not obvious that there is a well-defined elementary excitation, which resembles (1-9), for this Hamiltonian, since coupling between the electrons is far from weak. Nevertheless, as Landau, Silin, and Luttinger and Nozières[1] have shown, in the presence of electron-electron interaction one can introduce a distribution function for *quasi-particles*, of energy ξ_p measured relative to the Fermi energy (or chemical potential) for the interacting system, which takes the form

$$f_p(T) = \frac{1}{e^{\beta\xi_p} + 1} \tag{1-11}$$

at low-enough temperatures. From (1-11) one obtains, for example, the familiar linear dependence on temperature of the electronic contribution to the specific heat.

One may picture the quasi-particle as a particle accompanied by a co-moving cloud of other particles. As a particle moves along, it pushes other particles out of its way, drags other particles along with it, and the like; it is this co-moving cloud which acts to alter the energy-momentum relation from (1-9) to ξ_p.

The quasi-particle description applies only to excitations in the immediate vicinity of the surface of the filled Fermi sphere; only these excitations possess a lifetime sufficiently long to satisfy the criterion (1-3). The long lifetime of quasi-particle excitations in the immediate vicinity of the Fermi surface is a simple consequence of the Pauli principle, which limits the amount of phase space available for single-particle collisions in such a way that

$$\gamma_p \sim \frac{(p - p_o)^2}{p^2} \xi_p \tag{1-12}$$

(for a quasi-particle above the Fermi surface). At a temperature T, one sees directly from (1-11) that the quasi-particles which are excited will be those lying within the shell $p_o - \delta p \leq p_o \leq p_o + \delta p$, where $(\delta p/p_o) \sim \kappa T/\mu$. The lifetime of such an excited quasi-particle will therefore be

$$\gamma_p(T) \sim \left(\frac{\delta p}{p_o}\right)^2 \xi_p \cong \left(\frac{\kappa T}{\mu}\right)^2 \xi_p$$

so that the use of the distribution function (1-11) to describe the thermodynamic properties of the system is consistent as long as $\kappa T << \mu$.

When one considers the static electron-ion interaction, $\sum_{ij} v(\mathbf{r}_i - \mathbf{R}_{jo})$, the above picture changes somewhat. It is then preferable to begin with the model Hamiltonian, (1-8), representing electrons moving in a periodic potential; and to put in the electron-electron interaction subsequently. Thus one has, in the absence of electron-electron interaction, the well-known band theory of solids, according to which the electrons are labeled by their Bloch wave energies; $\varepsilon^0_{p\mu}$, where p is the momentum within a band and μ refers to the band under consideration. (We are using the extended zone scheme.) The general properties of the quasi-particle excitations (in the presence of electron interactions) have yet to be developed in any detail for this case. However, on the basis of the electron gas discussed above, it is clear that for metals the conduction-band quasi-particles in the immediate vicinity of the Fermi surface will be well-defined elementary excitations. Moreover, one can estimate the validity of a quasi-particle picture for a given band state by considering the phase-space restrictions imposed by the Pauli principle (and perhaps symmetry considerations as well) on the possibility of decay of that state as a consequence of electron-electron interaction.

Finally, we must consider the influence of *electron-phonon interaction* on the properties of our quasi-particles in solids. For metals that influence can be profound in some cases, since it gives rise to the phenomenon of superconductivity. As Bardeen, Cooper, and Schrieffer[2] have shown, superconductivity can arise in metals as a consequence of an attractive phonon-induced, electron-electron interaction. For superconductors, the quasi-particle spectrum takes the form

$$\xi_p^s = \left[\xi_p^2 + \Delta^2\right]^{1/2} \tag{1-13}$$

where ξ_p is the usual quasi-particle energy measured relative to the Fermi surface and Δ is a constant. The distribution function for the quasi-particles in a superconductor is given by

$$f_p^s(T) = \frac{1}{e^{\beta\xi_p^s} + 1} \tag{1-14}$$

Because of the energy gap, Δ, in the quasi-particle spectrum, the specific heat of a superconductor is proportional to exp $-(\beta\Delta)$ at sufficiently low temperatures.

It should be added that for normal metals (as distinct from superconductors) the electron-phonon interaction acts to change the quasi-particle energy and the specific heat. It also provides an additional quasi-particle damping mechanism and acts to limit the conductivity of metals at all temperatures. However, it does not alter the concept of the quasi-particle as a well-defined elementary excitation of the system in the immediate vicinity of the Fermi surface.

Plasmons

Yet another kind of elementary excitation is possible for an interacting electron gas, as described by the Hamiltonian (1-6). In such a system, as a consequence of the Coulomb interaction, one can have a collective oscillation of the electron particle density, the plasma oscillation. In the limit of long wavelengths, the frequency of the oscillation is given by the plasma frequency;

$$\omega_p = \left(\frac{4\pi N e^2}{m}\right)^{1/2} \tag{1-15}$$

where N is the electron density. The plasma oscillation has no counterpart in the noninteracting electron system; it corresponds directly to the oscillations studied by Langmuir and Tonks in classical gaseous discharges, or plasmas. The quantum of plasma oscillation is the plasmon; plasmons are bosons, and have a distribution function of the characteristic boson form at finite temperatures. A low-momentum plasmon has an energy $h\omega_p$; according to (1-15) plasmon energies range from about 5 to 30 ev for electron systems of metallic densities; consequently plasmons play no role in determining the thermodynamic properties of an electron system.

The plasmon is not a completely well-defined elementary excitation, in that it can decay into pairs of quasi-particles: however, at long wavelengths, the imaginary part of the energy of a plasmon of momentum p is proportional to $(p/p_F)^2\omega_p$, so that the excitation easily satisfies the criterion, (1-3).

When one takes into account the influence of the periodic ion potential on the plasmon spectrum, one finds that the plasmon lifetime depends on the strength of the electron interband transition of energy in the vicinity of $h\omega_p$. For many solids, $h\omega_p$ is large compared to the interband excitations of importance (the latter often being only a few electron volts). Consequently, the valence-electron plasmon is a well-defined excitation for a wide group of metals, semiconductors, semimetals, and insulators.

Other Elementary Excitations

We mention briefly certain other elementary excitations which one encounters in solids, and which we shall not have an opportunity to consider in detail in this book. In insulating polar crystals, an electron in the conduction band is strongly coupled to the optical mode of the lattice vibrations. As a result, when the electron moves, it is accompanied by a co-moving cloud of phonons, which may act to change its mass appreciably. The resultant quasi-particle is known as a *polaron*.[3]

In insulators, or in certain semiconductors, in consequence of electron-electron interaction, there may exist well-defined elementary excitations within the energy gap which separates the valence-electron band from the conduction-electron band. The excitations are known as *excitons*[3]: they correspond to a bound electron-hole pair state. The energy of an exciton lies within the gap as a consequence of the attractive Coulomb interaction between an electron excited from the valence band and the hole it has left behind there. Excitons, like plasmons, are bosons.

In a ferromagnet, the low-lying excitations correspond to oscillations in the electron-spin-density fluctuations, and are known as spin waves. The quantized spin waves are called magnons[4]; these obey Bose statistics, and may be used to treat the thermodynamic properties of a ferromagnetic system.

1-4 THE MEASUREMENT OF THE ELEMENTARY EXCITATION SPECTRUM

One measures directly the spectrum of elementary excitations in a solid by means of various kinds of external probes. The ideal external probe is one which is only very weakly coupled to the solid, so that the system response can be expressed in terms of the properties of the excitations in the absence of the probe. The great strides which have been made in the purification of solids have enabled the experimentalist to use more and more sophisticated external probes, often involving a combination of both static and time-dependent magnetic and electric fields. A high degree of purity is required because even quite small amounts of impurity may tend to mask the subtle resonance effects under investigation. One of the major consequences of the development of better probes and "better" solids is our vastly improved and by now quite detailed knowledge of the Fermi surface of a number of metals.[5]

Great advances have been made too in the development of external probes which do not depend on an applied magnetic field. Here we may mention three such, which we shall consider in some detail in the course of this book:

1. The direct measurement of the phonon spectrum in solids by means of the inelastic scattering of slow neutrons.
2. The direct measurement of the valence-electron excitation spectrum, and particularly the plasmons, by means of the inelastic scattering of fast electrons.
3. The extension of optical measurements of the electronic excitation spectrum to the region between 5 and 25 ev.

Both neutron scattering and fast electron scattering represent examples of longitudinal probes of the elementary excitations. In both cases, the external probe couples directly to a longitudinal excitation, the density fluctuation of the solid. On the other hand, measurements of the optical reflectivity of a solid constitute a transverse probe of the solid, in that the electromagnetic wave couples directly to the transverse current-density fluctuations of the electrons.

Concurrent with the experimental advances has been the realization on the part of theorists that for a weakly coupled external probe one can specify the system response in terms of the exact eigenstates of the many-particle system under consideration. Such a description may serve as a starting point for detailed theoretical calculations based on a specific model for the system. Moreover, one can, for example, relate the measurements of the density-fluctuation spectrum directly to the space-time particle-particle correlations and fluctuations in the solid, and so obtain a more detailed understanding of the system behavior.

1-5 SCOPE OF THE BOOK

As is clear from the title, the elementary excitations on which we shall focus our attention are electrons, phonons, and plasmons. Although some of our treatment will be comparatively general, for the most part the specific applications which are developed in the course of the book have to do with "simple" metals, that is, metals which display essentially free-electron-like behavior. Thus we shall often have in mind the alkali metals (the favorite metals of the theorist); we shall steer clear of the transition metals and rare earths. It should also be emphasized that it is not possible to treat the properties of even alkali metals with an accuracy of, say, 1 per cent. There are simply too many variables, too many approximations that one is forced to make along the way, to hope to arrive at this sort of accuracy for a calculation of solid-state properties from first principles. One therefore speaks of a "good" agreement between theory and experiment for the alkali metals if the agreement approaches, say 10 to 15 per cent. Such a close correspondence between theory and experiment is not to be hoped for, in general, when one is comparing theory and experiment for a given solid-state property.

Our general plan is to present the excitations, and their mutual interaction, in what might be regarded as an order of increasing complexity. Thus we begin with phonons, since these represent in many ways the simplest of the elementary excitations in solids. In Chapter 2 we review some general features of phonons in solids and discuss briefly the phonon dispersion relation in simple metals. We consider the phonon contribution to the specific heat and the stability of a solid against melting as simple examples of quantum statistical calculations based on the notion of independent elementary excitations. The use of slow neutrons as a probe of phonon spectra in solids is described in some detail, and a sketch is given of some of the general features of phonon-phonon interaction.

Following a review of the Sommerfeld-Hartree free electron model in Chapter 3, the Hartree-Fock approximation is discussed. There follows a preliminary and essentially historical survey of electron interactions in a dense electron gas. The approach of Wigner, Bohm, and Pines, and Gell-Mann and Brueckner, are described; the important physical concepts of screening and collective oscillation (plasmons) are presented in elementary fashion. There follows a somewhat formal section on the definition of the frequency and wave-vector-dependent dielectric constant, and of the dynamic form factor, and the way these concepts permit one to obtain in simple fashion a number of interrelated physical properties of an electron system. These include time-dependent density correlations, the scattering of a fast charged particle, the pair-distribution function, and the ground-state energy. Emphasis is placed here on the *exact* specification of the system response to longitudinal fields which vary in space and time. The dielectric constant is then derived in the random phase approximation, and the aforementioned physical properties in this approximation are derived and discussed. The concluding section of this chapter is devoted to a consideration of electron interactions in simple metals. Following a discussion of the inapplicability of the random phase approximation, the calculations that have been carried out for the correlation energy, the specific heat, and the spin susceptibility of the alkali metals are presented.

The first part of Chapter 4 is devoted to the way electron interaction in solids differs from that in a free-electron gas; in particular, the changes in screening behavior and the plasmon spectra are considered. The experimental observation of plasmon spectra in solids by means of fast-electron-scattering experiments is then presented in some detail. There follows a discussion of the optical properties of solids, in which considerable use is made of the formalism developed to treat the dielectric response of an electron system. A selected group of recent optical experiments on metals and semiconductors is then described; the emphasis is here placed on the high-frequency (5 to 25 ev) behavior of the electron systems in question.

Perhaps the principle emphasis in Chapter 5 is to sort out the consequences of dealing simultaneously with electron-electron and electron-phonon interaction in simple metals. The alteration in phonon frequencies arising from electron-phonon *and* electron-electron interaction is discussed in some detail, as is the phonon-induced electron-electron interaction, which plays such an important role in the theory of superconductivity. As a typical example of a nonequilibrium calculation involving large quantum systems described by coupled excitations, the way in which a system of coupled electrons and phonons approaches equilibrium is considered. The high-temperature conductivity of simple metals is discussed; the chapter concludes with a brief description of the low-temperature conductivity, and of quasi-particle properties in simple metals.

References

1. For review of the Landau Fermi liquid theory, and its application to the electron gas, see P. Nozières, "Interacting Fermi Systems," Dunod-Benjamin, 1963, Chapter 1.
2. For an excellent recent review of the BCS theory, see the article by J. Bardeen and J. R. Schrieffer, in "Progress in Low Temperature Physics," Vol. 3 (ed. by C. J. Gorter), North-Holland, Amsterdam, 1961.
3. See, for example, "Polarons and Excitons" (the Proceedings of the Scottish University Summer School in Theoretical Physics), 1962.
4. See, for example, the lectures by C. Kittel, in "Low Temperature Physics," edited by C. DeWitt, B. Dreyfus, and P. G. de Gennes, Gordon and Breach, New York, 1962.
5. See, for example, the lectures by A. B. Pippard in "Low Temperature Physics," op. cit.

Chapter 2

PHONONS

2-1 LATTICE DYNAMICS IN ONE DIMENSION

Lattice-Wave Dispersion Relation

We begin our study of phonons with a brief review of lattice dynamics and the quantization of the phonon field. It is recommended to the reader who is unfamiliar with these topics that he consult one of the standard texts (Peierls[1] or Ziman,[2] for example) where more of the mathematical details and physical discussion may be found.

Because we are here interested primarily in lattice motion, we shall restrict our attention to that part of the general Hamiltonian, (1-4), which involves ion motion only, H_{ion}. We return later (in Chapter 5) to a discussion of the coupled motion of ions and electrons in metals.

Most of the salient features of phonons may be understood from a study of a one-dimensional solid, i.e., a linear atomic array. For that reason, we begin our review there, and consider the appropriate three-dimensional generalization in a subsequent section.

The simplest linear crystal structure for similar ions is one of equal spacing. The equilibrium position of the nth ion is denoted by R_{no}. Obviously, we have $R_{no} = na$, where a is the interionic spacing. The actual position (under vibrations) of the nth ion is R_n. Defining δR_n as the departure from equilibrium of the nth ion, we obtain

$$R_n = R_{no} + \delta R_n \tag{2-1}$$

For our one-dimensional solid, the Hamiltonian of the system is

$$H = \sum_i \frac{P_i^2}{2M} + \frac{1}{2} \sum_{i \neq j} V(R_i - R_j) \tag{2-2}$$

where R_i and P_i are the position and momentum of the ith ion.

One assumes that the displacement from equilibrium of the ions is small, so that one can expand any quantity involving R_n, say, as a Taylor series in δR_n. Thus one expands $V(R_i - R_j)$ in a Taylor series about the equilibrium separation $R_{io} - R_{jo}$. Retaining up to the quadratic terms in δR_i, we may write (2-2) as

$$H = \sum_i \frac{P_i^2}{2M} + \frac{1}{2} \sum_{i \neq j} V(R_{io} - R_{jo}) + \sum_{i,j} \frac{A_{ij}}{2} \delta R_i \, \delta R_j \tag{2-3}$$

where

$$A_{ij} = \frac{\partial^2 V(R_i - R_j)}{\partial R_i \, \partial R_j} \qquad i \neq j \tag{2-4}$$

$$A_{ii} = \sum_{\substack{j \\ j \neq i}} \frac{\partial^2 V(R_i - R_j)}{\partial R_i^2} \tag{2-5}$$

The terms linear in δR_i do not contribute to (2-4) because of the equilibrium condition, $\partial V(R_i - R_j)/\partial R_i = 0$ (the force on any atom vanishes in equilibrium). The second term in the right-hand side of (2-4) is a constant and may be neglected hereafter.

The equation of motion for the ith ion is

$$\dot{P}_i = -\frac{\partial H}{\partial R_i} = M\delta \ddot{R}_i$$

or

$$M\delta \ddot{R}_i = -\sum_j A_{ij} \, \delta R_j \tag{2-6}$$

Focussing our attention on oscillatory solutions we let

$$\delta R_i(t) = e^{-i\omega t} \, \delta R_i \tag{2-7}$$

(The use of the same symbol for the time-dependent and time-independent displacement should not cause confusion.) This substitution gives for (2-6)

$$M\omega^2 \delta R_i = \sum_j A_{ij} \, \delta R_j \tag{2-8}$$

There are certain limitations placed on the solutions of (2-8), limitations which arise because of the periodic character of the equilibrium ionic array. Clearly the physical properties of the system are unaltered by the displacement,

$$R_n \rightarrow R_n + na$$

where n is an integral number. Put another way, there is nothing which distinguishes the motion of the ith atom from that of its neighbors. As a result, the solutions for R_i and R_{i+1} can differ at most by a phase factor. We therefore write

$$\delta R_{n+1} = e^{ika}\,\delta R_n \qquad (2\text{-}9)$$

A solution of (2-9) is obtained if we write

$$\delta R_n = q_k e^{ikR_{no}} = q_k e^{ikna} \qquad (2\text{-}10)$$

with q_k independent of n, as direct substitution of (2-10) into (2-9) shows. The mathematical proof that (2-9) and (2-10) are a direct consequence of periodicity is known as Floquet's theorem,[2a] and is given as a problem at the end of this chapter.

We see that the different solutions of (2-8) may be labeled by the wave vector k. So far no mention has been made as to what values of k we might expect. The exact specification of k depends on the boundary conditions. The most convenient choice is a periodic boundary condition as, for one thing, it provides a simple way to count available states. In our one-dimensional study we use a long "chain." We require, then, that if we go a distance L = Na, we obtain the same result for any physical property, such as the lattice displacement. Inspection of (2-10) shows that $kL = 2\pi n$, where n is an integer; that is,

$$k = \frac{2\pi n}{L} = \frac{2\pi}{a}\frac{n}{N} \qquad (2\text{-}11)$$

We can write down the density in k space, i.e., the number of normal modes per unit k. This becomes

$$\frac{dn}{dk} = \frac{L}{2\pi} \qquad (2\text{-}12)$$

More often, one is interested in the number of states per unit frequency, i.e.,

$$dn/d\omega = (dn/dk)\,[1/(\partial\omega/\partial k)] = L/2\pi\ \ [1/(\partial\omega/\partial k)]$$

We remark that not all values of k are independent; only a finite number are unique. Inspection of either (2-9) or (2-10) shows that the equation for δR_n is invariant if one changes k to $k + 2\pi a$. Thus only those values of k which lie in the range 0 to $2\pi/a$ constitute a unique set. However, it is often more convenient to let k be in the range defined by

$$-\pi/a \le k \le \pi/a \tag{2-13}$$

The number of independent k values is obtained with the aid of (2-12) as

$$\frac{dn}{dk}\,\Delta k = (L/2\pi)(2\pi/a) = L/a = N \tag{2-14}$$

The number of independent values of k is thus the same as the number of ions (in a chain of length L).

The dispersion relation which determines ω as a function of k is obtained by substituting (2-10) into (2-8). One finds

$$M\omega_k^{\,2} = \sum_j A_{ij}\, e^{ik(R_{jo}-R_{io})} \tag{2-15}$$

a result which involves only the distance between the atoms, as it should.

Equation (2-15) is the dispersion relation that determines ω^2(or ω) as a function of k. There are several quite general properties which this dispersion relation possesses. First, for k = 0,

$$M\omega^2(0) = \sum_j A_{ij} = 0 \tag{2-16}$$

That (2-12) is true may be seen either from the translational invariance of the system or by a direct substitution of (2-4) and (2-5) into (2-15) and the use of $\partial/\partial R_i = -\partial/\partial R_j$ in those equations. Hence, ω_k starts out at the value 0. The second observation is that ω^2 is an even function of k. This is easily obtained from the symmetry of the coefficients, A_{ij}. Hence it follows for small k that

$$\omega^2 = s^2k^2 + \cdots \tag{2-17}$$

Here s represents the speed of sound.

It is instructive to solve the dispersion relation (2-15) for the case of atoms interacting via nearest neighbor interactions only; the calculation is given as a problem for the reader.

Transformation to Normal Modes

We now consider the transformation from the N coordinates, R_i, which represent the positions of the atoms, to N new coordinates, q_k, which describe the normal modes of oscillation of the ions about their equilibrium positions. The transformation is given by

$$P_i = \left(\frac{M}{N}\right)^{1/2} \sum_k p_k e^{ikR_{io}} \tag{2-18a}$$

$$\delta R_i = \frac{1}{(NM)^{1/2}} \sum_k q_k e^{ikR_{io}} \tag{2-18b}$$

where p_k is the momentum conjugate to q_k. Here all the dynamical variables are time-dependent and from the reality condition for P_i and δR_i, we obtain 2N relations:

$$\begin{aligned} p_k^+ &= p_{-k} \\ q_k^+ &= q_{-k} \end{aligned} \tag{2-19}$$

These relations reduce the number of independent variables from 4N (real and imaginary parts of p_k and q_k) to 2N, as one would expect.

With the aid of the dispersion relation (2-15), the Hamiltonian (2-3) can be rewritten in terms of the new coordinates as

$$H = \sum_k \frac{p_k^+ p_k}{2} + \omega_k{}^2 \frac{q_k^+ q_k}{2} \tag{2-20}$$

where ω_k is determined by the dispersion relation (2-15). The Hamiltonian (2-20) describes a harmonic-oscillator field decomposed into independent normal modes.

Quantization of the Lattice Waves

Because the Hamiltonian for the lattice waves resembles a collection of independent harmonic oscillators, the quantization of the lattice waves proceeds along the well-known route followed for the harmonic oscillator.[3] We first remark that the commutation rules for the lattice coordinates, p_k and q_k, follow directly from those for individual ion coordinates, which read:

$$\begin{aligned} [P_i, \delta R_j] &= (\hbar/i)\, \delta_{ij} \\ [P_i, P_j] &= [R_i, R_j] = 0 \end{aligned} \tag{2-21}$$

It is an elementary exercise to show that because of (2-18a) and (2-18b), one finds

$$[p_k, q_{k'}] = (\hbar/i)\,\delta_{kk'}$$
$$[p_k, p_{k'}] = [q_k, q_{k'}] = 0 \tag{2-22}$$

One could, if one liked, discuss the properties of the quantized lattice waves in terms of the representation specified by the Hamiltonian (2-20) and the commutation rules (2-22). It is, however, far more convenient to transform to a different representation, in which the lattice-wave function describes only the number of quantized lattice waves present under given conditions. A quantized lattice wave is known as a *phonon*. In this representation the operators of interest are no longer the coordinates or momentum of a given lattice wave, but rather correspond to operators which change the number of phonons.

The transformation is specified by the equations

$$p_k = \left[\hbar\omega_k/2\right]^{1/2} i\,(a_k^+ - a_{-k})$$
$$q_k = \left[\hbar/2\omega_k\right]^{1/2} (a_k + a_{-k}^+) \tag{2-23}$$

The a_k and a_k^+ act to destroy, and create, a phonon of wave vector k, energy $\hbar\omega_k$, respectively. Their properties may be obtained directly from their commutation rules, which are a simple consequence of the transformation (2-23), and (2-22),

$$\left[a_k, a_{k'}^+\right] = \delta_{kk'}$$
$$\left[a_k, a_{k'}\right] = \left[a_k^+, a_{k'}^+\right] = 0 \tag{2-24}$$

The transformed Hamiltonian reads

$$H = \sum_k \hbar\omega_k \left[a_k^+ a_k + 1/2\right] \tag{2-25}$$

The various properties of the operators and eigenstates of the Hamiltonian, (2-25), may be found in any standard textbook on quantum mechanics.[3] Here we summarize those which are most essential for what follows, namely,

$$N_k^{op} = a_k^+ a_k \tag{2-26}$$

$$N_k^{op}|n_k\rangle = n_k|n_k\rangle \tag{2-27}$$

$$a_k|n_k\rangle = \sqrt{n_k}|n_k - 1\rangle \tag{2-28}$$

$$a_k^+|n_k\rangle = \sqrt{n_k + 1}|n_k + 1\rangle \tag{2-29}$$

$$a_k|0\rangle = 0 \tag{2-30}$$

In (2-26), N_k^{op} is the number operator; it commutes with the Hamiltonian, (2-25); according to (2-27) its eigenvalues, n_k, specify the number of phonons present of wave vector k. $|n_k\rangle$ denotes the system wave function in which there are n phonons of wave vector k present [the number of other phonons present not being relevant for equations (2-26) through (2-29)]. Equations (2-28) and (2-29) tell us that a_k and $a_k^\dagger$ do play the role of destruction and creation operators, while in (2-30) $|0\rangle$ is the ground-state wave function, in which there are no phonons present.

Finally one has

$$E_o = \sum_k \frac{\hbar\omega_k}{2} \tag{2-31}$$

so that the ground-state energy is a sum of the zero-point energies of the phonons, and

$$H|n_k\rangle = (E_o + n_k\hbar\omega_k)|n_k\rangle \tag{2-32}$$

so that each phonon may be regarded as possessing an energy $\hbar\omega_k$.

Phonon "Pseudomomentum"

It is tempting to assume that a phonon of wave vector k possesses a momentum $\hbar k$. This is not however true, as we may see most directly if we recall that there are only N independent values of k, lying between $-\pi/a < k < \pi/a$. The "momentum" of a phonon is thus not defined to within an integral multiple of $2\pi/a$. To put the matter another way, if one considers a momentum transfer $\hbar q$ to the ions, in a process in which only a single phonon is involved, the momentum conservation condition reads

$$\hbar q = \hbar k + \hbar K_n \tag{2-33}$$

where K_n is the reciprocal lattice wave vector, defined by

$$K_n = \pm n\frac{2\pi}{a} \tag{2-34}$$

where n is any integer. Thus $\hbar k$ plays the role of a "pseudomomentum," the lattice always being able, in consequence of the periodic ionic array, to supply a momentum $\hbar K_n$.

2-2 LATTICE DYNAMICS IN THREE DIMENSIONS

Phonon Dispersion Relation

We now consider the generalization of the foregoing results to a three-dimensional lattice, which possesses N atoms, of equilibrium position $\mathbf{R}_{io}$, and a particle interaction specified by $V(\mathbf{R}_i - \mathbf{R}_j)$. The system Hamiltonian is then given by

$$H = \sum_i \frac{P_i^2}{2M} + \sum_{i \neq j} \frac{1}{2} V(\mathbf{R}_i - \mathbf{R}_j) \tag{2-35}$$

As before, we take $\mathbf{R}_i = \mathbf{R}_{io} + \delta\mathbf{R}_i$ and expand the potential about the equilibrium positions of the ions to get

$$\begin{aligned} \sum_{i \neq j} V(\mathbf{R}_i - \mathbf{R}_j) &= \sum_{i \neq j} \Big\{ V(\mathbf{R}_{io} - \mathbf{R}_{jo}) + \big[(\delta\mathbf{R}_i \cdot \nabla_i)(\delta R_i \cdot \nabla_i) \\ &\quad + (\delta\mathbf{R}_i \cdot \nabla_i)(\delta\mathbf{R}_j \cdot \nabla_j)\big] V(\mathbf{R}_{io} - \mathbf{R}_{jo}) \Big\} \qquad (2\text{-}36) \\ &= \text{const.} + \sum_{i,j} \delta\mathbf{R}_i \cdot \mathcal{a}_{ij} \cdot \delta\mathbf{R}_j \end{aligned}$$

It will be useful to obtain an explicit expression for $\mathcal{a}_{ij}$. Let us suppose that the potential energy term is well behaved, so that we may expand it in a Fourier series:

$$V(r) = \sum_k V_k e^{i\mathbf{k}\cdot\mathbf{r}} \tag{2-37}$$

(Note that the summation here is over *all* values of k.) One can then show the dyadic $\mathcal{a}_{ij}$ is given by

$$\mathcal{a}_{ij} = \sum_k \mathbf{kk}V_k e^{i\mathbf{k}\cdot(\mathbf{R}_{io}-\mathbf{R}_{jo})} \qquad i \neq j \tag{2-38a}$$

$$\mathcal{a}_{ii} = -\sum_k \sum_{\substack{j \\ j \neq i}} \mathbf{kk}V_k e^{i\mathbf{k}\cdot(\mathbf{R}_{io}-\mathbf{R}_{jo})} \tag{2-38b}$$

We note that $V_k^+ = V_{-k}$ and therefore $\mathfrak{a}_{ij} = \mathfrak{a}_{ij}^+$; furthermore $\mathfrak{a}_{ij}$ is a symmetric dyadic.

We now proceed in a fashion directly analogous to the one-dimensional case. In a normal mode, the relation between displacements must be of the form

$$\delta \mathbf{R}_{i+1} = e^{i\mathbf{k}\cdot\mathbf{a}} \, \delta \mathbf{R}_i$$

where the lattice points are separated by the elementary lattice vector a. We then get at each lattice point

$$\delta \mathbf{R}_i = q_k \varepsilon_k e^{i\mathbf{k}\cdot\mathbf{R}_{io} - \omega_k t}$$

where ε_k is a unit polarization vector. The dispersion relation is obtained by inserting this in the equation of motion for the ith ion. A brief calculation leads to the result

$$M\omega_k{}^2 \varepsilon_k = \sum_j \mathfrak{a}_{ij} \cdot \varepsilon_k e^{i\mathbf{k}\cdot(\mathbf{R}_{jo} - \mathbf{R}_{io})} \tag{2-39}$$

Our result, (2-39), shows that, corresponding to a given direction of propagation and wavelength, there are three polarizations and three frequencies, the solutions of the above Hermitian eigenvalue problem. The three polarization eigenvectors are of course orthonormal. We introduce a suffix λ to distinguish the three polarizations corresponding to a given k. In the one-dimensional case, the frequencies corresponding to given wavelengths were given directly in the dispersion relation: in three dimensions, one must first solve the secular equation for the $\varepsilon_{k\lambda}$ and $\omega_{k\lambda}^2$ ($\lambda = 1, 2, 3$), before going on to the detailed solution of (2-39).

We have assumed that the lattice is a simple Bravais lattice for which the equilibrium points are given by

$$\mathbf{R}_{io} = \alpha_i \mathbf{a}_1 + \beta_i \mathbf{a}_2 + \gamma_i \mathbf{a}_3$$

where α_i, β_i, γ_i are integers and the $\mathbf{a}_\sigma$ are the basic lattice vectors; all combinations of integers α, β, γ will correspond to lattice points. In the general case, a "lattice with basis" has to be used, in which there will be several atoms in the unit cell with equilibrium positions $d_1, d_2, \ldots, d_r$. The normal mode spectrum will be somewhat more complex, owing to the greater number of degrees of freedom.[4]

Reciprocal Lattice

If we look at the space dependence of the displacements in the normal modes, we see immediately that not all **k** vectors are independent;

in fact k is completely equivalent to all other vectors formed by adding a vector of the "reciprocal lattice" $\mathbf{K}_n$; thus

$$\mathbf{k} \leftrightarrow \mathbf{k} + \mathbf{K}_n \tag{2-40a}$$

where

$$\mathbf{K}_n \cdot \mathbf{a}_\sigma = 2\pi p \tag{2-40b}$$

p is an integer, and $\mathbf{a}_\sigma$ is any lattice vector. All the $\mathbf{K}_n$ vectors can be expressed as a linear combination of the three basic reciprocal lattice vectors $\mathbf{b}_1$, $\mathbf{b}_2$, $\mathbf{b}_3$:

$$\mathbf{K}_n = n_1\mathbf{b}_1 + n_2\mathbf{b}_2 + n_3\mathbf{b}_3 \qquad n_1, n_2, n_3 \text{ integers} \tag{2-41}$$

where

$$\mathbf{b}_1 = 2\pi \frac{\mathbf{a}_2 \times \mathbf{a}_3}{\mathbf{a}_1 \cdot \mathbf{a}_2 \times \mathbf{a}_3} \qquad \mathbf{b}_2 = 2\pi \frac{\mathbf{a}_3 \times \mathbf{a}_1}{\mathbf{a}_1 \cdot \mathbf{a}_2 \times \mathbf{a}_3} \qquad \mathbf{b}_3 = 2\pi \frac{\mathbf{a}_1 \times \mathbf{a}_2}{\mathbf{a}_1 \cdot \mathbf{a}_2 \times \mathbf{a}_3} \tag{2-42a}$$

which we can write more compactly as

$$\mathbf{b}_\lambda \cdot \mathbf{a}_\sigma = 2\pi\delta_{\lambda\sigma} \tag{2-42b}$$

There is a close relation between the "direct" or configuration space lattice and the reciprocal lattice; for example, the inverse of a face-centered-cubic lattice is a body-centered-cubic lattice and conversely.[5]

We next consider the number of independent k vectors. The density of points in k space is given by

$$\frac{dn}{dk} = \left(\frac{L}{2\pi}\right)^3$$

if we put our system in a cube of side L and impose periodic boundary conditions. All the independent vectors can be taken in the parallelpiped defined by $\mathbf{b}_1$, $\mathbf{b}_2$, $\mathbf{b}_3$ with volume

$$\mathbf{b}_1 \cdot \mathbf{b}_2 \times \mathbf{b}_3 = \frac{(2\pi)^3}{\mathbf{a}_1 \cdot \mathbf{a}_2 \times \mathbf{a}_3} = \frac{(2\pi)^3}{V_o}$$

V_o is the volume per atom in configuration space. Hence, the number of independent points in k space is

$$\frac{(2\pi)^3}{V_o}\ \frac{L^3}{(2\pi)^3} = N, \text{ the number of particles}$$

The number of independent normal modes is equal to the number of atoms.

The First Brillouin Zone

The first Brillouin zone is defined as that within which all phonon wave vectors lie: Take from each set of equivalent **k** vectors (as defined above) the vector of least modulus; the resulting set of vectors lies symmetrically about $\mathbf{k} = 0$ and is the first Brillouin zone. Clearly any point in **k** space can now be reached by a $\mathbf{K}_n$ displacement from some point in the first zone. Other equivalent sets of **k** vectors are sometimes taken for the first zone, such as the set included in the b_1, b_2, b_3 parallelpiped. However, $\mathbf{k} = 0$ is *always included.*

The geometrical construction of the first Brillouin zone is analogous to the construction of the Wigner-Seitz zone in the direct lattice[6] and proceeds as follows: Starting at the point $\mathbf{k} = 0$ in the reciprocal lattice, we draw lines to all neighboring lattice points. Then the planes which contain all perpendicular bisectors of these lines are drawn in; these planes enclose the first Brillouin zone. In a simple square two-dimensional lattice, the construction would go as indicated in Fig. 2-1.

Orthogonality Relations and Normal Modes

For a general motion of the lattice, we expand the vibrations in normal modes:

$$\delta\mathbf{R}_i = \frac{1}{\sqrt{NM}} \sum_{\mathbf{k},\lambda} q_{\mathbf{k}\lambda}\, \varepsilon_{\mathbf{k}\lambda}\, e^{i\mathbf{k}\cdot\mathbf{R}_{io}} \tag{2-43a}$$

$$P_i = \sqrt{\frac{M}{N}} \sum_{\mathbf{k},\lambda} p_{\mathbf{k}\lambda}\, \varepsilon_{\mathbf{k}\lambda}\, e^{i\mathbf{k}\cdot\mathbf{R}_{io}} \tag{2-43b}$$

with reality conditions

$$p^+_{\mathbf{k}\lambda} = p_{-\mathbf{k}\lambda}$$

$$q^+_{\mathbf{k}\lambda} = q_{-\mathbf{k}\lambda}$$

$$\varepsilon_{\mathbf{k}\lambda} = \varepsilon_{-\mathbf{k}\lambda} \tag{2-44}$$

Since the number of atoms, N, is very large, the following orthogonality relation holds:

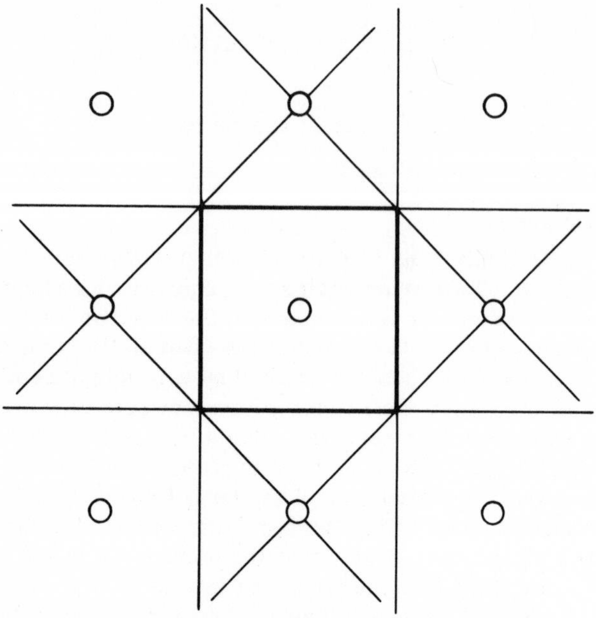

Fig. 2-1. Circles indicate lattice points; heavy lines, edge of first zone; light lines, perpendicular bisectors.

$$\sum_n e^{i(\mathbf{k}-\mathbf{k}')\cdot \mathbf{R}_{no}} = N\delta_{\mathbf{k},\mathbf{k}'+\mathbf{K}_n} = N\delta_{\mathbf{kk}'} \tag{2-45}$$

since $\mathbf{k}$ and $\mathbf{k}'$ are restricted to the first Brillouin zone.

Furthermore, since the $\varepsilon_{\mathbf{k}\lambda}$ are solutions of the Hermitian eigenvalue problem

$$M\omega_{\mathbf{k}\lambda}^2 \varepsilon_{\mathbf{k}\lambda} = \sum_j \mathfrak{a}_{ij} \cdot \varepsilon_{\mathbf{k}\lambda} e^{i\mathbf{k}\cdot(\mathbf{R}_{io}-\mathbf{R}_{jo})} \tag{2-39a}$$

we have

$$\varepsilon_{\mathbf{k}\lambda} \cdot \varepsilon_{\mathbf{k}\lambda'} = \delta_{\lambda\lambda'} \tag{2-46}$$

Combining the above results, we see that the different modes are indeed independent, as they should be. Thus,

$$\sum_n \varepsilon_{\mathbf{k}\lambda} \cdot \varepsilon_{\mathbf{k}'\lambda}\, e^{i(\mathbf{k}-\mathbf{k}')\cdot \mathbf{R}_{on}} = N\delta_{\mathbf{kk}'}\,\delta_{\lambda\lambda'} \tag{2-47}$$

With the aid of the dispersion relation (2-39) as well as the above orthogonality relations, one can show that the Hamiltonian (2-35) now takes the desired form:

$$H = \frac{1}{2} \sum_{k\lambda} p^{+}_{k\lambda} p_{k\lambda} + \omega^{2}_{k\lambda} q^{+}_{k\lambda} q_{k\lambda} \tag{2-48}$$

Quantization of the Phonon Field

The steps toward the quantization of the phonon field proceed along lines similar to the one-dimensional case. We start from the commutation relations between the coordinates $\delta\mathbf{R}_i$ and the conjugate momenta $\mathbf{P}_i$:

$$\begin{aligned} &[P_{i\alpha}, \delta R_{j\beta}] = \frac{\hbar}{i} \delta_{ij} \delta_{\alpha\beta} \\ &[P_{i\alpha}, P_{j\beta}] = 0 \qquad [R_{i\alpha}, R_{j\beta}] = 0 \end{aligned} \tag{2-49}$$

With the aid of the orthogonality relations discussed above, one can show that the relations (2-49) lead to the following commutation relations between the new dynamical variables, $q_{k\lambda}$ and $p_{k\lambda}$:

$$\begin{aligned} &[p_{k\lambda}, q_{k'\lambda'}] = \frac{\hbar}{i} \delta_{kk'} \delta_{\lambda\lambda'} \\ &[p_{k\lambda}, p_{k'\lambda'}] = 0 \qquad [q_{k\lambda}, q_{k'\lambda'}] = 0 \end{aligned} \tag{2-50}$$

The creation and annihilation operators, $a^{+}_{k\lambda}$ and $a_{k\lambda}$, are then introduced as

$$\begin{aligned} p_{k\lambda} &= \left(\frac{\hbar\omega_{k\lambda}}{2}\right)^{1/2} i\,(a^{+}_{k\lambda} - a_{-k\lambda}) \\ q_{k\lambda} &= \left(\frac{\hbar}{2\omega_{k\lambda}}\right)^{1/2} (a_{k\lambda} + a^{+}_{-k\lambda}) \end{aligned} \tag{2-51}$$

They obey the following commutation rules:

$$\begin{aligned} &[a_{k\lambda}, a^{+}_{k'\lambda'}] = \delta_{kk'} \delta_{\lambda\lambda'} \\ &[a_{k\lambda}, a_{k'\lambda'}] = 0 \qquad [a^{+}_{k\lambda}\ a^{+}_{k'\lambda'}] = 0 \end{aligned} \tag{2-52}$$

The wave functions for the phonon field may be constructed in the same fashion as in the one-dimensional case.

Alternative Form for the Phonon Dispersion Relation

In the light of the orthogonality relations, one can express the phonon dispersion relation (2-39) in a different form. To do so, we first substitute the values of $\mathfrak{a}_{ij}$, (2-38a) and (2-38b), into the dispersion relation (2-39), obtaining

$$M\omega_{k\lambda}^2 \varepsilon_{k\lambda} = -\sum_{jk'} k'(k' \cdot \varepsilon_{k\lambda}) V_{k'} e^{ik' \cdot (R_{io}-R_{jo})}$$

$$+ \sum_{jk'} k'(k' \cdot \varepsilon_{k\lambda}) V_{k'} e^{i(k'-k) \cdot (R_{io}-R_{jo})} \quad (2\text{-}53)$$

The restriction $j \neq i$ on the sums has been removed, since for $j = i$, the two sums cancel. On the right-hand side of (2-53), the sum over $\mathbf{k}'$ runs over all possible k values, coming, as it does, from the Fourier analysis of V(r).

We now make use of (2-45), to obtain

$$M\omega_{k\lambda}^2 \varepsilon_{k\lambda} = N \sum_{K_n} \left\{(k + K_n)(k + K_n) V_{k+K_n} - K_n K_n V_{K_n}\right\} \cdot \varepsilon_{k\lambda}$$

$$= NV_k kk \cdot \varepsilon_{k\lambda}$$

$$+ N \sum_{K_n \neq 0} V_{k+K_n}(k + K_n)(k + K_n) \cdot \varepsilon_{k\lambda} - V_{K_n} K_n K_n \cdot \varepsilon_{k\lambda} \quad (2\text{-}54)$$

Let us consider this three-dimensional sound-wave-dispersion relation in some detail. Our first observation is that the last term on the right-hand side of (2-54) will lead to transverse vibrations. We might thus say that the transverse vibrations arise from the periodicity of the crystal. To show this let us neglect the last term completely and prove that only longitudinal vibrations occur. Thus assume that

$$M\omega_{k\lambda}^2 \varepsilon_{k\lambda} = Nk(k \cdot \varepsilon_{k\lambda}) V_k \quad (2\text{-}55)$$

If one takes the unit propagation vector $\hat{k}$ to be parallel to ε_{k1} one then finds for ω_{k1}^2

$$M\omega_{k1}^2 = Nk^2 V_k \quad (2\text{-}56)$$

Since ε_{k2} and ε_{k3} are both perpendicular to ε_{k1} (and to each other) their scalar product with k (parallel to ε_{k1}) is zero. We therefore find

$$M\omega_{k2}^2 \varepsilon_{k2} = M\omega_{k3}^2 \varepsilon_{k3} = 0$$
$$\omega_{k2}^2 = \omega_{k3}^2 = 0 \qquad (2\text{-}57)$$

A Sum Rule

The phonon frequencies for a given direction of propagation satisfy a simple sum rule, which we now derive. Let us take the scalar product of (2-54) with $\varepsilon_{k\lambda}$ and then sum over λ. This gives

$$\sum_{\lambda} M\omega_{k\lambda}^2 = NV_k \sum_{\lambda} (\mathbf{k} \cdot \varepsilon_{k\lambda})^2 + N \sum_{K_n \neq 0} V_{k+K_n} \left\{(\mathbf{k}+\mathbf{K}_n) \cdot \varepsilon_{k\lambda}\right\}^2 - V_{K_n} (\mathbf{K}_n \cdot \varepsilon_{k\lambda})^2 \qquad (2\text{-}58)$$

By employing the relation

$$\sum_{\lambda} (\varepsilon_{k\lambda})_{\alpha} \cdot (\varepsilon_{k\lambda})_{\beta} = \delta_{\alpha\beta} \qquad \alpha, \beta = xyz \qquad (2\text{-}59)$$

which states that the three vectors $\varepsilon_{k,\lambda}$ form an orthonormal basis, we obtain

$$M \sum_{\lambda} \omega_{k\lambda}^2 = NV_k k^2 + N \sum_{K \neq 0} V_{k+K_n} (\mathbf{k}+\mathbf{K}_n)^2 - V_{K_n} K_n^2 \qquad (2\text{-}60)$$

which is our desired sum rule.

Solutions of the Phonon Dispersion Relation for Metals

The phonon dispersion relation, (2-39) or (2-54), is in general quite difficult to solve even for metals where the forces between the ions are primarily central in character. The required algebraic computations are far from trivial; still more important, one does not, in general, have a knowledge, based on first principles, of the relevant interatomic force constants. One possible approach is essentially phenomenological in nature. It is to assume that the only forces of importance are those between nearest neighbors, or nearest neighbors plus next neighbors. At first sight such an assumption appears absurd, in view of the long range of the Coulomb interaction between the ions. However, as we shall see in detail in the following chapters, the electrons act to screen the ionic motion in quite effective fashion, so that the use of a phenomenological short-range interaction offers no immediate difficulties in principle.

With such an assumption, one has a certain limited number of force constants; these may be chosen so that they are consistent with the elastic constants (there is obviously a close relation between the elastic constants and the behavior of long-wavelength phonons, which we shall not enter into here[6a]), plus whatever information is available concerning the short-wavelength phonon spectrum. (We consider the experimental study of that spectrum in Sec. 2-5.) In this way one learns a great deal about the general features of the influence of the periodicity of the ion structure on the phonon spectrum.[6a] Also, from the success or failure of a given phenomenological model in explaining the experimental data one may reach certain conclusions concerning the range of the effective interatomic forces. (We return to this question briefly in Sec. 2-5.)

A second approach, which may turn out to be quite useful for simple metals, is to begin from first principles, in that one assumes at the outset only Coulomb interactions between the ions, and between the ions and the electrons. (One might then subsequently attempt to take into account the non-Coulombic short-range part of the ion-ion interaction as a perturbation.) In such an approach one first solves the dynamic problem of the ions interacting via Coulomb interactions, and then subsequently allows for the response of the electrons to the ion motion. All the relevant forces are, of course, long range. We shall consider the major steps in such an approach in this book, although no detailed calculations which take account of the periodic field of the ions will be carried out.

Dispersion Relations for a Coulomb Lattice

We consider now a lattice of ions interacting via Coulomb interactions only. (In order that one have charge neutrality, and stability, it is necessary that the ions be assumed to be immersed in a uniform background of negative charge.) For such a system, the sum rule (2-60) takes a particularly simple form. We first note that for Coulomb interactions between the ions, one has

$$V_k = \frac{4\pi (Ze)^2}{k^2 L^3} \tag{2-61}$$

where Z is the charge on each ion. On substituting (2-61) into (2-60) one finds directly the result

$$\sum_\lambda \omega_{\mathbf{k}\lambda}^2 = \frac{4\pi N Z^2 e^2}{M L^3} = \Omega_p{}^2 \tag{2-62}$$

which was first obtained by Kohn.[7] In (2-62), $\Omega_p{}^2$ is the square of the ion plasma frequency.

The general character of the phonon dispersion relation is clear from (2-62). In the long-wavelength limit, we may speak of one longitudinal and two transverse modes of vibration. Moreover, in the limit $k \rightarrow 0$, the frequencies of the transverse waves vanish, so that at $k = 0$ one has simply a longitudinal wave, of frequency Ω_p. For small k, the longitudinal frequency takes the form

$$\omega_{k1}^2 = \Omega_p^2 - ak^2 \tag{2-63}$$

since the two transverse frequencies will be proportional to k. Detailed calculations on the frequency spectrum for this lattice have been carried out by Clark,[8] and by Coldwell-Horsfall and Maradudin.[9] The general character of the dispersion relation is shown in Fig. 2-2.

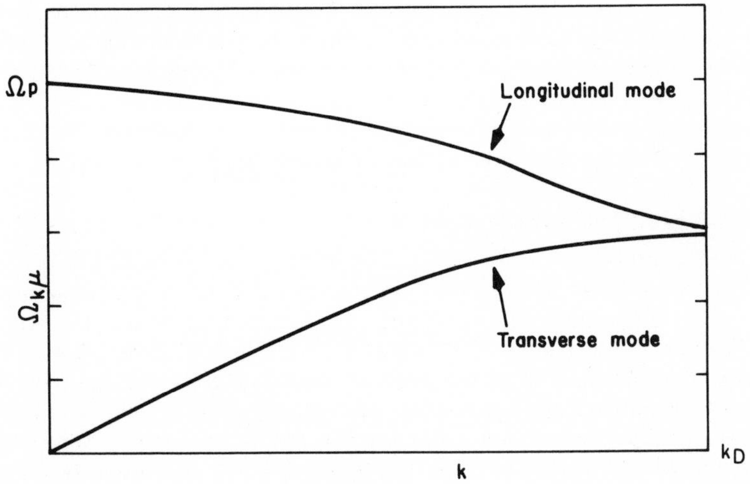

Fig. 2-2

It should be emphasized that the frequencies we have been considering must be modified when one considers an actual metal. The reason is that the electrons will have a profound effect on the longitudinal mode. Essentially, when an ion moves, it is accompanied by a screening cloud of electrons; as a result of the screening, the frequency of the long-wavelength longitudinal mode is altered from Ω_p to sk. We shall see how this comes about in some detail in Chapter 5.

Lattice with a Basis

We consider briefly the question of a lattice with a basis. Suppose one considers a solid made up of two distinct kinds of ions of masses M_1 and M_2. One can then regard the lattice as composed of N unit cells, each containing the two different ions. If we then specified the motion of each cell, say, we would have a description quite like that we have just considered, in which one was led to 3N phonons in all. Now, however, there remains the additional freedom of motion of the ions within a given cell. There are in general two possibilities: in one, the ions move in phase with one another, in the other, they move out of phase.

Hence, one is led to speak of 6N phonon modes, corresponding to these two distinct modes of vibration for each value of **k**. The modes in which the ions in a given cell are in phase with one another are called *acoustic modes;* the out-of-phase modes are known as *optical modes*. It is intuitively clear that, for a given **k**, the optical modes will have a frequency considerably higher than their acoustic counterparts, since the out-of-phase motion of the two neighboring ions can give rise to a substantial frequency of vibration. The optical modes are so-called because in an ionic crystal they are strongly coupled to electromagnetic waves, since one then has a strong charge separation between the positive and negative ions.

2-3 LATTICE SPECIFIC HEAT

Average Energy in a Phonon Mode

In common with all quantum phenomena, the quantization of the lattice waves will be seen to play an important role in any phenomenon for which the energy of importance is comparable to $\hbar\omega$, the energy of the phonon in question. The "classic" application of the phonon concept is the calculation of the phonon contribution to the specific heat of a solid, and we shall consider that briefly in this section. In the following sections we shall discuss the stability of a crystal against melting and the measurement of phonon spectra in solids by means of inelastic neutron scattering.

It is well to recall that the calculation of the phonon contribution to the specific heat was first performed by Einstein,[10] and that it represented one of the first applications of Planck's quantization of energy. We review the calculation here, because many of the results we obtain will be of use to us later on.

We are interested in the thermal excitation of phonons, and wish to calculate the average energy in a phonon mode at a temperature T. The probability of a quantum state of energy E is given by

$$W(E) = e^{-\beta E}$$

where $\beta = 1/\kappa T$. The average energy in a mode of frequency ω is

$$\langle E \rangle = \frac{\sum_{n=0}^{\infty} (n+1/2)\,\hbar\omega e^{-\beta(n+1/2)\hbar\omega}}{\sum_{n=0}^{\infty} e^{-\beta n\hbar\omega}} = -\frac{\partial}{\partial\beta}\ln z_\beta \qquad (2\text{-}64)$$

where z_β, the partition function, is given by

$$z_\beta = \sum_{n=0}^{\infty} e^{-\beta(n+1/2)\hbar\omega} = \frac{e^{-\beta h\omega/2}}{1 - e^{-\beta\hbar\omega}} \tag{2-65}$$

and hence

$$\langle E \rangle = \hbar\omega\left\{\frac{1}{2} + \frac{1}{e^{\beta\hbar\omega} - 1}\right\} = \frac{\hbar\omega}{2} \coth \frac{\beta\hbar\omega}{2} \tag{2-66}$$

We have also, since $\langle E \rangle = \left\{\langle N \rangle + \frac{1}{2}\right\}\hbar\omega$, the result

$$\langle N \rangle = \frac{1}{e^{\beta\hbar\omega} - 1} \tag{2-67}$$

for the average number of phonons of frequency ω present at a temperature T. The total energy of the system is then given by

$$E = \sum_{\mathbf{k}\lambda} \hbar\omega_{\mathbf{k}\lambda}\left\{\frac{1}{2} + \frac{1}{e^{\beta\hbar\omega_{\mathbf{k}\lambda}} - 1}\right\} \tag{2-68}$$

The summation, (2-68), is in general difficult to perform. However, one obtains simple results in both the high-temperature and low-temperature limits. In the high-temperature limit, $\beta\hbar\omega \ll 1$, and we find

$$\langle N \rangle \cong \frac{\kappa T}{\hbar\omega}$$

for the average number of phonons present of frequency ω. We note that $\langle N \rangle \gg 1$, so that quantum effects are unimportant. One finds for the average energy in the $\mathbf{k}$, λ normal mode

$$\langle E_{\mathbf{k}\lambda} \rangle = \kappa T\left\{1 + \frac{1}{12}\left(\frac{\hbar\omega_{\mathbf{k}\lambda}}{\kappa T}\right)^2 + \cdots\right\} \tag{2-69}$$

so that to lowest order in $(\beta\hbar\omega)^2$, one recovers the classical result of the equipartition theory. Clearly the total energy is $3N\kappa T$, while the specific heat, $\partial E_T/\partial T$, is seen to be $3N\kappa$, its classical value.

Low-Temperature Limit

In the low-temperature limit, matters are quite otherwise. We cannot define the low-temperature range by $\hbar\omega_{\mathbf{k}\lambda}\beta \gg 1$ for all modes because the lowest frequency is zero. However, those modes for which $\hbar\omega_{k\lambda}$ is much larger than κT will contribute negligibly to the total energy; one sees directly from (2-67) that they will be frozen out. Thus at sufficiently low temperatures only the lowest frequencies in the spectrum will contribute. For these modes we can take $\omega = sk$, where s is the sound velocity. For example, consider a temperature in the liquid helium range, 3°K. Here κT is 1/4000 ev, or 4×10^{-16} ergs. The important modes are then those for which $\hbar\omega \lesssim \kappa T = 4 \times 10^{-16}$ ergs. If we take $\omega = sk$ with $s = 2 \times 10^5$ cm/sec, we find that the condition $\hbar\omega\beta \lesssim$ is equivalent to $k \leq 2 \times 10^6\ \text{cm}^{-1}$, or $\lambda \geq \pi \times 10^6$ cm. The important wavelengths are thus the order of 100 interparticle spacings. Since they are large compared to the effective range of the interparticle forces, we may expect to be in the sound-wave range for which ω is proportional to k.

The general sound-wave relation is $\omega_{k\lambda} = s_\lambda k$. The sound velocity s_λ for a given polarization direction depends on the direction of k. Let θ and ϕ be angular coordinates in k space and let $d\Omega$ be an element of solid angle. The energy E_T in excess of the zero-point energy is given by the sum

$$E_T = \sum_{k,\lambda} \frac{\hbar s_\lambda k}{e^{\beta\hbar s_\lambda k} - 1} \tag{2-70}$$

If the volume L^3 is large enough, the density $(L/2\pi)^3$ of states in k space will be large enough that the sum (2-70) can be replaced by the integral

$$E_T = \frac{L^3}{(2\pi)^3} \sum_\lambda \int d\Omega \int \frac{(\hbar s_\lambda k)^3}{e^{\beta\hbar s_\lambda k} - 1}\, dk \tag{2-71}$$

Since the larger wavenumbers do not contribute, we can take the integral with respect to k from 0 to ∞. If one now lets $x = \hbar s' k/\kappa T$, one finds

$$E_T = \frac{L^3}{(2\pi)^3} \frac{(\kappa T)^4}{\hbar^3} \sum_\lambda \int \frac{d\Omega}{s_\lambda^3(\theta, \varphi)} \int_0^\infty \frac{x^3\, dx}{e^x - 1} \tag{2-72}$$

The integral with respect to x is $\pi^4/15$. It is convenient to define an effective, or average, sound velocity by

$$\frac{1}{s_{av}^3} = \frac{1}{12\pi} \sum_\lambda \int \frac{d\Omega}{s_\lambda^3(\vartheta, \varphi)} \tag{2-73}$$

which will be equal to the actual sound velocity when the latter is a constant independent of direction or polarization. Equation (2-72) then becomes

$$E_T = \frac{\pi^2}{10} \frac{L^3}{\hbar^3} \frac{(\kappa T)^4}{s_{av}^3} \tag{2-74}$$

Thus in the low-temperature range the increase in energy above the zero-point energy goes as the fourth power of the absolute temperature. The specific heat then goes as T^3. This has been well confirmed by experiment.

Einstein Model

We next consider two approximate models, due to Einstein and Debye, that give the energy over the whole temperature range.

Einstein made the simplifying assumption that all atoms vibrate with a single frequency ω. The total energy is then

$$E = 3N \left\{ \frac{\hbar\omega}{2} + \frac{\hbar\omega}{e^{\hbar\omega\beta} - 1} \right\} \tag{2-75}$$

Here E approaches the classical limit $3N\kappa T$ when T becomes large compared to the Einstein temperature $T_E = \hbar\omega/\kappa$. At low temperatures the energy above the zero-point energy varies as a Boltzmann function $e^{-\hbar\omega/\kappa T}$. This comes from the fact that a nonvanishing energy $\hbar\omega$ is required to reach even the lowest excited state. The Einstein model introduced the essential quantum mechanical effects and explains, at least quantitatively, the decrease in specific heat at low temperatures. Quantitatively the Einstein approximation gives a very good fit to the measured curve except at low temperature.

Debye Model

We have seen that at low temperature $\omega_{k\lambda} = s_\lambda k$. Debye used this assumption throughout the whole temperature range and assumed that s_λ was equal to a constant, s, independent of direction in k space or direction of polarization. Thus, at low temperatures where (2-74) holds, the Debye approximation reduces to (2-74) with $s = s_{av}$. At intermediate temperatures it must fail. However, at high temperatures it reduces to the classical limit. Since it is good at both high and low temperatures we expect it to be at least a fair approximation in the connecting range.

There are N permissible and meaningful different values of k. Instead of integrating over the basic cell in the reciprocal lattice, Debye defined an equivalent sphere in k space such that the sphere contains the correct number of degrees of freedom. Thus k_D, defined by

$$k_D^3 = \frac{(2\pi)^3 3N}{L^3 4\pi} = \frac{6\pi^2 N}{L^3} \tag{2-76}$$

is taken as the upper limit of integration with respect to k.

It is convenient to express s by the relation

$$\hbar\omega_D = \hbar s k_D = \kappa\theta_D \tag{2-77}$$

where θ_D is defined as the Debye temperature. We now have the same result as in the low-temperature case except that $s_\lambda = s$ and the upper limit of integration in (2-72) is not infinity but $x_o = \hbar s k_D/\kappa T = \theta_D/T$. Therefore instead of (2-74), we have

$$E_T = L^3 \frac{(\kappa T)^4}{(2\pi\hbar)^3} \frac{12\pi}{s^3} \int_0^{\theta_D/T} dx \frac{x^3}{e^x - 1} \tag{2-78}$$

When s is expressed in terms of θ_D this becomes

$$E_T = 9N\kappa T \left(\frac{T}{\theta_D}\right)^3 \int_0^{\theta_D/T} dx \frac{x^3}{e^x - 1} \tag{2-79}$$

The integral has been tabulated as a function of θ_D/T.[10a]

At any temperature (2-79) can be made to agree with measurements by adjusting θ_D. If the Debye approximation were really exact, θ_D so determined would be constant. In view of the assumptions made in the derivation, in particular the assumption $\omega = sk$, the result should not be expected to hold accurately except at high and very low temperatures. Blackman has shown that the observed deviations from the Debye approximation are not greater than would be expected from a careful consideration of the vibration spectrum.[11] The Debye approximation should be regarded as a useful interpolation connecting the high- and low-temperature ranges and reducing to the correct form in both limits.

2-4 MELTING CRITERION

Another application of simple quantum concepts is to the problem of determining the melting temperature of a solid. Let us assume, with Lindemann,[12] that a solid melts because the vibrations of the atoms about their equilibrium positions become too large. We are thus to consider the mean-square amplitude of vibration $\langle \delta \mathbf{R}_i^2 \rangle$ at a given temperature. If our hypothesis is correct, the solid will melt when $\langle \delta \mathbf{R}_i^2 \rangle$ becomes comparable to the square of the interatomic spacing R_o. Whether the idea possesses general validity can then be seen comparing the calculated values of

$$\gamma = \frac{\langle \delta \mathbf{R}_i^{\,2} \rangle}{R_o^{\,2}} \tag{2-80}$$

for a number of different solids.

From (2-43a) we have

$$\delta \mathbf{R}_i^{\,2} = \frac{1}{MN} \sum_{\substack{\mathbf{k},\lambda \\ \mathbf{k}',\lambda'}} q_{\mathbf{k}\lambda} q_{\mathbf{k}'\lambda'}\, e^{\,i(\mathbf{k}-\mathbf{k}')\cdot \mathbf{R}_{io}} \quad \boldsymbol{\varepsilon}_{\mathbf{k}\lambda} \cdot \boldsymbol{\varepsilon}_{\mathbf{k}'\lambda'} \tag{2-81}$$

In carrying out $\langle \delta R_i^{\,2} \rangle$ we are interested only in the terms in (2-81) which are diagonal in the phonon occupation number, n_k; the other terms describe transitions between states with different phonon occupation numbers, and will therefore not contribute to the sum over states. Thus we keep the terms with $k = k'$, $\lambda = \lambda'$, and obtain

$$\langle \delta R_i^{\,2} \rangle = \frac{1}{MN} \sum_{k\lambda} \langle q_{k\lambda}^{+}\, q_{k\lambda} \rangle \tag{2-82}$$

a result which is independent of the position of the ith atom, as it should be. The average in (2-82) is easily carried out. We write

$$\begin{aligned} \langle \delta R_i^{\,2} \rangle &= \frac{\hbar}{2MN} \sum_{k\lambda} \frac{1}{\omega_{k\lambda}} \langle (a_{k\lambda} + a_{-k\lambda}^{+}) \quad (a_{k\lambda}^{+} + a_{-k\lambda}) \rangle \\ &= \frac{\hbar}{MN} \sum_{k\lambda} \frac{1}{\omega_{k\lambda}} \left\{ \langle n_{k\lambda} \rangle + \frac{1}{2} \right\} \\ &= \frac{1}{MN} \sum_{k\lambda} \frac{E_{k\lambda}}{\omega_{k\lambda}^{2}} \end{aligned} \tag{2-83}$$

where $\langle n_{\mathbf{k}\lambda} \rangle$ and $\langle E_{\mathbf{k}\lambda} \rangle$ are the average number and average energy of phonons in the mode $(\mathbf{k}, \lambda)$. We obtain, therefore,

$$\gamma = \sum_{k\lambda} \frac{\langle E_{\mathbf{k}\lambda} \rangle}{MN\omega_{k\lambda}^{2} R_o^{\,2}} \tag{2-84}$$

For low temperatures we need to consider only the zero-point vibrations. Making the Debye assumption, $\omega_{\mathbf{k}\lambda} = sk$, we have

$$\gamma = \sum_{k\lambda} \frac{\hbar}{2MN\omega_{k\lambda} R_o^2} = \frac{3\hbar}{2MNsR_o^2} \sum_k \frac{1}{k}$$

$$= \frac{3}{2} \frac{\hbar}{MNsR_o^2} \frac{L^3}{(2\pi)^3} \int_0^{k_D} 4\pi k \, dk \tag{2-85}$$

$$= \frac{3}{8\pi^2} \frac{\hbar k_D^2 L^3}{MNsR_o^2}$$

If we now use

$$N = \frac{k_D^3}{6\pi^2} = \frac{3}{4\pi R_o^3}$$

we finally obtain

$$\gamma \cong 0.4 \frac{\hbar k_D}{Ms} \cong 0.4 \frac{\kappa\theta_D}{Ms^2} \tag{2-86}$$

as our low-temperature estimate of γ.

For high temperatures, as we have seen in the previous section, we may set

$$\langle E_{k\lambda} \rangle = \kappa T$$

Again using the approximation, $\omega_{k\lambda} = sk$, we obtain

$$\gamma \cong 1.6 \frac{\kappa T}{Ms^2} = 1.6 \frac{\hbar^2 k_D^2}{M\theta_D^2} \kappa T \tag{2-87}$$

Comparing (2-87) with the result (2-86), we see that the mean-square displacement due to classical effects dominates that arising from quantum effects when $1.6T > 0.4\theta_D$, or $T > \theta_D/4$. (Of course, our assumption of the equipartition of energy is true only when $T > \theta_D$.) The calculation of γ at intermediate temperatures is given later on in this chapter.

Thus, if the melting temperature T_m is greater than the Debye temperature, we can write the following relation between the Debye temperature and the melting temperature:

$$\theta_D = \left(\frac{1.6}{\gamma_m}\right)^{1/2} \left[\frac{\hbar^2}{M} \kappa T_m \left(\frac{2.4}{R_o}\right)^2\right]^{1/2} \tag{2-88}$$

In (2-88) we have introduced γ_m, the critical value of γ for which melting is assumed to take place. Equation (2-88) may also be written

$$\theta_D \cong C \left[\frac{\kappa T_m}{A V_o^{2/3}}\right]^{1/2} \tag{2-89}$$

where C is a constant, A is the atomic weight, $A = 6.02 \times 10^{23}$ M, and V_o is the atomic volume, 1/N. It was in this form that the relation between the Debye temperature and the melting temperature was first given by Lindemann.[12]

In Table 2-1 we give the results for T_m, θ_D, and C for a number of metals.

Table 2-1
Lindemann's Constant for a Number of Metals[a]

Metal	Li	Na	K	Cu	Ag	Au	Ca
T_m, °K	459	370	355	1356	1233	1336	1033
θ_D (obs)	400	160	100	315	215	170	230
C	115	115	116	134	140	142	131

[a]From N. F. Mott and H. Jones, "The Theory of the Properties of Metals and Alloys," Dover, New York, 1958, p. 13.

We remark that C is fairly constant for the alkali metals, the noble metals, and does not differ markedly for calcium. This is strong evidence for the theory that melting occurs when lattice vibrations become too large. We notice also that γ_m is not strongly dependent on the core size. We notice it differs only slightly from Li to Au.

A convenient form of (2-88) and (2-89) is the following:

$$\theta_D = \frac{40}{\sqrt{\gamma_m}} \sqrt{\frac{T_m}{A R_s^2}} \tag{2-90}$$

where R_s is the interatomic spacing measured in units of the Bohr radius. From (2-90) one finds that for sodium,

$$\gamma_m \cong 1/16$$

Thus melting takes place when the root-mean-square vibration of an atom is roughly one-eighth the interatomic spacing R_o, a not-unreasonable result. (Remember that R_o is the radius of a sphere of volume V_o surrounding each atom. The spacing *between* the atoms is thus $2R_o$.)

2-5 NEUTRON SCATTERING IN SOLIDS

General Considerations

In the past decade the scattering of neutrons by solids has developed into a powerful tool for the investigation of the details of the lattice vibrations.[13] Slow neutrons emerging from a reactor represent an excellent probe of the lattice vibrations because

1. The neutron-phonon coupling is weak.
2. The De Broglie wavelength of the neutrons is roughly comparable to interatomic spacing, so that large momentum transfers may be easily observed.
3. The energy of the (roughly thermal) neutrons is sufficiently low that one can easily measure the energy transfer from the neutrons to the phonons.

It is this latter quality which makes the neutrons a superior probe to X rays, the energy in an X-ray quantum being enormous compared to that of phonon. If there is no change in energy between the incident and scattered neutron, the process is known as "elastic" scattering; a process in which the neutron and lattice exchange energy is referred to as an "inelastic" scattering. Because of the periodic structure of a lattice, it is possible for the scattered neutrons to interfere with each other coherently; such a coherent scattering can occur either elastically or inelastically. On the other hand, there are a number of factors, such as randomly distributed different isotopic states or spin states of nuclei, which act to destroy the coherent nature of scattering; again the incoherent scattering can be either elastic or inelastic.

Neutron scattering experiments provide the following information concerning the lattice vibrations:

1. A measurement of the angular distribution of those neutrons which have undergone coherent inelastic scattering, in which a single phonon is involved, yields directly the frequency vs. wavenumber dispersion relation for the phonons involved.
2. In cubic crystals, the cross section for incoherent one-phonon inelastic scattering is directly proportional to the spectral density $g(\omega)$ of the lattice vibrations, and can therefore be used to measure that quantity.
3. The one-phonon coherent inelastic scattering offers also a way to measure the phonon-phonon interaction in a crystal; the neutron peaks which correspond to such scattering are broadened as a consequence of that interaction, and their width may be measured as a function of temperature and of the wavenumber of the phonon under consideration.

The relevant neutron scattering cross sections may be calculated with the aid of two important assumptions:

1. The interaction between the neutron and a given atomic nucleus may be described by a pseudo-potential,[14]

$$V(r) = \frac{2\pi\hbar^2}{m_n} a\,\delta(r) \tag{2-91}$$

where m_n is the neutron mass and a is the scattering length for the atom under consideration.

2. The scattering process may be described by the Born approximation.

Both assumptions are valid in practice. Because (2) is valid, it is possible to regard the neutron-phonon coupling as weak. Therefore one can use the "golden rule" of second-order perturbation theory to calculate the scattering cross sections of interest. We wish to sketch the main features of the calculation; the interested reader may find further details in, for example, Kothari and Singwi.[13]

The Hamiltonian, H_{int}, which describes the interaction between the neutrons and the atoms in the solid, may be written, according to (2-91),

$$H_{int} = \sum_i V(\mathbf{x} - \mathbf{R}_i) = \sum_{k,j} \frac{2\pi\hbar^2}{m_n} a_i e^{-i\mathbf{k}\cdot(\mathbf{x}-\mathbf{R}_i)} \tag{2-92}$$

where $\mathbf{x}$ denotes the position of the neutron and a_i refers to the scattering length of the ith atom. Consider a transition in which the neutron is scattered from a plane-wave state of momentum $\hbar\mathbf{k}_1$, to another state, $\hbar\mathbf{k}_2$; the matrix element for the transition is given by

$$H_{int}(\mathbf{k}) = \langle k_2 | H_{int} | k_1 \rangle = \int d\mathbf{x}\, e^{-i\mathbf{k}_2\cdot\mathbf{x}} H_{int}\, e^{i\mathbf{k}_1\cdot\mathbf{x}}$$

$$= \frac{2\pi\hbar^2}{m_n} \sum_i a_i e^{i\mathbf{k}\cdot\mathbf{R}_i} \tag{2-93}$$

where

$$\hbar\mathbf{k} = \hbar(\mathbf{k}_1 - \mathbf{k}_2) \tag{2-94}$$

is the momentum transfer, and we are now working in a box of unit volume. The probability per unit time that the neutron transfer momentum $\hbar\mathbf{k}$ and energy $\hbar\omega$ to the lattice is then given by the "golden-rule" of second-order perturbation theory as

$$W(\mathbf{k}\omega) = \frac{2\pi}{\hbar} \sum_{nm} w(n) \left| \langle m | H_{int}(\mathbf{k}) | n \rangle \right|^2 \delta\{\hbar[\omega - (E_m - E_n)]\} \tag{2-95}$$

Here E_n is the initial energy of the lattice, E_m the final energy; w(n) represents the probability of finding the lattice in a state of energy E_n, the delta function expresses conservation of energy, and one has, as well,

$$\hbar\omega = \hbar(k_2^2 - k_1^2)/2m_n = E_m - E_n \tag{2-96}$$

Upon making use of (2-93), we may write:

$$W(\mathbf{k}\omega) = \frac{8\pi^3\hbar^2}{m_n} \sum_{nm} w(n) \left\langle m \left| \sum_i a_i e^{i\mathbf{k}\cdot\mathbf{R}_i} \right| n \right\rangle^2 \delta(\omega - \omega_{mn}) \tag{2-97}$$

where

$$\omega_{mn} = (E_m - E_n)/\hbar \tag{2-98}$$

For the case of coherent scattering, in which all the a_i are equal to a single value a, we may write (2-97) as

$$W(\mathbf{k}\omega) = \frac{8\pi^3\hbar^2 a^2}{m_n} S(\mathbf{k}\omega) \tag{2-99}$$

where

$$S(\mathbf{k}\omega) = \sum_{mn} w(n) \left| \left\langle m \left| \sum_i e^{i\mathbf{k}\cdot\mathbf{R}_i} \right| n \right\rangle \right|^2 \delta(\omega - \omega_{mn}) \tag{2-100}$$

As van Hove[15] and Glauber[16] first emphasized, the quantity $S(\mathbf{k}\omega)$ provides one with complete information about the correlations in space and time between different atoms in the crystal. We shall have occasion to study the corresponding quantity in some detail for the electron gas in Chapter 3.

The information which neutron scattering can provide us on crystal dynamics is contained in (2-97), since a measurement of the differential cross section for inelastic scattering into a given solid angle corresponds to a measurement of the momentum and energy transfer to the lattice. We now proceed to the discussion of several cases of experimental interest.

Elastic Scattering

We consider first elastic scattering, in which $|\mathbf{k}_1| = |\mathbf{k}_2|$, or $E_n = E_m$. The transition probability, (2-97), may then be written

$$W(\mathbf{k}) = \frac{8\pi^3\hbar^2}{m_n} \sum_{n} w(n) \left\langle n \left| \sum_i a_i e^{i\mathbf{k}\cdot\mathbf{R}_i} \right| n \right\rangle^2 \rho_F \tag{2-101}$$

where ρ_F is the density of the final states per unit energy per unit solid angle (corresponding to scattering in the direction of **k**),

$$\rho_F = m_n k_2/(2\pi)^3\hbar^2 \qquad (2\text{-}102)$$

The important factor in (2-101) is

$$\sum_n w(n) \left| \left\langle n \left| \sum_i a_i e^{i\mathbf{k}\cdot\mathbf{R}_i} \right| n \right\rangle \right|^2 \qquad (2\text{-}103)$$

which we may write as

$$\sum_n w(n) \left| \sum_i a_i e^{i\mathbf{k}\cdot\mathbf{R}_{oi}} \left\langle n \right| e^{i\mathbf{k}\cdot\delta\mathbf{R}_i} \left| n \right\rangle \right|^2 \qquad (2\text{-}104)$$

where $\delta\mathbf{R}_i$ represents, as before, the displacement of the ith atom from its equilibrium position. The properties of the lattice vibrations enter only through the factor $\langle n| e^{i\mathbf{k}\cdot\delta\mathbf{R}_i} | n\rangle$; it turns out, for the averaging process involved (in which one is considering all possible phonon states n present at a given temperature) that such averages do not depend on the particular lattice displacement under consideration [compare (2-82)]. Hence one can write (2-104) as

$$\sum_n w(n) \left| \left\langle n \left| \sum_i a_i e^{i\mathbf{k}\cdot\mathbf{R}_i} \right| n \right\rangle \right|^2 = \left| \sum_i a_i e^{i\mathbf{k}\cdot\mathbf{R}_{io}} \right|^2 e^{-2W} \qquad (2\text{-}105)$$

where the factor $\left| \sum_i a_i e^{i\mathbf{k}\cdot\mathbf{R}_{io}} \right|^2$ depends on the structure of the solid, while the remaining factor, e^{-2W}, carries the temperature-dependent effects. The latter is the well-known Debye-Waller factor; it is

$$e^{-2W} = \sum_n w(n) \left| \left\langle n \right| e^{i\mathbf{k}\cdot\delta\mathbf{R}_i} \left| n \right\rangle \right|^2 \qquad (2\text{-}106)$$

We first discuss the character of the sum, $\left| \sum_i a_i e^{i\mathbf{k}\cdot\mathbf{R}_{io}} \right|^2$, which contains the coherent vs. incoherent aspects of scattering as well as the effect of the periodic structure of the lattice. To evaluate the sum we write

$$|\sum_i a_i e^{i\mathbf{k}\cdot\mathbf{R}_{io}}|^2 = \sum_{i,j} a_i a_j e^{i\mathbf{k}\cdot(\mathbf{R}_{io}-\mathbf{R}_{jo})}$$

$$= N\langle a^2\rangle + \sum_{i\neq j} a_i a_j e^{i\mathbf{k}\cdot(\mathbf{R}_{io}-\mathbf{R}_{jo})} \qquad (2\text{-}107)$$

where

$$\langle a^2\rangle = \frac{\sum_{i=1}^{N} a_i^2}{N} \qquad (2\text{-}108)$$

When $i \neq j$, we assume that the scattering length of the ith atom is independent of that of the jth atom. Then, defining

$$\langle a\rangle = \frac{\sum_i a_i}{N} \qquad (2\text{-}109)$$

we obtain

$$|\sum_i a_i e^{i\mathbf{k}\cdot\mathbf{R}_{io}}|^2 = N\langle a^2\rangle + \langle a\rangle^2 \sum_{i\neq j} e^{i\mathbf{k}\cdot(\mathbf{R}_{io}-\mathbf{R}_{jo})}$$

$$= N\left(\langle a^2\rangle - \langle a\rangle^2\right) + \langle a\rangle^2 |\sum_i e^{i\mathbf{k}\cdot\mathbf{R}_{io}}|^2$$

$$(2\text{-}110)$$

We now recall that, as a consequence of periodicity,

$$|\sum_i e^{i\mathbf{k}\cdot\mathbf{R}_{io}}|^2 = \frac{N\cdot(2\pi)^3}{V_o}\sum_n \delta(\mathbf{k}-\mathbf{K}_n) \qquad (2\text{-}111)$$

so that we can write

$$|\sum_i a_i e^{i\mathbf{k}\cdot\mathbf{R}_{io}}|^2 = \Big\{N\left(\langle a^2\rangle - \langle a\rangle^2\right)$$

$$+ \frac{N\cdot(2\pi)^3}{V_o}\langle a\rangle^2 \sum_n \delta(\mathbf{k}-\mathbf{K}_n)\Big\} \qquad (2\text{-}112)$$

The first term in brackets on the right-hand side of (2-112) represents the incoherent contribution; the remaining term is the coherent one.

The Debye-Waller factor may be evaluated in a number of ways: a particularly elegant one is due to Glauber,[16] while a simple recent one is due to Lipkin.[17] We here quote the result:

$$e^{-2W} = \sum_n w(n) \left| \left\langle n \right| e^{i\mathbf{k}\cdot\delta\mathbf{R}_i} \left| n \right\rangle \right|^2$$

$$= \exp - \sum_n w(n) \left\langle n \right| (\mathbf{k}\cdot\delta\mathbf{R}_i)^2 \left| n \right\rangle \tag{2-113}$$

We have already carried out the relevant average of the mean-square lattice displacement in Sec. 2-4. On transposing the result obtained there, we have

$$e^{-2W} = \exp - \sum_{\mathbf{k}'\lambda} \frac{(\mathbf{k}\cdot\boldsymbol{\varepsilon}_{\mathbf{k}'\lambda})^2}{2NM\omega_{\mathbf{k}'\lambda}} \coth \frac{\hbar\omega_{\mathbf{k}'\lambda}\beta}{2} \tag{2-114}$$

The Debye-Waller factor is a decreasing function of temperature. If we assume the Debye model, $\omega = sk$, it may be evaluated explicitly as

$$e^{-2W} = \exp\left\{-3\frac{\hbar^2 k^2}{M\kappa\theta_D}\left[\frac{1}{4} + \left(\frac{T}{\theta_D}\right)^2 \int_0^{\theta_D/T} dx \frac{x}{e^x - 1}\right]\right\} \tag{2-115}$$

For low temperatures it takes the form

$$e^{-2W} = \exp\left(-\frac{\hbar^2 k^2}{2M}\frac{3}{2\kappa\theta_D}\right) \tag{2-116}$$

while for high temperatures it is

$$e^{-2W} = \exp\left(-3\frac{\hbar^2 k^2}{M}\frac{T}{\theta_D}\frac{1}{\kappa\theta_D}\right) \tag{2-117}$$

One can easily transform from the result, (2-101), to the appropriate differential cross section per nucleus per unit solid angle by dividing the result there by $NI_o = N\hbar k_1/m_n$, where I_o is the initial neutron flux. One then finds

$$\left(\frac{d\sigma}{d\Omega}\right)_{\text{elastic}}^{\text{incoherent}} = \left\{\left\langle a^2\right\rangle - \left\langle a\right\rangle^2\right\} e^{-2W} \tag{2-118}$$

$$\left(\frac{d\sigma}{d\Omega}\right)_{\text{elastic}}^{\text{coherent}} = \frac{8\pi^3}{V_o} \langle a \rangle^2 e^{-2W} \sum_n \delta(\mathbf{k} - \mathbf{K}_n) \tag{2-119}$$

Inelastic Neutron Scattering: One-Phonon Processes

Let us return to our basic equation for the transition probability, (2-97), which involves the matrix element

$$\left\langle m \,\middle|\, \sum_i a_i e^{i\mathbf{k}\cdot\mathbf{R}_{oi}} e^{i\mathbf{k}\cdot\delta\mathbf{R}_i} \,\middle|\, n \right\rangle \tag{2-120}$$

between two lattice vibration states n and m. As we have seen, $\delta\mathbf{R}_i$ may be expanded in terms of the appropriate phonon creation and annihilation operators as

$$\delta\mathbf{R}_i = \sum_{k'\lambda'} \left(\frac{\hbar}{2NM\omega_{\mathbf{k}'}}\right)^{1/2} (a_{\mathbf{k}'\lambda'} + a^+_{-\mathbf{k}'\lambda'}) \quad \varepsilon_{\mathbf{k}'\lambda'} e^{i\mathbf{k}'\cdot\mathbf{R}_{io}} \tag{2-121}$$

Because $\delta\mathbf{R}_i$ appears in an exponential in (2-118), clearly the states n and m can differ by an arbitrary number of phonons (since $e^{i\mathbf{k}\cdot\delta\mathbf{R}_i}$ is equivalent to its power-series expansion). We shall here confine our attention to one-phonon processes, in which the states n and m differ by the presence (or absence) of a single phonon; these represent, in fact, the most important experimental tool for the study with neutrons of phonon spectra in solids.

The one-phonon processes are of course governed by energy conservation; thus the condition (2-96) must be satisfied for the phonon of wave vector $\mathbf{k}'$ and energy $\hbar\omega(\mathbf{k}')$. In the case of coherent scattering, one has as well the "pseudo-momentum" conservation condition, which reads

$$\mathbf{k}_1 - \mathbf{k}_2 = \mathbf{k} = \mathbf{k}' + \mathbf{K}_n \tag{2-122}$$

This condition is the generalization to coherent one-phonon processes of the coherent elastic scattering result (2-111). The conservation laws determine the main features of the scattering process, as has been emphasized by Placzek and van Hove,[18] to whose paper the reader is referred for further details.

The transition probability for a one-phonon process involving a phonon of wave vector $\mathbf{k}'$ may be shown to be[16]

$$W(\mathbf{k},\mathbf{k}') = \frac{8\pi^3\hbar^2}{Nm_nM} \sum_i | a_i e^{i\mathbf{k}\cdot\mathbf{R}_{oi}} e^{-i\mathbf{k}'\cdot\mathbf{R}_{oi}} |^2$$

$$\times \sum_{nm\lambda'} w(n) | \langle m | \mathbf{k}' \cdot \boldsymbol{\varepsilon}_{\mathbf{k}'\lambda'} q_{\mathbf{k}'\lambda'} | n \rangle^2$$

$$\times e^{-2W} \delta\left[\hbar^2 \frac{(k_1^2 - k_2^2)}{2m_n} \pm \hbar\omega_{\mathbf{k}'}\right] \tag{2-123}$$

where the upper sign in the delta function refers to scattering with energy gain by the neutron, the lower to phonon emission and energy loss: The structure factor, $| \sum_i a_i e^{i(\mathbf{k}-\mathbf{k}')\cdot\mathbf{R}_{oi}} |^2$, then gives rise to the scattering law, (2-122), in the case of coherent scattering; for incoherent scattering there are no restrictions on $\mathbf{k}'$. The remaining average in (2-123) is easy to carry out; it is left as a problem for the reader to show that the differential cross sections per unit angle are given by[18]

$$\left(\frac{d\sigma_1}{dk}\right)^{\text{inc}} = \frac{\hbar}{m_nMk_1} \left\{\langle a^2\rangle - \langle a\rangle^2\right\}$$

$$\times e^{-2W} \frac{V_o}{8\pi^3} \sum_{\lambda'} \int d\mathbf{k}' \left(\frac{\mathbf{k}\cdot\boldsymbol{\varepsilon}_{\mathbf{k}'\lambda'}}{\omega_{\mathbf{k}'\lambda'}}\right)^2$$

$$\times \begin{Bmatrix} N_{\mathbf{k}'\lambda'} \\ \\ N_{\mathbf{k}'\lambda'} + 1 \end{Bmatrix} \delta\left(k_1^2 - k_2^2 \pm \frac{2m_n\omega_{\mathbf{k}'\lambda'}}{\hbar}\right) \tag{2-124}$$

$$\left(\frac{d\sigma_1}{dk}\right)^{\text{coh}} = \frac{\hbar}{m_nMk_1} \left\{\langle a\rangle^2 e^{-2W} \sum_{\lambda} \frac{(\mathbf{k}\cdot\boldsymbol{\varepsilon}_{\mathbf{k}\lambda})^2}{\omega_{\mathbf{k}\lambda}}\right.$$

$$\times \begin{Bmatrix} N_{\mathbf{k}\lambda} \\ \\ N_{\mathbf{k}\lambda} + 1 \end{Bmatrix} \delta\left\{k_1^2 - k_2^2 \pm \frac{2m\omega_{\mathbf{k}\lambda}}{\hbar}\right\} \tag{2-125}$$

where $N_{\mathbf{k}\lambda}$ is the phonon distribution function (2-67), and one uses $N_{\mathbf{k}\lambda}$ for a phonon absorption process, $N_{\mathbf{k}\lambda} + 1$ for an emission process.

For crystals of cubic symmetry, the cross section for incoherent scattering can be simplified: first, because the Debye-Waller factor is then independent of the direction of k; second, because the average over polarizations under the integral sign is straightforward, and the integral may be carried out explicitly, and shown to yield[18]

$$\left(\frac{d\sigma}{dk}\right)^{inc} = \frac{\hbar^2}{2Mm_nk_o}\left\{\langle a^2\rangle - \langle a\rangle^2\right\}\left\{e^{-2W}\right\}\frac{k^2}{\omega}\left\{\begin{matrix} N(\omega) \\ N(\omega)+1 \end{matrix}\right\} g(\omega) \tag{2-126}$$

where $g(\omega)$ is the spectral density of the lattice vibrations, i.e., the number of normal modes per unit frequency interval.

Experimental Results

We consider now some of the experimental results which have been obtained by inelastic neutron scattering.[19] As we have seen, the angular distribution of neutrons which are coherently scattered by one-phonon processes consists of delta-function peaks whose position is governed by the conservation laws. In general these peaks will be superposed on a continuous background associated both with coherent multiphonon processes and with incoherent scattering processes.

Detailed studies of the phonon spectra have now been carried out for a number of solids.[20] In Fig. 2-3, the dispersion curves for lead at 100°K, as determined by Brockhouse et al.,[20] are shown. One sees that such an experiment provides a detailed survey of the phonon spectra, one which goes far beyond the information hitherto available on the long-wavelength dispersion relation.

As we have mentioned earlier, one may use the data to learn something of the interatomic forces for the solid in question. To do this, one begins with the basic phonon dispersion relation, (2-39). For a particular mode, in a particular symmetric direction, this may be written[21]

$$M\omega^2 = \sum_{n=1}^{N} \Phi_n \left[1 - \cos(n\pi q/q_M)\right] \tag{2-127}$$

where q_M is half the distance to the nearest reciprocal lattice point in the direction of the phonon wave vector q, while Φ_n corresponds to a force constant for the planes of atoms normal to q and n atoms away. Using (2-127) and the experimental data, one then attempts to determine by means of a least-squares fit just how many force constants Φ_n are necessary to fit the experimental data. In this way, Brockhouse et al.[20] found that the interatomic forces in lead were of long range and sometimes of alternating sign, and hence could not be fit by a simple model calculation based on (2-127). For sodium, on the other hand, Woods et al.[20] found that a good fit could be obtained with fourth and fifth neighbor forces. Similar experiments on the phonon modes in germanium have shown that relatively long-range interactions are present, with interactions between fifth or sixth distant

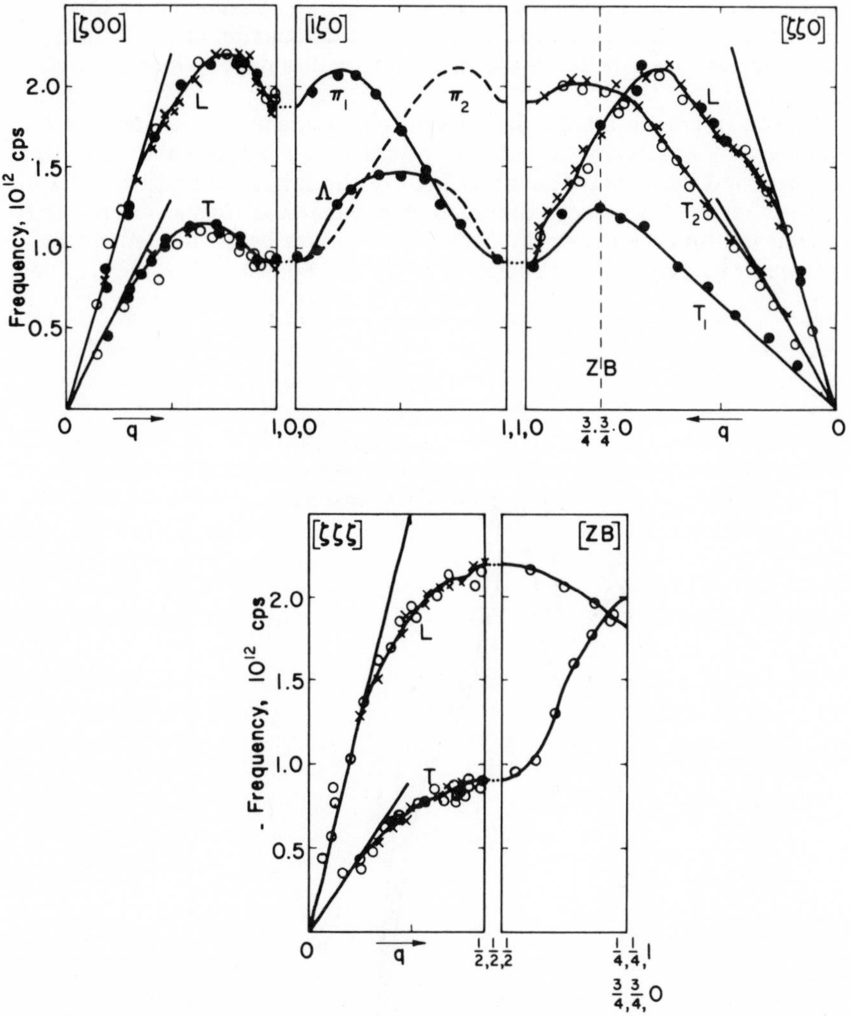

Fig. 2-3. The dispersion curves for lead at 100°K, plotted so as to show the interrelation of the various braches. The straight lines through the origin give the initial slopes of the curves as calculated from the elastic constants. (From Brockhouse et al.[20])

neighbors being required to fit the data.[22] The way is clearly open for the theorist interested in calculating lattice dynamics from first principles.

In addition, Brockhouse et al.[20] have found that certain images of the Fermi surface are present in the phonon spectrum of lead. This effect, which was predicted by Kohn[23] will be considered in Chapter 5. We postpone until the following section a discussion of the widths of the neutron loss lines and the information this provides on phonon lifetimes.

We turn now to a consideration of experiments on the incoherent one-phonon scattering in cubic crystals which, as we have seen, serve to measure the spectral density $g(\omega)$ of the lattice vibrations. Experiments on the frequency distribution in vanadium (for which the scattering is almost entirely incoherent) have now been carried out by several groups[24]; some recent results are shown in Fig. 2-4. The

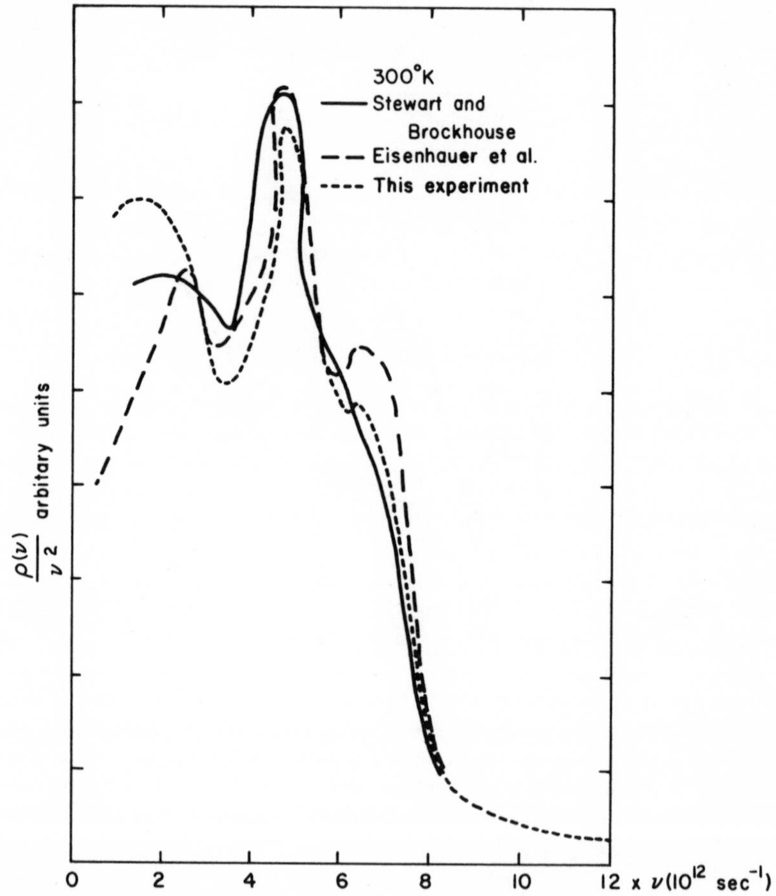

Fig. 2-4. Comparison of three measurements of the frequency distribution of vanadium at room temperature. (From Turberfield and Egelstaff[24].)

appearance of three peaks in the spectrum is in sharp contrast with the Debye theory for the lattice vibrations. For a Debye spectrum one finds

$$g_D(\omega) = \left(\frac{dn}{dk}\right) \frac{d\omega_D(k)}{dk} = \frac{\omega^2}{2\pi^2 S^2} \tag{2-128}$$

so that $g_D(\omega)/\omega^2$ should be a constant.

Singularities in the normal-mode distribution are found if one calculates the normal modes on the basis of the basic dispersion relations, (2-39). Van Hove[25] has shown that the $g(\omega)$ function of a crystal contains a finite number of singularities resulting from the periodic structure of the atomic array. The singular frequencies are those for which

$$\textbf{grad}\ \omega_\lambda(\mathbf{k}) = 0 \qquad \lambda = 1, 2, \text{ or } 3 \tag{2-129}$$

The analytic form of $g(\omega)$ in the neighborhood of such a singularity has been given by van Hove. Again, the calculation of the position of the singularities in the frequency distribution offers a sensitive test of the force model assumed for a given solid.

2-6 PHONON-PHONON INTERACTIONS

Thus far in our discussion of lattice vibrations we have confined our attention to the "harmonic" term in the expansion of the potential energy of interaction between the ions, i.e., that term which is quadratic in the displacement of the ions from their equilibrium positions. Within this approximation the phonons are, of course, completely well defined elementary excitations of the solid. We now consider briefly the effects of the anharmonic terms in the potential energy, those terms which are of higher order—cubic and quadratic for example—in the lattice displacements.[26]

These anharmonic terms give rise to macroscopic phenomena, such as thermal expansion and a linear term in the specific heat at high temperatures.[27] From a microscopic point of view, they give rise to an interaction between the phonons. As a result, the phonon is no longer a completely well-defined excitation, in that it becomes possible for phonons to scatter against one another, for one phonon to decay into two, etc. Consequently the anharmonic terms offer an important mechanism for the thermal resistance of a nonmetallic solid.[28] Moreover, they play a large role in measurements of one-phonon coherent inelastic neutron scattering as a result of the finite lifetime and shift in energy of the phonon in question.[29]

Consider, for example, the cubic term, which may be written

$$V_c = \sum_{\ell jmn} \frac{\mathbf{B}_{\ell mn}}{6} \delta\mathbf{R}_\ell \delta\mathbf{R}_m \delta\mathbf{R}_n \tag{2-130}$$

where $\mathbf{B}_{\ell mn}$ is a tensor of the third rank. If we introduce normal modes, according to (2-43), we find that (2-130) becomes

$$V_c = 1/6 \sum_{\substack{kk'k'' \\ \mu\nu\lambda \\ \ell mn}} \frac{1}{(NM)^{3/2}} \mathbf{B}_{\ell mn}\, \varepsilon_{\mathbf{k}\mu}\, \varepsilon_{\mathbf{k}'\nu}\, \varepsilon_{\mathbf{k}''\lambda}\, q_{\mathbf{k}\mu}\, q_{\mathbf{k}'\nu}\, q_{\mathbf{k}''\lambda}$$

$$\times\, e^{i\mathbf{k}\cdot\mathbf{R}_{o\ell}}\, e^{i\mathbf{k}'\cdot\mathbf{R}_{om}}\, e^{i\mathbf{k}''\cdot\mathbf{R}_{on}} \tag{2-131}$$

If we now recall the expansion of $q_{\mathbf{k}\mu}$ into phonon creation and annihilation operators, we see that (2-131) therefore gives rise to processes which involve three phonons. Because of the periodic character of the lattice, there is a "pseudo-momentum conservation" law, which reads

$$\mathbf{k} + \mathbf{k}' + \mathbf{k}'' = \mathbf{K}_n \tag{2-132}$$

as one sees at once if one remarks that V_c must be unchanged if the position of every atom is shifted by a lattice vector. In any scattering process one has conservation of energy as well. Thus through V_c, one phonon may decay into two, or, in a scattering process, two phonons may be destroyed, while one is created, etc.

In the same way, the quadratic term in the expansion of $V(\mathbf{R}_i - \mathbf{R}_j)$ gives rise to four-phonon processes in which two phonons scatter against one another, one phonon decays into three, or there is a scattering process in which three phonons are destroyed and one is created. Again there will be a conservation law which reads

$$\mathbf{k} + \mathbf{k}' + \mathbf{k}'' + \mathbf{k}''' = \mathbf{K}_n \tag{2-133}$$

for the four phonons involved in the interaction. In general, it is not possible to decide without a detailed analysis whether the cubic or the quartic terms are more important for the process under consideration.

Peierls has emphasized that the conservation laws play a most important role in determining the temperature dependence of the thermal conductivity for those insulating crystals for which phonon-phonon scattering provides the dominant resistance mechanism. (This means a pure crystal of moderate size at not-too-low temperature, so that effects due to impurity and boundary scattering of the phonons may be neglected.) His argument proceeds along the following lines. Suppose we neglect the effects of periodicity in the conservation laws, (2-132) and (2-133); that is, put $\mathbf{K}_n = 0$. In that case the sum of the phonon wave vectors will not change in the collision process and the net phonon "current"

$$\mathbf{J}_{ph} = \sum_{k\lambda} \mathbf{k} N_{\mathbf{k}\lambda} \tag{2-134}$$

will be conserved in phonon-phonon collisions. A finite value of $\mathbf{J}_{ph}$ implies that there are more phonons travelling in one direction than in another, so that it implies a net energy transport. In general one would have a value of $\mathbf{J}_{ph}$ which is initially different from zero (as a simple consequence of statistical fluctuations). Since phonon-phonon collisions then provide no mechanism for changing either $\mathbf{J}_{ph}$ or the associated energy transport, one would have an energy transport without a thermal gradient, and hence an infinite thermal conductivity.

The phonon-phonon contribution to thermal resistance therefore comes from collisions in which $\mathbf{K}_n \neq 0$; these are called Umklapp processes, following the German name which Peierls gave them in his original work on the subject.[30] We next remark that at low temperatures ($T << \theta_D$), most of the phonons which are present possess long wavelengths, such that their vectors, $\mathbf{k} << \mathbf{K}_o$, the smallest $\mathbf{K}_n$ value which can appear in (2-132). (Recall that $\mathbf{K}_o$ is of the order of an inverse lattice spacing, while for $T << \theta_D$, thermally excited phonons possess wavelengths which are of the order of some hundreds of lattice spacings.) A simple geometrical consideration shows that one of the phonons involved in the collision must have a wave vector comparable to $\mathbf{K}_o$, and hence a certain minimum frequency, ω_{min}, such that $\hbar\omega_{min} \sim K\theta_D$. Hence, from (2-67), since $\kappa T << \hbar\omega_{min}$, the number of such phonons is proportional to

$$\exp\ (-\hbar\omega_{min}/\kappa T) = \exp\ (-\alpha\theta_D/T)$$

where α depends on the geometry of the scattering process, and whether three or four phonon collisions provide the most important resistive mechanism. Finally, since such phonons are essential for a U process, and hence for thermal resistance, the thermal resistance itself must vary with temperature as $\exp\ (-\alpha\theta_D/T)$. Experiments by Berman et al.[31] confirm such a temperature dependence for diamond ($\alpha = 1/2.6$), solid helium ($\alpha = 1/2.3$), and sapphire ($\alpha = 1/2.1$).

Much more detailed information on the strength and character of the phonon-phonon interactions is offered by the inelastic neutron scattering experiments. As we have remarked, these interactions act both to shift and broaden the peaks in the neutron scattering spectrum which are predicted in the harmonic approximation. Experiments that show such anharmonic effects have been carried out by Brockhouse et al.[29] on lead and by Larsson et al.[30] on aluminium. Their results show that the neutron line widths are temperature-dependent, and vary almost linearly with temperature in the region from the Debye temperature to the melting point of the metal in question. For temperatures of the order of the Debye temperatures, the line widths are small for all phonons considered, a result which shows that the lifetime of the phonon is small compared to its energy. In other words, phonons at this temperature continue to be a well-defined elementary excitation of the solid. On the other hand, at temperatures large compared to the Debye temperature, the short-wavelength phonons possess a lifetime which is of the order of their energy, that is, $\hbar/\tau_{ph} \cong \hbar\omega_{ph}$. Such phonons do not properly represent well-defined excitations of the crystal, according to the criterion we have set forth in Chapter 1. In Fig. 2-5 we show the measurements of Brockhouse et al.[29] on the width of the scattering peaks in Pb at a temperature (425°K) which is large compared to the Debye temperature (70°K). The width is seen to increase rapidly with wavenumber (more so than the corresponding increase in phonon frequencies). Thus long-wavelength phonons are relatively long-lived, a result which can

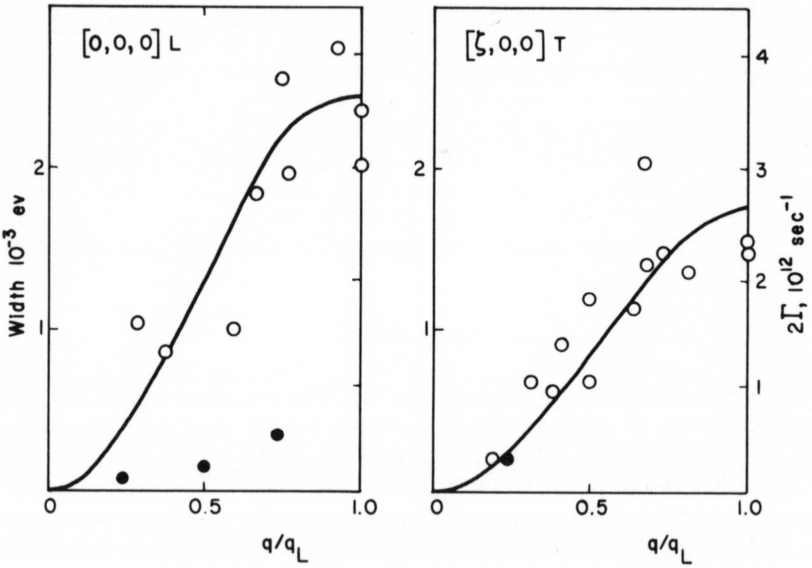

Fig. 2-5. Width of the scattering peaks for lead at 425°K. The circles are the experimental points of Brockhouse et al.,[29] the squares represent the results of the calculation of Maradudin and Fein.[32] The solid line is the best fit of the experimental data by a function of the form $\sin^2(\pi q/2q_L)$. (From Kokkedee.[29])

probably be understood in terms of the phase space available for the decay of such a phonon as a result of phonon-phonon interaction.

A fundamental theoretical analysis of the influence of the anharmonic terms on inelastic coherent neutron scattering has been carried out by Kokkedee.[29] His analysis is based on perturbation theory and is thus restricted to temperatures such that the anharmonic terms represent a relatively small perturbation and the phonon continues to be a well-defined excitation of the solid. He finds in suitable approximation a width proportional to the temperature, in agreement with experiment. A detailed calculation of line widths is complicated by lack of basic knowledge of the relevant anharmonic force constants. Maradudin and Fein[32] have attempted to overcome this difficulty by taking a simple model for a given solid (in their case Pb), assuming only nearest-neighbor interactions, and then choosing the force constants in such a way that the model yields relevant macroscopic experimental data. Their results are compared with experiment in Fig. 2-5. In view of the necessarily rough character of the approximations made, this order-of-magnitude agreement can be regarded as satisfactory.

References

1. R. E. Peierls, "Quantum Theory of Solids," Oxford, London, 1955.
2. J. M. Ziman, "Electrons and Phonons," Oxford, London, 1960.
2a. For an elementary discussion of Floquet's theorem, see N. F. Mott and H. Jones, "The Theory of the Properties of Metals and Alloys," Dover, N. Y., 1958, p. 57.
3. See, for example, L. Schiff, "Quantum Mechanics," McGraw-Hill, New York, 1955.
4. See, for example, L. Brillouin, "Wave Propagation in Periodic Structures," Dover, New York, 1953, pp. 147-148.
5. L. Brillouin,[4] pp. 148-155; J. M. Ziman,[2] pp. 22-27.
6. L. Brillouin,[4] pp. 155-157; F. Seitz, "Modern Theory of Solids," McGraw-Hill, New York, 1940.
6a. See, for example, the review article by J. de Launay, in F. Seitz and D. Turnbull (eds.), "Solid State Physics," Academic, New York, 1956, Vol. 2.
7. W. Kohn, private communication.
8. C. B. Clark, *Phys. Rev.*, **109**, 1133 (1958).
9. R. A. Coldwell-Horsfall and A. A. Maradudin, *J. Math. Phys.*, **1**, 395 (1960).
10. A. Einstein, *Ann. Physik*, **22**, 180, 800 (1907); **34**, 170 (1911).
10a. Landolt-Börnstein, "Physikalisch-Chemische Tabellen," 5th ed, Berlin, 1927.
11. M. Blackman, "Handbuch der Physik," Springer, Berlin, 1955, Vol. VII-1.

12. F. Lindemann, *Phys. Z.*, **11**, 609 (1910).
13. Some general references on neutron scattering include: L. van Hove, N. Hugenholtz, and L. Howland, "Quantum Theory of Many-Particle Systems," Benjamin, New York, 1962; W. Marshall, "Neutron Scattering," Benjamin, New York, 1963; C. G. Shull and E. D. Wollan, in F. Seitz and D. Turnbull (eds.), "Solid State Physics," Academic, New York, 1956, Vol. 2, and L. Kothari and K. S. Singwi, *ibid.*, 1959, Vol. 8.
14. E. Fermi, *Ricerca Sci.*, **7**, 13 (1936): English translation available as USAEC Rept. NP-2385.
15. L. van Hove, *Phys. Rev.*, **95**, 249 (1954).
16. R. J. Glauber, *Phys. Rev.*, **98**, 1692 (1955).
17. H. J. Lipkin, *Ann. Phys.*, **9**, 332 (1960).
18. G. Placzek and L. van Hove, *Phys. Rev.*, **93**, 1207 (1954).
19. For a review of experimental results up to 1959, see Kothari and Singwi.[13] See also "Inelastic Scattering of Neutrons in Solids and Liquids," Intern. Atomic Energy Agency, Vienna, 1961, which represents the proceedings of a symposium held on that subject in October 1960 and which contains both review papers and recent experimental results.
20. For example see the studies on the phonon spectra in Al which have been carried out by B. N. Brockhouse and A. T. Stewart [*Rev. Mod. Phys.*, **30**, 236 (1958)]; and by K. E. Larsson, S. Holmryd, and D. Dahlborg in "Inelastic Scattering of Neutrons in Solids and Liquids,"[19] p. 587; in Pb by B. N. Brockhouse, T. Arase, G. Caglioti, K. R. Ras, and A. D. B. Woods, *Phys. Rev.*, **128**, 1099 (1962); in Na by A. D. B. Woods, B. N. Brockhouse, R. H. March, A. T. Stewart, and R. Bowers, *Phys. Rev.*, **128**, 1112 (1962).
21. See, for example, Brockhouse et al.[20]
22. B. N. Brockhouse and P. K. Iyengar, *Phys. Rev.*, **111**, 747 (1958); A. Ghose, H. Palevsky, D. J. Hughes, I. Pelah, and C. M. Eisenhauer, *Phys. Rev.*, **113**, 49 (1959).
23. W. Kohn, *Phys. Rev. Letters*, **2**, 393 (1959); E. J. Woll, Jr., and W. Kohn, *Phys. Rev.*, **126**, 1693 (1962).
24. A. T. Stewart, and B. N. Brockhouse, *Rev. Mod. Phys.*, **30**, 250 (1958); C. M. Eisenhauer, M. I. Pelak, D. J. Hughes, and H. Palevsky, *Phys. Rev.*, **109**, 1046 (1958); K. C. Turberfield and P. A. Egelstaff, *Phys. Rev.*, **127**, 1017 (1962).
25. L. van Hove, *Phys. Rev.*, **89**, 1189 (1953).
26. Excellent references on the anharmonic terms, and the effects they produce, include R. E. Peierls,[1] and L. van Hove et al.[13]
27. See, for example, R. E. Peierls.[1]
28. For a discussion of the thermal conductivity, see R. E. Peierls[1] and P. Carruthers, *Rev. Mod. Phys.*, **33**, 92 (1961).
29. Experimental investigations have been carried out for lead by B. N. Brockhouse, T. Arase, C. Galioti, M. Sakamato, R. N.

Sinclair and A. D. B. Woods, in "Inelastic Scattering of Neutrons in Solids and Liquids,"[19] p. 531, and for aluminium by Larsson et al.[20] A detailed theoretical analysis has been carried out by J. J. J. Kokkedee, *Physica*, 28, 374 (1962), where references to other theoretical investigations may be found.

30. R. E. Peierls, *Ann. Phys.*, (5) 3, 1055 (1929).
31. R. Berman, F. Simon, and J. Wilks, *Nature*, **168**, 277 (1951).
32. A. Maradudin and A. Fein, *Phys. Rev.*, **128**, 2589 (1962).

Problems

2-1 Apply Floquet's theorem to obtain the restrictions imposed by periodicity on the solutions of (2-8).

2-2 Consider a one-dimensional solid in which only nearest-neighbor interactions are of importance. Show that the sound-wave dispersion relation takes the form

$$M\omega_k^2 = 2A_{ii} \sin^2 (ka/2)$$

2-3 Discuss the stability of solid He^4 on the basis of the melting criterion of Sec. 2-4, under the assumption that the phonons of importance are longitudinal phonons of frequency sk, where $s = 240$ m/sec for He^4. (Note that the same considerations apply to He^3, since γ depends only on Ms^2, a mass-independent quantity.)

2-4 Show how conservation of energy and pseudo-momentum determines the main features of one-phonon inelastic neutron scattering.

2-5 Derive the cross sections for one-phonon inelastic scattering, (2-124), (2-125), and (2-126).

Chapter 3

ELECTRONS AND PLASMONS

3-1 SOMMERFELD NONINTERACTING ELECTRON GAS

Ground-State Wave Function

In this chapter we wish to study the interactions between electrons in a metal. We shall do so by adopting a simple model for a metal, in which we replace the periodic potential due to the ions by a uniform background of positive charge. Such an "interacting electron gas" model will work best for simple, nearly free-electron-like metals (such as the alkalis) for which the periodic potential can be regarded as producing a relatively small perturbation in the motion of the electrons. It is probably not a bad approximation for all metals with the notable exception of the transition metals and the rare earths; in these latter systems periodicity plays an essential role.

The earliest (and simplest) quantum treatment of the interacting electron gas is due to Sommerfeld.[1] In the Sommerfeld approximation one neglects the interaction between the electrons; the many-electron aspect of the problem is taken into account by assigning plane-wave states to the electrons in accordance with the Pauli principle. Thus if we choose periodic boundary conditions in a box of side L, the individual electron solutions are given by

$$\varphi_{\alpha_i}(\mathbf{r}_i, \zeta_i) = \chi_i(\zeta_i)\, e^{i\mathbf{k}\cdot\mathbf{r}_i}$$

χ_i is the spin wave function; the index α includes both the spin direction and the momentum vector. The energy of the electron is independent of its spin direction, and is

$$\varepsilon_k = \frac{\hbar^2 k^2}{2m} \qquad (3\text{-}1)$$

since we are considering only the kinetic-energy part of the electron Hamiltonian. To build the many-electron wave function, one simply forms a product of one-electron functions

$$\Psi = \prod_{i=1}^{N} \varphi_{\alpha_i}(x_i) \tag{3-2}$$

x signifies both the position and spin coordinates. (Since electrons are fermions, the wave function should rather be taken as a Slater determinant of plane waves; we consider this modification presently.) The energy of the system is then

$$E_o = \Sigma_{\alpha_i} \varepsilon_{\alpha_i}$$

The k vectors are limited by the periodic boundary condition to the values (compare Chapter 2)

$$\mathbf{k} = \frac{2\pi}{L} n$$

where n has integral components. Hence the density of points in k space (for a single spin direction) is

$$\frac{dn_x \, dn_y \, dn_z}{d^3k} = \left(\frac{L}{2\pi}\right)^3 = \rho(k)$$

and for a function f(**k**) of **k**, the transformation between the summation and the integration goes as

$$\sum_{\mathbf{k}} f(\mathbf{k}) = \left(\frac{L}{2\pi}\right)^3 \int f(\mathbf{k}) \, d^3k$$

How does one assign the wave vectors **k**, which appear in the wave function (3-2)? According to the Pauli principle, no two electrons can have identical quantum numbers; in the present case this means that to each value of **k** we can assign at most two electrons, of opposite spin. At T = 0, the system energy is clearly minimized if we fill the N lowest-energy states in a way consistent with the Pauli principle. We are led therefore to a picture of the momentum distribution as consisting of two filled "Fermi spheres," one for each spin direction, all states being occupied up to some maximum momentum $\hbar k_o$ (Fig. 3-1). We obtain k_o by requiring there be N/2 vectors in momentum space (each occupied twice):

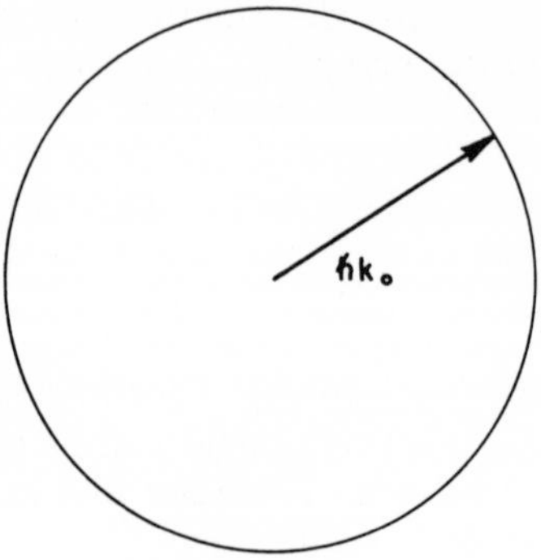

Fig. 3-1

$$N = \sum_{k} 2 = 2 \int_{0}^{k_o} 4\pi k^2 \, dk \left(\frac{L}{2\pi}\right)^3 = \frac{L^3 k_o^3}{3\pi^2} \; ; \quad k_o = (3\pi^2 n)^{1/3} \tag{3-3}$$

with $n = N/L^3$, the density in configuration space. The volume per electron can be described by a characteristic radius r_o:

$$V_e = \frac{1}{n} = \frac{4}{3}\pi r_o^3$$

It is convenient to work with the dimensionless quantity $r_s = r_o/a_o$, where $a_o = \hbar^2/me^2 = 0.529$ A, the Bohr radius. Then

$$k_o r_o = \left(\frac{9\pi}{4}\right)^{1/3} = 1.92 \qquad k_o = \frac{3.64}{r_s} \, A^{-1} \tag{3-4}$$

The maximum or Fermi energy is given by

$$\varepsilon_F = \frac{\hbar^2 k_o^2}{2m} = \left(\frac{9\pi}{4}\right)^{2/3} \frac{1}{r_s^2} \frac{me^4}{2\hbar^2} = \frac{3.68}{r_s^2} \text{ rydbergs} \tag{3-5}$$

the rydberg $= 1/2\,(me^4/\hbar^2) = 13.5$ ev $= 2.17 \times 10^{-11}$ erg, the ionization potential for hydrogen. The *average* energy per particle is

$$E_{kin} = \sum_{k} E_k \Big/ \sum_{k} 1 = \frac{3}{5}\varepsilon_F = \frac{2.21}{r_s^2} \text{ rydbergs} \tag{3-6}$$

as is easily verified.

Most metals have densities falling within the range represented by

$$2 \leq r_s \leq 5.5$$

then the values of k_o and ε_F will fall within the ranges

$$1.82 \geq k_o \geq 0.662\ \text{A}^{-1}$$

$$12.5 \geq \varepsilon_F \geq 1.66\ \text{ev}$$

Specific Heat

At finite temperatures, the probability of finding an electron of momentum $\hbar k$, energy ε_k, is given by the Fermi-Dirac distribution function,

$$f_k(T) = \frac{1}{\exp [\beta (\varepsilon_k - \mu_o) + 1]} \tag{3-7}$$

where $\beta = 1/\kappa T$ and μ_o, the chemical potential, is equal to ε_F, the energy of an electron on the Fermi surface. In Fig. 3-2 a plot of $f_k(T)$ is given. One sees there the smearing out, at finite temperatures, of the discontinuity in $f_k(0)$ at $k = k_o$. The smearing occurs within a region δk of k_o, where

$$\frac{\delta k}{k_o} \cong \frac{\kappa T}{\varepsilon_F}$$

One may say that only a fraction, $\sim \kappa T/\varepsilon_F$, of the electrons are free to take part in thermally activated processes; the remainder are frozen out by the Pauli principle.

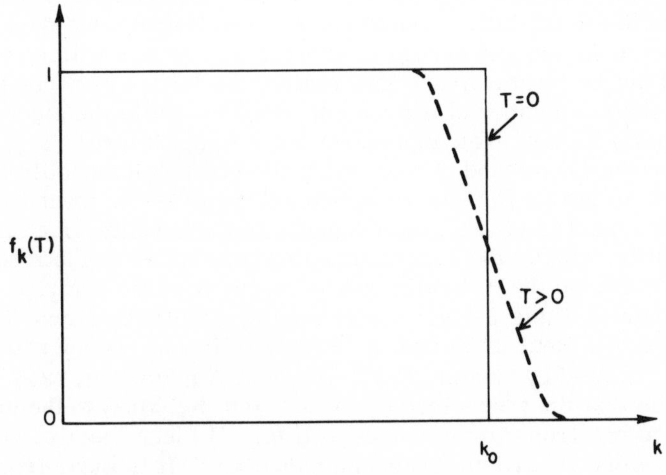

Fig. 3-2

Let us now consider some properties of the Sommerfeld model for a metal. We begin with the specific heat. It is straightforward to show that the electronic specific heat is given by[2]

$$C_v = \frac{\pi^2 \kappa^2 T}{3} \frac{\rho_F(E)}{N} \tag{3-8}$$

where $\rho_F(E)$ is the density of single-particle states per unit energy at the Fermi surface. We can write

$$\rho_F(E) = \left(\frac{dn}{d\varepsilon}\right)_{\varepsilon=\varepsilon_F} = \left[\left(\frac{dn}{dk}\right) \frac{1}{\partial \varepsilon_k / \partial k}\right]_{k=k_o} = \frac{mk_o}{\pi^2 \hbar^2} \tag{3-9a}$$

and using (3-3) for N, obtain

$$C_v = \frac{\pi^2 m}{\hbar^2 k_o^2} \kappa^2 T \tag{3-9b}$$

In (3-9b), k_o is determined by the number of free electrons per atom, N_a, one assumes for the metal in question; the experimental results for C_v can then be expressed as a ratio of the measured C_v,

$$C_v^{\text{expt}} = \frac{\pi^2 m_e}{\hbar^2 k_o^2} \kappa^2 T \tag{3-9c}$$

to the free-electron value, (3-9b); or, by what is equivalent, m_e/m.

Experimentally, the electronic specific heat cannot be observed by calorimetric techniques except at very low temperatures when the T^3 law is valid for the lattice contribution. The linear term then dominates the cubic one and errors in subtracting out the lattice contribution will not be large. Above this region, the lattice part rises rapidly to $N\kappa$, with N = number of degrees of freedom, while the electronic part is quite linear, even high above room temperature ($\kappa T_{room}/E_o \simeq 1/80$). A second method of measuring the electronic specific heat, one which is usable for superconductors, involves the measurement of the threshold field, i.e., the magnetic field intensity which is just sufficient to destroy the superconducting properties of the metal. This field can be theoretically related to the specific heat.

The data in Table 3-1 are taken from an article by Daunt, Electronic Specific Heat in Metals in "Progress in Low Temperature Physics," edited by Gorter, North-Holland, Amsterdam, 1955.

We see that the free-electron model, with N_a equal to the number of valence electrons/atom, works well for all these metals, which we may therefore regard as "free-electron-like." It is clear from Table 3-1 that neither the influence of the periodic ion potential, of the

Table 3-1

Metal	N_a	m_e/m	Metal	N_a	m_e/m
Cu	1	1.5	Al	3	1.6
Ag	1	1.0	Ga	3	0.4
Be	2	0.46	In	3	1.3
Mg	2	1.33	Tl	3	1.15
Ca	2	0.8	La	3	4.3
Zn	2	0.9	Sn	4	1.2
Cd	2	0.75	Pb	4	2.1
Hg	2	2			

electron-electron interactions, nor of the electron-phonon interactions, has an important qualitative effect on the electronic specific heat of these metals, in that m_e is not far from m. Indeed the quantitative effects of all these neglected couplings are not large—and that is one of the properties of electrons in metals which it behooves the theorist to explain. Such good agreement is not found for either semimetals, like Bi or Sb, or the transition metals. In both these cases, the influence of the periodic lattice potential is very large, and must be taken into account at the outset if one hopes to obtain agreement with experiment.

Spin Susceptibility

Next we consider the paramagnetic, or spin, susceptibility of the free-electron gas. In the presence of a magnetic field, we expect that the energies of electrons of spin parallel to the field (spin up) or antiparallel to the field (spin down) will no longer be the same. Thus one has

$$E_{k\uparrow} = \frac{\hbar^2 k^2}{2m} + \mu_e H$$

$$E_{k\downarrow} = \frac{\hbar k^2}{2m} - \mu_e H$$

where μ_e is the magnetic moment of the electron. The resultant spin polarization, p, of the electron gas may be calculated by assuming that one has for the density of up and down spin electrons,

$$n_\uparrow = \frac{n}{2}(1 - p) = k_{o\uparrow}^3/6\pi^2$$

$$n_\downarrow = \frac{n}{2}(1 + p) = k_{o\downarrow}^3/6\pi^2$$

and then expanding the ground-state energy per particle in powers of p/n. This latter quantity will always be small, since the fraction of electrons influenced by the magnetic field is of order $\mu_e H/\varepsilon_F$. One finds the quite general result:

$$E(p) = E(0) + \alpha p^2 - p\mu_e H \tag{3-10a}$$

where E(0) is the ground-state energy per particle in the absence of the field. From (3-10a) one obtains

$$p = \frac{\mu_e H}{2\alpha}$$

for the number of aligned spins, and hence

$$\chi_s = n\mu_e^2/\alpha \tag{3-10b}$$

for the spin susceptibility per unit volume.

In the free-electron approximation, one considers only the contribution to α from the kinetic energy of the electrons. It is a straightforward exercise to obtain

$$\alpha_{free} = \frac{2}{3}\varepsilon_F$$

whence one has

$$\chi_s^{free} = \frac{3}{2}\frac{N\mu_e^2}{\varepsilon_F} \tag{3-11}$$

the result first obtained by Pauli.[3]

The spin susceptibility of the conduction electrons in Li and Na has been measured directly by Slichter and Schumacher,[4] using a combination of electron-spin-resonance and nuclear-magnetic-resonance techniques. Their results are compared with the free-electron values in Table 3-2. One sees again that the free-electron theory leads to a good order-of-magnitude agreement with experiment.

Table 3-2

χ_s (10^6 cgs units)

Metal	χ_{free}	χ_s^{expt}
Li	0.81	2.08 ± 0.1
Na	0.64	0.89 ± 0.04

Width of Conduction Band

Another quantity of interest is the total width of the Fermi distribution, $\Delta = \varepsilon_F - \varepsilon_o$, which corresponds to the width of the conduction band in a metal. This can be measured by knocking out core electrons and observing the soft X rays emitted as conduction electrons fall into the gap provided, as shown in Fig. 3-3. The radiation will have energies between E_1 and $E_1 + \Delta$, with a smearing out beyond these limits (see Fig. 3-4), due primarily to electron-electron interactions. After corrections for this broadening have been made, rather good agreement between theory and experiment is found, as may be seen in Table 3-3.

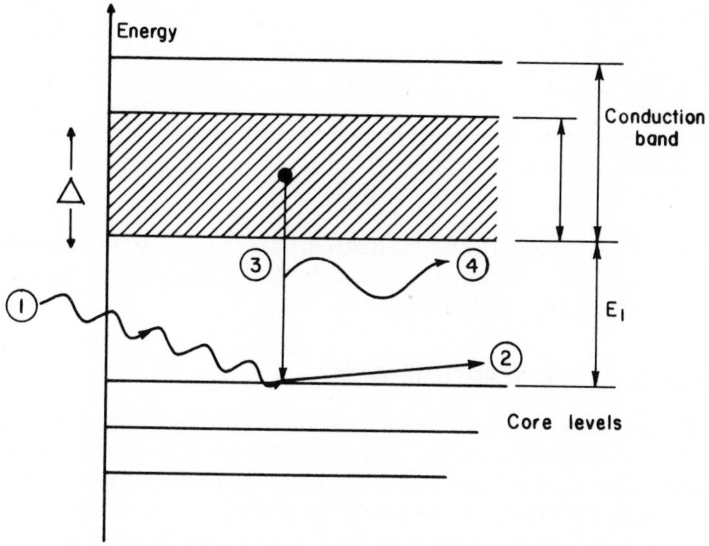

Fig. 3-3. (1) Hard X ray impinges on metal. (2) Core electron is knocked out. (3) Conduction electron falls into emptied level. (4) Soft X ray is emitted ($E_1 \sim 50$ ev).

Table 3-3
Band Width of Certain Metals (in ev)

Metal	Δ_{free}	Δ_{expt} [a]
Li	4.8	3.7 ± 0.5
Na	3.2	3.5 ± 0.3
Be	14.6	13.8 ± 1.0
Mg	7.3	6.2 ± 0.3
Al	11.9	11.8 ± 0.5

[a]These values are due to H. B. W. Skinner, *Phil. Trans. Roy. Soc.*, **A239**, 95 (1940).

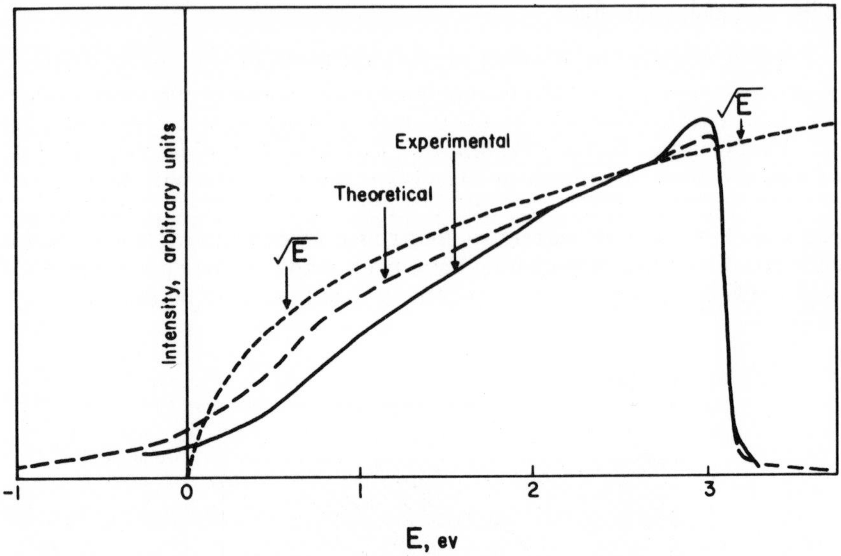

Fig. 3-4. Experimental and theoretical $L_{II,\ III}$ emission curves of sodium. (From P. T. Landsberg, *Proc. Phys. Soc. (London)*, **A62**, 806 (1949).

Improvements on the Sommerfeld Model

In all the cases we have discussed the agreement between the first crude theory one might make, and experiment, may be viewed as satisfactory. The corrections one would like to make are the following:

1. Include the effect of the periodic lattice. For the specific heat, and for the spin susceptibility, both of which depend only on the behavior of electrons in the immediate vicinity of the Fermi surface, this can be done by the introduction of an effective mass, m^*, defined (for a spherical Fermi surface) by

$$\partial \varepsilon_k^*/\partial k_{\ k=k_o} = \hbar^2 k_o/m^*$$

where ε_k^* is the one-electron energy in the presence of the periodic field. (For a nonspherical Fermi surface, m^* represents an average of the gradient of the one-electron energy over all directions in k space.) For the conduction-electron band width, one has rather to calculate the change in the binding of an electron at the bottom of the conduction band, of energy ε_o^* say, and that at the top of the band, $\varepsilon_{ko}^* - \hbar^2 k_o^{\ 2}/2m$. Both of these corrections may, in principle, be obtained from a standard band-theory calculation for the metal in question.[4a]

2. Include the effect of electron-electron interactions. These will likewise act to change the energy of a single particle of momentum k near the Fermi surface, and hence influence both the specific heat and the spin susceptibility. The influence of electron-electron interactions on the band width is still more complicated; there is a change in the energy of a particle at the Fermi surface, and, as well, of an electron or, rather, a hole, at the bottom of the conduction band. Moreover, this latter state is not well defined, since any electron higher up in the band may jump into such a hole; it is this effect which is responsible for the broadening of the X-ray spectrum we have discussed.

3. Include the effect of electron-phonon interactions. These turn out to affect the specific heat, but not the spin susceptibility or the bandwidth to any appreciable extent.

The first correction is a "solid-state" effect; the second and third corrections arise from the replacement of the free-particle spectrum by the quasi-particle spectrum appropriate to the interactions considered.

The general philosophy one follows in making such corrections is to use the best "solid-state correction" available for the one-electron energy considered. One then adds to this the corresponding correction from electron interaction, computed on the basis of an interacting-electron-gas model, in which the influence of the periodic lattice is neglected. This choice is one born of necessity; there exist at present no satisfactory treatments of the influence of electron-electron interaction on quasi-particle properties in which solid-state effects are included, that is, in which one considers a collection of interacting "Bloch" electrons. It is probably not a bad approximation, for corrections come from all possible momentum transfers in the electron-electron interaction, so that solid-state effects tend to average out as far as the electron-electron interaction is concerned. In computing the influence of the electron-phonon interaction, one can in principle include "solid-state effects" on the coupling of the electrons to the phonons in simple metals. We return to a discussion of these in Chapter 5.

3-2 HARTREE AND HARTREE-FOCK APPROXIMATIONS

Perturbation-Theoretic Calculation of the Ground-State Energy

Let us now consider the effect of the interaction between the electrons in our electron gas immersed in a uniform background of positive charge. The Hamiltonian for the system is given by

$$H = \sum_i \frac{p_i^2}{2m} + \frac{1}{2} \sum_{i \neq j} \frac{e^2}{|\mathbf{r}_i - \mathbf{r}_j|} \tag{3-12}$$

It is convenient to express the interaction term in terms of the density fluctuations of the electron gas. We have

$$\rho(\mathbf{r}) = \sum_i \delta(\mathbf{r} - \mathbf{r}_i) = \sum_k \rho_k e^{i\mathbf{k}\cdot\mathbf{r}} \tag{3-13}$$

where $\rho(\mathbf{r})$ is the particle density at the point $\mathbf{r}$ and ρ_k is the fluctuation about the average particle density

$$\rho_o = N$$

(We take our volume L^3 to be unity in this section.) On performing the Fourier analysis indicated in (3-13), one finds

$$\rho_k = \sum_i e^{-i\mathbf{k}\cdot\mathbf{r}_i} \tag{3-14}$$

We leave it to the reader as an exercise to show that one may rewrite H in (3-12) as

$$H = \sum_i \frac{p_i^2}{2m} + \sum_k V_k \left(\frac{\rho_k^+ \rho_k}{2} - N \right) \tag{3-15}$$

where

$$V_k = 4\pi e^2/k^2$$

is the Fourier transform of the Coulomb interaction.

Because we deal with a gas of electrons immersed in a uniform background of positive charge, the term with $k = 0$ in (3-15) is to be omitted. This follows directly from the fact that the $k = 0$ component of the electron density fluctuations corresponds to a uniform distribution of negative charge; in its effect on any given electron it is simply canceled by the uniform positive charge. The smeared-out background of positive charge has no effect on the behavior of the $k \neq 0$ components of the density fluctuations; this is no longer true when one takes into account the actual background of positive ions arrayed in a periodic lattice.

We shall, moreover, find it convenient to work with the Hamiltonian, (3-15), expressed in the representation of second quantization. A brief description of the derivation of the Hamiltonian in this representation is given in Appendix A. One has

$$H = \sum_{p\sigma} \varepsilon_p \, c^+_{p\sigma} c_{p\sigma} + \frac{1}{2} \sum_{\substack{pqk \\ \sigma\sigma'}} V_k \, c^+_{p+k\sigma} \, c_{q-k\sigma'} \, c_{q\sigma'} \, c_{p\sigma} \tag{3-16}$$

where

$$\varepsilon_p = p^2/2m$$

is the free-electron energy, and the creation and annihilation operators satisfy the anticommutation rules:

$$\begin{aligned} \left[c_{p\sigma}, c_{p'\sigma'}\right]_+ &= \left[c^+_{p\sigma}, c^+_{p'\sigma'}\right]_+ = 0 \\ \left[c_{p\sigma}, c^+_{p'\sigma'}\right]_+ &= \delta_{pp'} \, \delta_{\sigma\sigma'} \end{aligned} \tag{3-17}$$

Let us now consider the approximations of Hartree, and Hartree and Fock, for the ground-state energy and elementary excitations of the Hamiltonian, (3-15). We shall here adopt a somewhat different view from that normally found in textbooks (cf., for example, the excellent discussion in Seitz[5]): rather than regarding the approximations as variational calculations, we shall discuss them as first steps in a perturbation-theoretic treatment of the free-electron gas. In such a treatment one regards the kinetic energy as the dominant term in determining the system behavior; the potential energy is then regarded as a relatively small perturbation. As we shall see, such an approach is well justified in the limit of very high density electron systems.

If one ignores the potential energy altogether, the ground-state wave function, $|0\rangle$, is that compatible with a filled Fermi sphere, as discussed in the previous section. In configuration space it corresponds to a determinant formed from plane waves made up of the lowest momentum states available to the electrons, i.e., with $p \le \hbar k_o$: In the representation of second quantization we may specify $|0\rangle$ by (A-22) and (A-23) of Appendix A, according to which

$$\begin{aligned} n_{p\sigma} = \langle 0 | c^+_{p\sigma} c_{p\sigma} | 0 \rangle &= 1 \qquad p \le \hbar k_o \\ &= 0 \qquad p \ge \hbar k_o \end{aligned} \tag{3-18}$$

The ground-state energy of the system per particle is, in lowest (or zeroth) order, the mean kinetic energy per electron

$$E_{kin} = (1/N) \langle 0 | \sum_{p\sigma} \varepsilon_p \, c^+_{p\sigma} c_{p\sigma} | 0 \rangle = \frac{2.21}{r_s^2} \text{ rydbergs} \tag{3-19}$$

a result we obtained in the previous section; cf. (3-6).

We proceed to calculate the ground-state energy in the first order of the perturbation. The first-order energy per particle is formally written as

$$E_1 = (1/N) \left\langle 0 \left| \sum_{\substack{p,q,k \\ \sigma,\sigma'}} (V_k/2)\, c^+_{p+k,\sigma} c^+_{q-k,\sigma'} c_{q,\sigma'} c_{p,\sigma} \right| 0 \right\rangle \qquad (3\text{-}20)$$

In order to obtain a nonzero contribution from the right-hand side, we must consider a process in which two particles are destroyed from the ground state and then two particles are created in such a way to permit the system to come back to the original ground state. Two such possibilities may be pointed out:

One is a direct process in which annihilation and creation occur in the pairs: $(c^+_{p+k,\sigma}, c_{p,\sigma})$, $(c^+_{q-k,\sigma'}, c_{q,\sigma'})$. Figure 3-5a gives a schematic picture of this process. We may also draw a diagram corresponding to this process as in Fig. 3-5b, where circles in solid lines represent nonpropagating electron lines and a dotted line describes an interaction.[6] This contribution arises from the k = 0 part of the interaction; it represents the Hartree contribution to the ground-state energy.

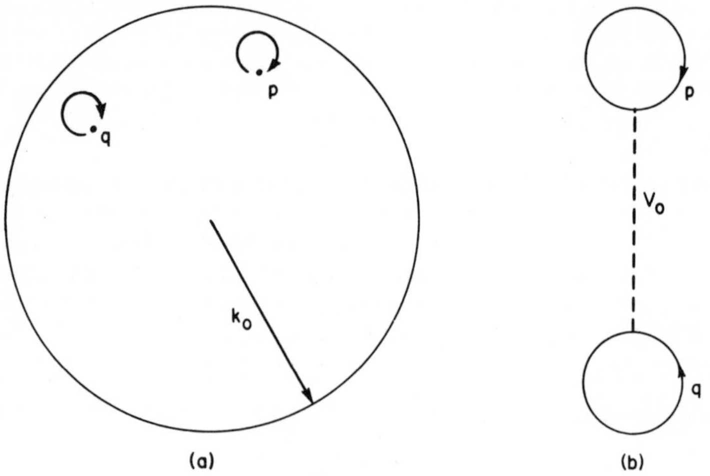

Fig. 3-5

But, as we have just seen, for the electron gas in a uniform background of positive charge there is no k = 0 part of the interaction. Hence the Hartree approximation is completely equivalent to the Sommerfeld free-electron gas model. Another way of seeing this is to remark that in the Hartree approximation, each particle moves in an average self-consistent field produced by all the other particles. For the free-electron gas, the single-particle wave functions are plane waves, so that the self-consistent field is a uniform distribution of negative charge. The latter is then canceled by the uniform background of positive charge.

The other possibility is an exchange process in which particles are annihilated and created in such a way as to make pairs: $(c^+_{p+k,\sigma}, c_{q,\sigma'})$, $(c^+_{q-k,\sigma'}, c_{p,\sigma})$. Such a process is permitted only when $\sigma = \sigma'$, i.e., for electrons with parallel spin. Diagrams corresponding to this process are shown in Fig. 3-6. On keeping only the terms with $q = p + k$, and $\sigma = \sigma'$ in (3-20), one finds for the energy per particle

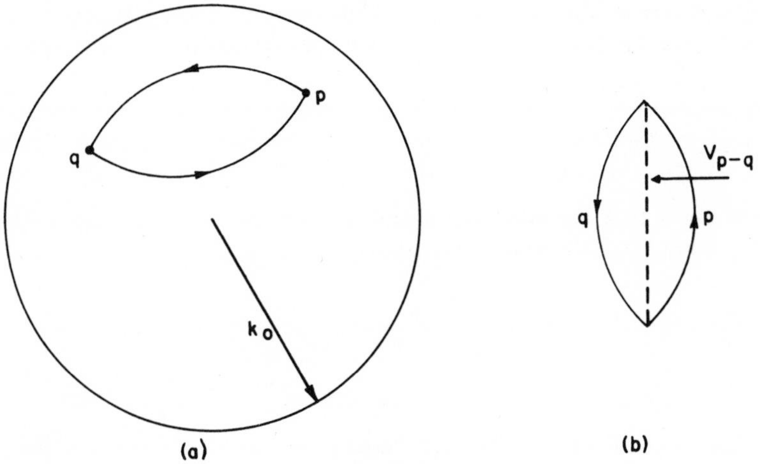

Fig. 3-6

$$E_{exch} = \frac{1}{N} \langle 0 | \sum_{\substack{pk\\ \sigma}} (V_k/2)\, c^+_{p+k\sigma} c^+_{p\sigma}\, c_{p+k\sigma} c_{p\sigma} | 0 \rangle$$

$$= -\frac{1}{N} \sum_{\substack{pk\\ \sigma}} (V_k/2)\, n_{p+k\sigma} n_{p\sigma} \qquad (3\text{-}21)$$

on applying the anticommutation rules, (3-17). This term in the energy, may also be written

$$E_{exch} = -\frac{1}{N} \sum_{\substack{p<p_F\\ q<p_F}} \frac{2\pi e^2}{|p - q|^2} \qquad (3\text{-}22)$$

on changing the dummy variable **k** to **q** - **p**; the evaluation of (3-22) is straightforward, and one finds

$$E_{exch} = -\frac{0.916}{r_s} \text{ rydbergs} \tag{3-23}$$

Comparison with Variational Calculation

The Hartree and the Hartree-Fock approximations were presented originally as applications of Schrödinger's variational principle in quantum mechanics.[5] In this section we sketch this approach to the extent required to reproduce the results obtained in the previous section.

In the Hartree approximation, one starts with a wave function for the whole system which is a product of one-electron wave functions ψ_i:

$$\Psi = \prod_\alpha \psi_\alpha(\mathbf{r}_\alpha) \tag{3-24}$$

One can show that the wave functions, ψ_α, which minimize the system energy, must obey the Hartree equation:

$$\frac{p^2}{2m} + e^2 \sum_{\substack{\beta \\ \beta\neq\alpha}} \left\langle \psi_\beta(\mathbf{r}') \middle| \frac{1}{|\mathbf{r} - \mathbf{r}'|} \middle| \psi_\beta(\mathbf{r}') \right\rangle \psi_\alpha(\mathbf{r}) = \varepsilon_\alpha \psi_\alpha(\mathbf{r}) \tag{3-25}$$

where the second term on the left-hand side takes into account the average field acting on the electron.

The method is self-consistent if the ψ_α's chosen initially are eigenfunctions of this equation. When this is not the case, one proceeds by successive iterations. For a free-electron gas, the ψ_α's are the plane-wave solutions of the equation

$$\frac{p^2}{2m} \psi_\alpha(\mathbf{r}) = \varepsilon_\alpha \psi_\alpha(\mathbf{r}) \tag{3-26}$$

Owing to the uniform background of positive charge, the average field acting on one electron vanishes, so that the plane waves provide a consistent solution. The Hartree approximation therefore gives the same result as the free-electron model, as we have already remarked.

The first disadvantage of this approximation is that the cohesive energy comes out completely wrong, as we shall see later from numerical examples. This is due to the fact that the interactions between electrons have been completely neglected. There is no repulsion among the electrons, and two electrons can occupy precisely the same site. A second disadvantage is that the method does not take into account the Pauli exclusion principle, in that the wave function (3-24) is not antisymmetric with respect to the interchange of any two electrons.

In the Hartree-Fock approximation, as first developed by Dirac and Fock, one uses instead of the wave function, (3-24), a properly antisymmetrized wave function. The normalized antisymmetric wave function can be written as a Slater determinant:

$$\psi = \frac{1}{\sqrt{N}} \begin{vmatrix} \psi_1(r_1)\, \psi_2(r_1) & \cdots & \psi_N(r_1) \\ \psi_1(r_2) & \cdots & \\ & & \\ \psi_1(r_N) & \cdots & \psi_N(r_N) \end{vmatrix} \tag{3-27}$$

Instead of (3-25), the one-electron wave functions have now to be consistent with Hartree-Fock equations:

$$\frac{p^2}{2m}\psi_\alpha(\mathbf{r}) + e^2 \sum_\beta \left\langle \psi_\beta(\mathbf{r}') \left| \frac{1}{|\mathbf{r}-\mathbf{r}'|} \right| \psi_\beta(\mathbf{r}') \right\rangle \psi_\alpha(\mathbf{r})$$

$$- e^2 \sum_{\substack{\beta \\ ||\,\text{spins}}} \left\langle \psi_\beta(\mathbf{r}') \left| \frac{1}{|\mathbf{r}-\mathbf{r}'|} \right| \psi_\alpha(\mathbf{r}') \right\rangle \psi_\beta(\mathbf{r}) = \varepsilon_\alpha \psi_\alpha(\mathbf{r}) \tag{3-28}$$

If we compare this with (3-25) we see that the only new term is the third term on the left-hand side. This is the exchange term, which is due solely to the antisymmetric properties of the wave function (3-27).

The problem can still be solved in a consistent way, using plane waves for the one-electron wave functions. Taking into account the fact that plane waves are eigenfunctions of (3-25), we have only to show that they are also eigenfunctions of the exchange term; we have

$$H_{ex} e^{i\mathbf{k}\cdot\mathbf{r}} = -e^2 \sum_{\substack{\mathbf{k}' \\ ||\,\text{spins}}} \int d\mathbf{r}'\, e^{-i\mathbf{k}'\cdot\mathbf{r}'} \frac{1}{|\mathbf{r}-\mathbf{r}'|} e^{i\mathbf{k}\cdot\mathbf{r}'} e^{i\mathbf{k}'\cdot\mathbf{r}}$$

$$= -e^2 \sum_{\substack{\mathbf{k}' \\ ||\,\text{spins}}} \int d\mathbf{r}' \frac{e^{-i(\mathbf{k}-\mathbf{k}')\cdot(\mathbf{r}-\mathbf{r}')}}{|\mathbf{r}-\mathbf{r}'|} e^{i\mathbf{k}\cdot\mathbf{r}}$$

$$= - \sum_{\substack{\mathbf{k}' \\ ||\,\text{spins}}} \frac{4\pi e^2}{|\mathbf{k}-\mathbf{k}'|^2} e^{i\mathbf{k}\cdot\mathbf{r}} \tag{3-29}$$

The summation over **k'** here excludes **k'** = **k**. Equation (3-29) shows that plane waves are actually eigenfunctions of H_{ex}. The energy of each electron in the Hartree-Fock approximation is

$$\tilde{\varepsilon}_{k\sigma} = \frac{\hbar^2 k^2}{2m} - \sum_{\substack{k' \\ \parallel \text{spins}}} 4\pi e^2/|\mathbf{k} - \mathbf{k}'|^2$$

$$= \frac{\hbar^2 k^2}{2m} - \sum_{q} V_q N_{q+k\sigma} \tag{3-30}$$

Therefore the grand-state energy per particle is

$$E_{HF} = \left\{\sum_{k} \hbar^2 k^2/2m - \frac{1}{2} \sum_{\substack{k \pm k' \\ \parallel \text{spins}}} 4\pi e^2/|\mathbf{k} - \mathbf{k}'|^2\right\}/N$$

$$= 2.21/r_s^2 - 0.916/r_s \quad \text{rydbergs} \tag{3-31}$$

in agreement with (3-19) and (3-23).

Physical Interpretation of Exchange Hole and Exchange Energy

Let us now investigate the physical significance of the Hartree and the Hartree-Fock approximations in some detail. For this purpose we shall find it helpful to introduce certain correlation functions. The time-independent density-density correlation function, p(r), is defined as

$$p(\mathbf{r}) = (1/N) \langle \Psi_0 | \rho(\mathbf{r} + \mathbf{r}') \rho(\mathbf{r}') | \Psi_0 \rangle \tag{3-32}$$

where ρ is the particle density, (3-13), and Ψ_0 is here the exact ground-state wave function of the system. We call p(**r**) "time-independent" because $\rho(\mathbf{r} + \mathbf{r}')$ and $\rho(\mathbf{r}')$ are to be taken at the same time; later a time-dependent density-density correlation will be introduced. If the system is invariant under the space and time translation, the correlation function (3-32) is independent of **r'**; we have assumed such translational invariance for our system. As r increases indefinitely, the correlation obviously must vanish (i.e., the quantities in regions widely separated are statistically independent), and thus the function p(r) tends to N for sufficiently large **r**.

On substituting the density, $\rho(\mathbf{r})$, appropriate to a system of point particles, (3-13), we find

$$p(\mathbf{r}) = (1/N) \langle \Psi_0 | \sum_{ij} \delta(\mathbf{r} + \mathbf{r}' - \mathbf{r}_j)\, \delta(\mathbf{r}' - \mathbf{r}_j) | \Psi_0 \rangle \tag{3-33}$$

The particle coordinates $\mathbf{r}_i$ and $\mathbf{r}_j$ always commute as long as a simultaneous observation is concerned; we may make use of translational invariance to rewrite (3-33) as

$$p(\mathbf{r}) = (1/N) \langle \Psi_o | \sum_{ij} \delta(\mathbf{r} + \mathbf{r}_i - \mathbf{r}_j) | \Psi_o \rangle$$

$$= \delta(\mathbf{r}) + (1/N) \langle \Psi_o | \sum_{i \neq j} \delta(\mathbf{r} + \mathbf{r}_i - \mathbf{r}_j) | \Psi_o \rangle$$

$$= \delta(\mathbf{r}) + (N - 1) g(\mathbf{r}) \tag{3-34}$$

where

$$g(\mathbf{r}) = \frac{1}{N(N-1)} \langle \Psi_o | \sum_{i \neq j} \delta(\mathbf{r} + \mathbf{r}_i - \mathbf{r}_j) | \Psi_o \rangle \tag{3-35}$$

is the pair distribution function; it gives the probability that when one particle is observed at a point (say, $\mathbf{r}_o$), another particle will be found in a characteristic volume $v_o = 1/(N - 1)$ located at a distance r away from the point $\mathbf{r}_o$. It is then apparent that if there is no correlation between the positions of two different particles, $g(\mathbf{r})$ becomes unity. What we have done in (3-34) is to separate out that singular part of $p(\mathbf{r})$ which involves the correlation of a particle with itself.

Let us calculate the Fourier transform of the density-density correlation function, $p(\mathbf{r})$.

$$\int d\mathbf{r}\, p(\mathbf{r}) e^{-i\mathbf{k}\cdot\mathbf{r}} = 1/N \int d\mathbf{r} \langle \Psi_o | \sum_{ij} \delta(\mathbf{r} + \mathbf{r}_i - \mathbf{r}_j) | \Psi_o \rangle e^{-i\mathbf{k}\cdot\mathbf{r}}$$

$$= (1/N) \langle \Psi_o | \sum_{ij} e^{-i\mathbf{k}\cdot(\mathbf{r}_i - \mathbf{r}_j)} | \Psi_o \rangle$$

$$= (1/N) \langle \Psi_o | \sum_i e^{i\mathbf{k}\cdot\mathbf{r}_i} \sum_j e^{-i\mathbf{k}\cdot\mathbf{r}_j} | \Psi_o \rangle$$

$$= (1/N) \langle \Psi_o | \rho_k^+ \rho_k | \Psi_o \rangle = S(k) \tag{3-36}$$

S(k), the Fourier transform of p(r), is known as the form factor (or sometimes structure factor); it plays a central role in X-ray and neutron scattering experiments. It is seen to be simply the mean-square density fluctuation in the ground state. We remark that the expectation value of the potential energy (per particle), according to (3-36) and (3-15), is given by

$$E_{int} = 1/N \left\langle \Psi_o \left| \sum_k V_k/2 \quad \rho_k^+ \rho_k - N \right| \Psi_o \right\rangle$$

$$= \sum_k (V_k/2) \{S(k) - 1\} \tag{3-37}$$

For a gas of noninteracting particles, S(k) = 1. To see this, write

$$S(k) = (1/N) \left\langle \Psi_o \left| \sum_{i,j} e^{-ik\cdot(r_i - r_j)} \right| \Psi_o \right\rangle$$

$$= 1 + (1/N) \left\langle \Psi_o \left| \sum_{i\neq j} e^{-ik\cdot(r_i - r_j)} \right| \Psi_o \right\rangle \tag{3-38}$$

If there is no correlation between the positions of two different particles, the second term on the right-hand side vanishes for $k \neq 0$, and thus we obtain S(k) = 1. We note that for k = 0 the form factor takes the value N, independent of the nature of the interactions, since $\rho_o = N$, a constant of the motion.

In the representation of second quantization, we may write

$$S(k) = 1 + (1/N) \left\langle \Psi_o \left| \sum_{\substack{pq \\ \sigma\sigma'}} c_{p+k\sigma}^+ c_{q-k\sigma'}^+ c_{q\sigma'} c_{p\sigma} \right| \Psi_o \right\rangle \tag{3-39}$$

a form which emphasizes the close connection between the calculation of E_{int} and that of S(k). Let us now consider S(k) and g(**r**) in the Hartree and Hartree-Fock approximations.

In the Hartree approximation, we keep only the term with k = 0 in (3-39); we find then

$$S_H(k) = 1 + (1/N)\, N(N-1)\, \delta_{ok}$$

$$= \begin{cases} N & k = 0 \\ 1 & k \neq 0 \end{cases} \tag{3-40}$$

[the N(N-1) occurs because one cannot have q = p in (3-39)]. This is just the spectrum we might have anticipated for noninteracting electron gas. The corresponding value of g(r) is determined by an expression obtained from (3-34) and (3-36):

$$g(\mathbf{r}) = \frac{1}{N-1} \sum_k (S(k) - 1)\, e^{ik\cdot r} \tag{3-41}$$

In the Hartree approximation, we have

$$g_H(r) = \frac{1}{N-1}\sum_k (N-1)\,\delta_{ok} e^{ik\cdot r} = 1 \tag{3-42}$$

In other words, there is *no* correlation between the electrons. If we have one electron located at the origin, it is equally likely that we shall find another at any distance **r** away.

In the Hartree-Fock approximation, we have

$$\begin{aligned} S_{HF}(k) &= 1 + (1/N)\left\langle 0 \left| \sum_{\substack{pq \\ \sigma\sigma'}} c^+_{p+k\sigma} c^+_{q-k\sigma'} c_{q\sigma'} c_{p\sigma} \right| 0 \right\rangle \\ &= 1 + (N-1)\,\delta_{o,k} - (1/N) \sum_{\substack{p\sigma \\ k\neq 0}} n_{p+k\sigma} n_{p\sigma} \\ &= N\delta_{o,k} + \sum_{\substack{p\sigma \\ k\neq 0}} n_{p\sigma}(1 - n_{p+k\sigma}) \end{aligned} \tag{3-43}$$

The last term is a sum of all the states such that (p,σ) is occupied but $(p+k,\sigma)$ is unoccupied. It may be calculated by computing the volume of the shaded region shown in Fig. 3-7. One obtains[7]

$$S_{HF}(k) = \begin{cases} N\delta_{ok} + \dfrac{3}{4}\dfrac{k}{k_o} - \dfrac{1}{16}\dfrac{k^3}{k_o^{\,3}} & k < 2k_o \\[2em] 1 & k > 2k_o \end{cases} \tag{3-44}$$

The pair distribution function is now calculated as[8]

$$\begin{aligned} g_{HF}(r) &= 1 - \frac{1}{N-1}\sum_{k<2k_o}\left[1 - \frac{3}{4}\frac{k}{k_o} + \frac{1}{16}\frac{k^3}{k_o^{\,3}}\right] e^{ik\cdot r} \\ &= 1 - \frac{9}{2}\left[\frac{\sin k_o r - k_o r\cos k_o r}{k_o^{\,3} r^3}\right]^2 \end{aligned} \tag{3-45}$$

A plot of $g_{HF}(r)$, together with that of $g_H(r)$, is shown in Fig. 3-8.

We may understand the behavior of $g_{HF}(r)$ in the following way. First, in the Hartree-Fock approximation we have taken the Pauli principle into account; hence two electrons of the same spin cannot be

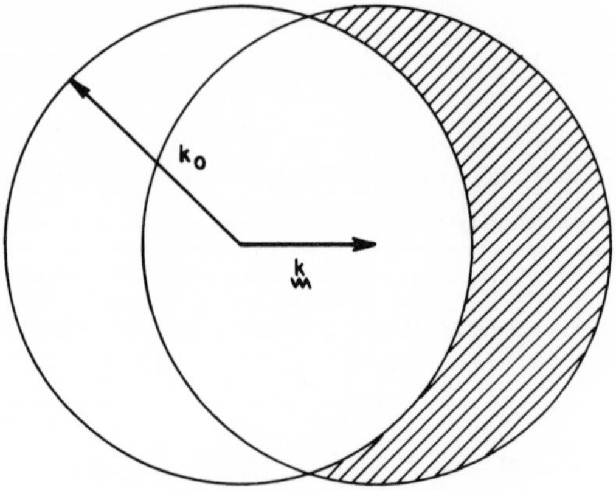

Fig. 3-7

at the same place. Nonetheless, $g_{HF}(r) = 1/2$ at $r = 0$, because we have not yet taken into account any correlations between electrons of antiparallel spin. As r increases from zero, $g_{HF}(r)$ increases, corresponding to the fact that the Pauli principle restriction gradually weakens. For distances much greater than the DeBroglie wavelength of an electron at the top of the Fermi distribution, the Pauli principle restriction has nearly ceased to operate, and one has nearly the free-electron behavior characteristic of $g_H(r)$. Finally, the oscillatory behavior of $g_{HF}(r)$ may be understood as arising from the sharpness of the Fermi surface; it is a reflection of the discontinuity in the derivative of $S_{HF}(k)$ at $k = 2k_o$.

It is this correlation between electrons of parallel spin which gives rise to the exchange energy. Because we are dealing with a repulsive

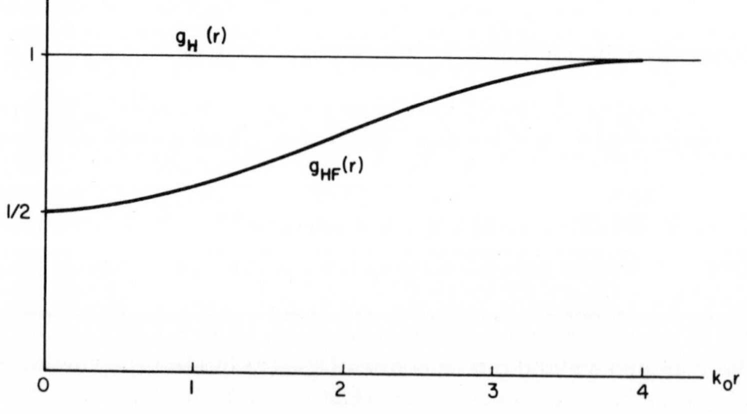

Fig. 3-8

interaction, any tendency of the electrons to stay away from one another will give rise to a reduction in the ground-state energy of the system. We may regard the exchange energy as arising from the *spin-induced* correlations in the electron gas; the fact that the electrons possess a charge, and interact via the Coulomb interaction, plays no role in determining $S_{HF}(k)$ or $g_{HF}(r)$.

Another way of looking at the exchange energy is to remark that, thanks to the Pauli principle, the mean-square density fluctuation has been reduced for small k, and it is this reduction which is responsible for the lowering of the system energy.

Equation-of-Motion Method

It is illuminating to obtain the ground state wave function and elementary excitations in the Hartree-Fock approximation in yet another way, by a study of the equations of motion of the operators which determine the single-particle elementary excitations in the system.[8a] In the equation-of-motion method, one works entirely in the representation of second quantization. One assumes that the ground-state wave function Ψ_o is known, and then seeks directly the operators, say 0_k^+ and 0_k, which act to create and destroy an elementary excitation of momentum $\hbar k$. These operators are determined by the requirement that they satisfy the oscillatory equations of motion

$$\left[H, 0_k^+\right] = \hbar\omega_k 0_k^+ \tag{3-45a}$$

$$\left[H, 0_k\right] = -\hbar\omega_k 0_k \tag{3-45b}$$

where H is the system Hamiltonian. Consider the commutator, $[H, 0_k]$, applied to some state Ψ_1 of energy E_1. Since $H\Psi_1 = E\Psi_1$, by (3-45b), we see that

$$[H, 0_k]\Psi_1 = H0_k\Psi_1 - 0_k H\Psi_1 = H0_k\Psi_1 - 0_k E_1\Psi_1 = -\omega_k 0_k \Psi_1$$

and

$$H0_k\Psi_1 = (E_1 - \hbar\omega_k)\, 0_k\Psi_1$$

The state $0_k\Psi_1$ thus has an energy $E_1 - h\omega_k$, so that to the extent that a solution of (3-45a) and (3-45b) may be found, 0_k is seen to destroy an excitation of energy $\hbar\omega_k$. In the same way, 0_k^+ acts to create an excitation of energy $\hbar\omega_k$. Finally, there must exist a state of lowest energy, the ground state Ψ_o, for which

$$0_k\Psi_o = 0 \tag{3-45c}$$

These equations possess, in general, a series of approximate, self-consistent solutions, which determine Ψ_o, 0_k, and ω_k to a given order of approximation.

Let us now take for 0_k the electron annihilation operator, $c_{k\sigma}$. It is furthermore convenient to add a term, $-\mu N$, to the basic Hamiltonian (3-16), where μ is the chemical potential, or, what is equivalent, the energy of a particle at the Fermi surface. By direct application of the anticommutation rules, (3-17), one finds that the equation of motion for $c_{k\sigma}^{+}$ then reads

$$\left[H - \mu N, c_{k\sigma}^{+}\right] = (\varepsilon_k - \mu)c_{k\sigma}^{+} + \sum_{pq\sigma'} V_q c_{k+q\sigma}^{+} c_{p-q\sigma'}^{+} c_{p\sigma'} \tag{3-45d}$$

Thus the creation operator for an electron is coupled to a trilinear term which acts in general to create an electron *plus* an electron-hole pair. This result is exact: One might next try to write down the equation of motion for the trilinear term; one would obtain thereby a coupling between a trilinear term, a linear term, and a quintuple term (involving the creation of an electron plus *two* electron-hole pairs), etc. In this way one generates a whole series of coupled equations which are simply another way of writing the Schrödinger equation and which are, of course, too difficult to solve exactly. The approximations enter in the way one obtains a solution to the chain of equations by cutting them off at a given order, and searching for a self-consistent solution.

In the Hartree-Fock approximation one keeps only linear terms, so that the single equation we have considered is sufficient. What we must do is separate out those terms in the trilinear term on the right-hand side of (3-45d) which are essentially linear. There are two such; those with $q = 0$ (for which the spin σ' may be arbitrary), which do not contribute for the electron gas, and those with $q = p - k$ (for which σ' must be equal to σ). We find then

$$\begin{aligned}\left[H - \mu N, c_{k\sigma}^{+}\right] &= \left\{\varepsilon_k^o - \mu - \Sigma_p V_{p-k}\, n_{p\sigma}\right\} c_k^{+} \\ &\quad - \Sigma_p V_{p-k} \left\{c_{p\sigma}^{+} c_{p\sigma} - n_{p\sigma}\right\} c_k^{+} \\ &\quad + \sum_{\substack{pq \\ q\neq 0 \\ q\neq p-k}} V_q c_{k+q\sigma}^{+} c_{p-q\sigma}^{+} c_{p\sigma}\end{aligned} \tag{3-45e}$$

where $n_{p\sigma}$ is the expectation value, $\langle\Psi_o|\, c_{p\sigma}^{+} c_{p\sigma} \,|\Psi_o\rangle$. On neglecting the second term on the right-hand side of (3-45e), which corresponds to neglecting fluctuations about $n_{p\sigma}$, and the remaining truly trilinear term, we obtain

$$\left[H - \mu N, c^{+}_{k\sigma}\right] = (\tilde{\varepsilon}_{k\sigma} - \mu)\, c^{+}_{k\sigma} \tag{3-45f}$$

where

$$\tilde{\varepsilon}_{k\sigma} = \varepsilon_k - \sum_p V_{p-k}\, n_{p\sigma} \tag{3-45g}$$

In the same way one has

$$\left[H - \mu N, c_{k\sigma}\right] = -(\tilde{\varepsilon}_{k\sigma} - \mu)\, c_{k\sigma} \tag{3-45h}$$

Equations (3-45f) and (3-45h) determine directly the energy of the elementary excitation, here a quasi-particle of energy $\tilde{\varepsilon}_{k\sigma}$. The ground-state wave function, Ψ_o, is likewise determined; suppose k is such that $\tilde{\varepsilon}_{k\sigma} > \mu$; it then follows from (3-45c) that c^{+}_{k} plays the role of a creation operator, and

$$c_k |\Psi_o\rangle = 0 \quad \tilde{\varepsilon}_{k\sigma} > \mu \tag{3-45i}$$

On the other hand, if $\tilde{\varepsilon}_{k\sigma} < \mu$, it is now $c_{k\sigma}$ which plays the role of a creation operator, and one must have

$$c^{+}_{k\sigma} |\Psi_o\rangle = 0 \quad \tilde{\varepsilon}_{k\sigma} < \mu \tag{3-45j}$$

In order that Ψ_o be compatible with (3-45i) and (3-45j), it must take the form

$$\Psi_o = \prod_{k\sigma} c^{+}_{k_n\sigma_n} \cdots c^{+}_{k_2\sigma_2} c^{+}_{k_1\sigma_1} |0\rangle \qquad \tilde{\varepsilon}_{k\sigma} < \mu \tag{3-45k}$$

where $|0\rangle$ is the vacuum state. This is, of course, the wave function for the filled Fermi sphere; the radius of the sphere being k_o. Moreover, it is clear that

$$\mu = \tilde{\varepsilon}_{k_o}$$

is the energy of a particle on the Fermi surface. One can likewise obtain the usual result for the ground-state energy.

This method is by no means the easiest way to obtain the Hartree-Fock approximation; we have presented it here because it does enable us to obtain the quasi-particle energy ε_k directly, and, more important, it is a comparatively simple method of quite general applicability to the determination of the elementary excitations in solids. We shall have occasion to use it, in slightly modified form, for the calculation of the random phase approximation for the electron gas later on in this chapter and in Chapter 5 for the coupled electron-phonon system. The reader interested in further applications of the method will find them in Refs. 6 and 8a.

Cohesive Energy

To get a quantitative idea of the accuracy of the Hartree-Fock method we look at the cohesive energy of the alkali metals. The cohesive energy is defined as the difference in energy between a collection of free atoms and these atoms brought together to make a metal.[9] In the Hartree approximation the contributions to the cohesive energy are: (1) E_{ion}, a constant representing the difference between the energy by which the most tightly bound conduction electron (i.e., that at the bottom of the conduction band) is bound, and the ionization energy of the free atom; (2) the average kinetic energy of the electrons, $(2.21/r_s^2)(m/m_{av}^*)$; (3) the average effect of the Coulomb interaction between electrons, $1.2/r_s$ rydbergs. The quantities E_{ion} and m_{av}^* are determined from a one-electron calculation in which the effect of the periodic ion-core potential is taken into account. The most reliable calculations of this kind have been carried out for the alkali metals; for that reason, discussions of the cohesive energy often reduce to discussions of the cohesive energy of the alkali metals.

The Hartree method then gives for the total cohesive energy per particle

$$E_H = E_{ion} + (2.21/r_s^2)(m/m_{av}^*) + 1.20/r_s \quad \text{rydbergs}$$

We obtain the result of the Hartree-Fock method if we add to this the exchange energy, (3-23),

$$E_{HF} = E_{ion} + (2.21/r_s^2)(m/m_{av}^*) + 0.284/r_s \quad \text{rydbergs}$$

The values of E_H, E_{HF}, and the experimental cohesive energy, E_{exp}, for the alkali metals are given in Table 3-4 (the units of energy are kcal/mole).

Table 3-4
Cohesive Energy of the Alkali Metals[a]

Metal	m_c/m	E_{ion}	E_H	E_{HF}	E_{exp}
Li	1.45	-87.2	74.4	-17.0	-36.5
Na	0.98	-71.3	67.6	-6.8	-26.0
K	0.93	-51.6	56.1	-4.3	-22.6
Rb	0.89	-47.6	53.4	-3.4	-18.9
Cs	0.83	-43.9	49.9	-2.9	-18.8

[a]From D. Pines.[15]

We remark that the Hartree-Fock approximation represents a great improvement over the Hartree approximation, in that the alkali metals are bound. Nonetheless, the values obtained for the cohesive energy E_{HF} are wide of the mark. The reason is that in the Hartree-Fock approximation no account is taken of the repulsion between electrons of antiparallel spin, yet is is clear that the Coulomb interaction between such electrons will tend to keep them apart, and so further reduce the system energy.

Quasi-particles

What will single-particle motion be like in the Hartree-Fock approximation? As an electron moves along, other electrons which possess the same spin will tend to stay out of its way, a tendency measured explicitly by the correlation function $g_{HF}(r)$. One may speak then of an exchange "hole" in the vicinity of a given electron, i.e., a region in which the density of other electrons is reduced. (For a detailed discussion of the exchange hole, cf. J. Slater.[7]) We therefore deal no longer with free particles but rather with electrons plus their associated exchange holes. We call such "modified" electrons *quasi-particles*.

A quasi-particle will have an energy vs. momentum dependence which differs from that of a free particle. For the quasi-particle in the Hartree-Fock approximation, one obtains directly from (3-30)

$$
\begin{aligned}
\tilde{\varepsilon}_{k\sigma} &= \frac{\hbar^2 k^2}{2m} - \sum_q V_q n_{q+k\sigma} \\
&= \frac{\hbar^2 k^2}{2m} - \frac{e^2 k_o}{2\pi}\left(2 + \frac{k_o^2 - k^2}{kk_o}\,\ell n \left|\frac{k + k_o}{k - k_o}\right|\right) \\
&= \frac{\hbar^2 k^2}{2m} - \frac{e^2 k_o}{2\pi} F(k/k_o) \qquad (3\text{-}46)
\end{aligned}
$$

The shape of F(x) is shown in Fig. 3-9.

From (3-46) we can calculate the width of the conduction band

$$\Delta_{HF} = \tilde{\varepsilon}_{k_o} - \tilde{\varepsilon}_o$$

For the Hartree method we found $\Delta_H = \hbar^2 k_o^2/2m$. The Hartree-Fock result is obtained by expanding the logarithmic term in (3-47) to obtain the proper limit for k = 0. One finds

$$
\begin{aligned}
\Delta_{HF} &= \hbar^2 k_o^2/2m + (2/\pi)e^2 k_o \\
&= \Delta_H + 1.22/r_s \quad \text{rydbergs}
\end{aligned}
$$

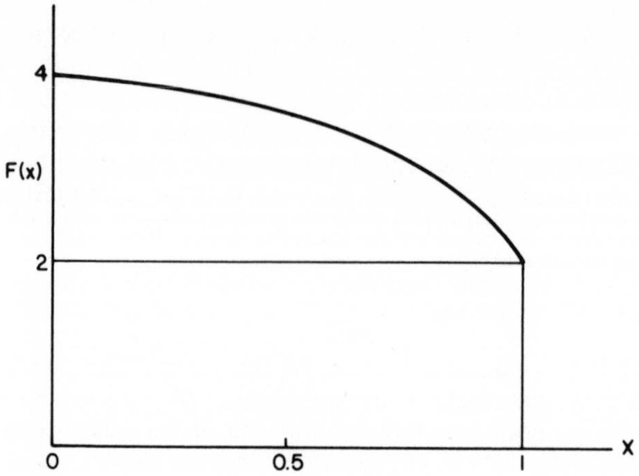

Fig. 3-9

The added term is large and spoils the agreement of Δ_H with experiment obtained in the Hartree approximation (or Sommerfeld model), as seen in Table 3-5.

Table 3-5

Element	Li	Na	Be	Hg	Al
Δ_{exp}(ev)	3.7	3.5	13.8	6.2	11.8
Δ_H(ev)	4.8	3.2	14.6	7.3	11.9
Δ_{HF}(ev)	8.5	7.4	20.7	13.6	20

The behavior of the E(k) curve also changes the dependence of the electronic specific heat on temperature. In (3-8) we have seen that the specific heat is proportional to the density of single-particle states per unit energy at the Fermi surface. Quite generally, one may write this [compare (3-9a) and (1-11)]

$$\rho_F(\varepsilon) = \left(\frac{dn}{d\varepsilon}\right)_{\varepsilon=\mu} = \left[\left(\frac{dn}{dk}\right) 1/(\partial\tilde{\varepsilon}_k/\partial k)\right]_{k=k_o} = \frac{k_o^2}{\pi^2} \Bigg/ \left(\frac{\partial\tilde{\varepsilon}_k}{\partial k}\right)_{k=k_o} \tag{3-47}$$

where $\tilde{\varepsilon}_k$ is the energy of a quasi-particle of momentum k and $\mu = \tilde{\varepsilon}_{k_o}$, the energy of a quasi-particle on the Fermi surface. In the Hartree-Fock approximation, according to (3-46), one has

$$\left(\frac{\partial \tilde{\varepsilon}_k}{\partial k}\right)_{k=k_o} = \infty$$

and hence $\rho_F(\varepsilon) = 0$. Thus, in fact, the simple expression (3-8) fails, and one must calculate in detail how the Fermi distribution changes with temperature. Such a calculation was first carried out by Bardeen[11]; he found

$$C_v \sim T/\ln T$$

a result which is not at all in accord with experiment. In the same way other quantities, such as transition probabilities, which depend on the density of states at the top of the Fermi distribution, will change markedly (and not for the better) in the Hartree-Fock approximation.

Finally, we mention the difficulties arising in connection with the magnetic properties of the electron gas in the Hartree-Fock approximation. The spin susceptibility may be readily calculated with the aid of (3-10a) and (3-10b); one simply takes account of the change in the Fermi spheres for up and down spins in the calculation of the dependence of the exchange energy upon p. The result is

$$\alpha_{HF} = \frac{2}{3}\,\varepsilon_F + \frac{4}{9}\,E_{exch}$$

Actually, we can easily include as well the influence of the periodic ion potential on χ_s. For, as we have already noted, it acts to change the mass of an electron at the Fermi surface from m to m^*, where

$$\frac{\hbar k_o}{m^*} = \left(\frac{\partial \varepsilon_k^*}{\partial k}\right)_{k=k_o}$$

and ε_k^* is the one-electron energy with the effects of ion periodicity taken into account. (We are for simplicity considering a spherical Fermi surface.) Thus we can write

$$\alpha_{HF} = \frac{2}{3}\,\varepsilon_F\,\frac{m}{m^*} + \frac{4}{9}\,E_{exch}$$

The values of χ_{HF} so obtained are compared with $\chi^*_{free} = \chi_{free}\,\dfrac{m^*}{m}$ and χ_s^{expt} in Table 3-6.

Table 3-6
χ (10^6 cgs units)

Metal	$\left(\frac{m^*}{m}\right)^a$	χ_{free}	χ^*_{free}	χ^*_{HF}	χ_s^{expt}
Li	1.66	0.81	1.35	12.2	2.08 ± 0.1
Na	1.00	0.64	0.64	1.86	0.89 ± 0.04

[a]From F. Ham, *Phys. Rev.* (to be published).

It is easy to understand why χ_s^{HF} is greater than χ_s^{free}; the exchange energy favors a polarization of the spins, while the kinetic energy opposes it (naturally the external field also favors spin alignment). Hence, inclusion of exchange effects (for a system with repulsive interactions) acts to increase χ_s.

In fact, the inclusion of the exchange energy leads one to predict the ferromagnetism of an electron gas of moderate density ($r_s = 5.5$) in the Hartree-Fock approximation. To see this, we compare the energy of two states of a free-electron gas, one where up and down spin states are filled equally (nonmagnetic), and one where all spins are lined up (ferromagnetic). Because of the exclusion principle, in the ferromagnetic case, the top of the Fermi distribution lies higher—it costs us energy to line the spins up. On the other hand, we gain exchange energy, since in the ferromagnetic case all (instead of half) of the electrons give an exchange energy contribution. Numerically, if k_o is the top of the nonmagnetic distribution, then $k_{max} = 2^{1/3}k_o$ is the top of the ferromagnetic Fermi distribution, for the total number of electrons is to be the same in both cases. The energy needed to line the spins up is therefore

$$E_{kin}\left(2^{1/3}k_o\right) - E_{kin}\left(k_o\right) = \frac{3}{5}\,\frac{\hbar^2 k_o{}^2}{2m}\left(2^{2/3} - 1\right)$$

$$= \frac{2.21 \times 0.588}{r_s{}^2} \quad \text{rydbergs}$$

and the energy gain due to the exchange energy contribution is

$$E_{ex}\left(2^{1/3}k_o\right) - E_{ex}\left(k_o\right) = -\frac{0.916}{r_s}\left(2^{1/3} - 1\right)$$

$$= -\frac{0.916 \times 0.26}{r_s} \quad \text{rydbergs}$$

so that the total energy difference becomes

$$\Delta_{\text{ferr}} = \frac{1.30}{r_s^2} - \frac{0.238}{r_s} \quad \text{rydbergs}$$

This expression vanishes for $r_s = r_s^\circ = 5.46$; for $r_s > r_s^\circ$, Δ_{ferr} is negative and the substance should be ferromagnetic. However, such a consideration is naive; it neglects the fact that there is also a correlation between electrons of antiparallel spin, and a consequent lowering of the system energy. Such correlations act to oppose ferromagnetic spin alignment, since in the ferromagnetic state there could be *no* contribution to the ground-state energy from electrons of antiparallel spin. The correlations between electrons of opposite spin are, in fact, quite strong enough to prevent a free-electron gas of any density from becoming ferromagnetic.[7,12]

In summary, the quasi-particle properties in the Hartree-Fock approximation are in disagreement with experiment, the disagreement being most noticeable in the case of the density of states per unit energy at the Fermi surface. The logarithmic singularities in (3-47) may be traced directly to the long range of the Coulomb force. If, in place of a Coulomb interaction, the effective electron interaction were screened, with a screening radius of the order of β^{-1}, the logarithmic singularity in (3-47) is removed [$\ln(k+k_0)/(k-k_0)$ is replaced by $\ln(k+k_0)/\beta$ for $k \cong k_0$]. Such a screened interaction was proposed some time ago by Landsberg,[11a] in connection with his calculation of the tail of the soft X-ray spectrum of sodium. (We have remarked that the tail is due to the spread in energy of the bottom of the band owing to electron-electron interaction.) It was likewise noted by Wohlfarth[11] that screening would eliminate the difficulties with the specific-heat calculation. In general, if a screening radius of the order of the interparticle spacing is chosen, the quasi-particle energy then gives rise to results in reasonable accord with experiment for the properties we have considered.[15] On the other hand, such screening would reduce the exchange energy E_{HF} markedly, so that the alkali metals would no longer be bound. It is for this reason that the introduction of an empirical screening radius for electron-electron interactions cannot of itself offer a consistent account of metallic properties, since it necessarily leads to an inadequate cohesive energy calculation.

3-3 CORRELATION AND CORRELATION ENERGY: AN INTRODUCTORY SURVEY

Difficulty with the Second-Order Perturbation-Theoretic Calculation

We now wish to look for a better scheme of calculation of the ground-state energy than the Hartree-Fock approximation. We shall therefore be calculating the correlation energy of the free-electron gas. The correlation energy is defined as the difference in energy between the Hartree-Fock value (3-34) and any better calculation. It is so called because the Hartree-Fock method takes into account only the accidental correlations due to the Pauli principle and neglects the correlations in particle positions brought about by their mutual interaction; any improved calculation will take the latter correlations into account.

One thing we might attempt to do in this connection is to calculate the correlation energy by considering the next term in the perturbation expansion for the ground-state energy. From the perturbation-theoretic point of view, the Hartree-Fock approximation represents a first-order calculation; we therefore consider the second-order contribution.

In second order, the Rayleigh-Schrödinger perturbation theory gives

$$E_2 = -\sum_n \frac{\langle n | H_{int} | 0 \rangle^2}{E_n - E_o} \tag{3-48}$$

where

$$H_{int} = \frac{1}{2} \sum_{\substack{pqk \\ \sigma\sigma'}} V_k c^+_{p-k\sigma} c^+_{q+k\sigma'} c_{q\sigma'} c_{p\sigma} \tag{3-49}$$

What now are the states n which enter into this sum, and how do we go about calculating (3-48)?

A typical transition introduced by H_{int} is one in which electrons in states **p** and **-q**, say, are scattered into states **p + k** and **-q - k**. Because of the Pauli principle, the states **p** and **-q** must lie within the Fermi sphere, while the states **p + k** and **-q - k** must lie outside it. The matrix element for this transition, where allowed, is simply

$$V_k = \frac{4\pi e^2}{k^2}$$

The excitation energy is

$$E_{pq}(k) = \frac{(p+k)^2}{2m} + \frac{(-q-k)^2}{2m} - \frac{p^2}{2m} - \frac{q^2}{2m} = \frac{k \cdot (p+q+k)}{m}$$

Suppose, moreover, we write E_2 in the following way:

$$E_2 = - \sum_n \frac{\langle 0 | H_{int} | n \rangle \langle n | H_{int} | 0 \rangle}{E_n - E_o}$$

We see then, that having arrived at the excited state n, characterized by electrons in states p + k, -q - k, holes in states p, -q, we must then use H_{int} once more to return to the ground state. Here we may distinguish between two different processes, which correspond to distinct contributions to the ground-state energy.

In the first, the so-called "direct" process, one comes back down just the way one went up, via a matrix element V_k. The direct process is therefore that depicted in Fig. 3-10. Here electrons in the

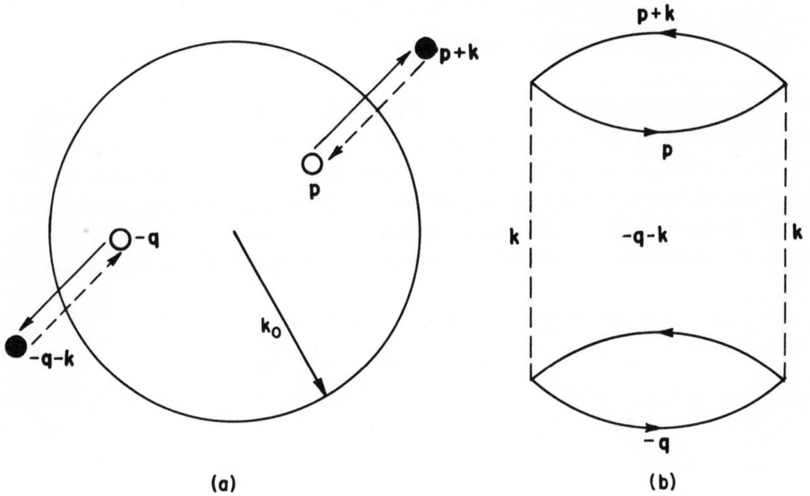

Fig. 3-10

states p and -q interact each other, being knocked out from the Fermi sphere to states p + k and -q - k (the process expressed by solid lines in Fig. 3-10a); these excited electrons then come back to the original states by another interaction (dashed lines in Fig. 3-10a). A diagrammatic expression for such a process is shown in Fig. 3-10b, where the solid lines represent the propagating electron and hole lines and the dashed lines describe the interactions with momentum transfer $\hbar$k.

The contribution which the direct process makes to E_2 is

$$E_2^{(a)} = -4 \sum_{pqk} \left(\frac{4\pi e^2}{k^2}\right)^2 \frac{m}{\hbar^2 k \cdot (p + q + k)} n_p(1 - n_{p+k})n_q(1 - n_{q+k}) \quad (3\text{-}50)$$

where the Pauli principle restrictions on the intermediate states n which enter are expressed with the aid of the distribution functions

$$n_p = \begin{cases} 0 & |p| < k_o \\ 1 & |p| < k_o \end{cases}$$

and the factor 4 allows for the sum over spins.

In the second, the so-called "exchange" process, the electron in the state $p + k$ makes a transition to the state $-q$, while that in the state $-q - k$ returns to the state p. The matrix element for this transition is

$$-V_{p+q+k} = -\frac{4\pi e^2}{(p + q + k)^2}$$

The minus sign arises because a different ordering of creation and annihilation operators is involved. We note, too, that the exchange process can *only* occur for states p and q which have parallel spins, while the direct process is available for states p and q of both parallel and antiparallel spin. A typical exchange process is pictured in Fig. 3-11. The contribution which exchange processes make to E_2 is given by

$$E_2^{(b)} = 2 \sum_{pqk} \frac{4\pi e^2}{k^2} \frac{4\pi e^2}{(p + q + k)^2} \frac{m}{\hbar^2 k \cdot (p + q + k)}$$

$$\times\, n_p(1 - n_{p+k})\, n_p(1 - n_{q+k}) \qquad (3\text{-}51)$$

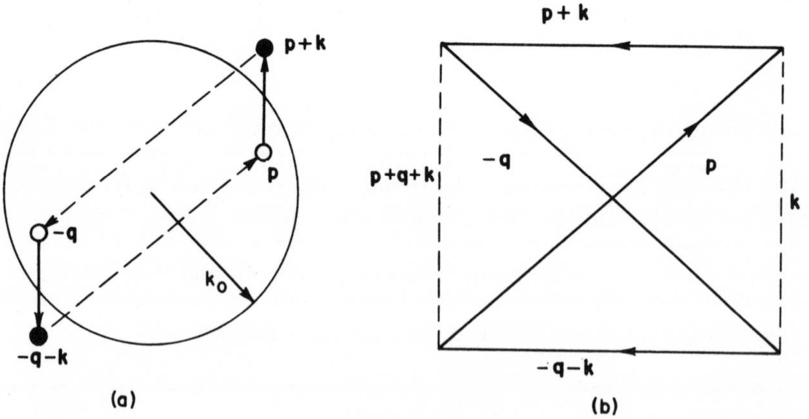

Fig. 3-11

We shall now see that the direct contribution, $E_2^{(a)}$, is logarithmically divergent. To see this, we consider (3-50) in the limit of small momentum transfers. We first remark that both **p** and **q** must be nearly equal to k_o, since the requirement that $p < k_o$, $|\mathbf{p} + \mathbf{k}| > k_o$, limits the value of p to a thin shell in the immediate neighborhood of the Fermi surface (compare Fig. 3-7). Moreover, the width of that shell will be of order k. The form of the Pauli principle restriction for small momentum transfers may be easily obtained with the aid of the relation

$$n_p(1 - n_{p+k}) = n_p(1 - n_p - \mathbf{k} \cdot \nabla_p n_p)$$
$$= n_p \left[(\mathbf{k} \cdot \mathbf{p})/p\right] \delta(p - p_F) \quad \mathbf{k} \cdot \mathbf{p} \geq 0 \qquad (3\text{-}52)$$

In writing (3-52) we have used the expression

$$\nabla_p n_p = - (\mathbf{p}/p)\, \delta(p - p_F)$$

plus the requirement that $p < p_F$, $|\mathbf{p} + \mathbf{k}| > p_F$, which means that $\mathbf{k} \cdot \mathbf{p} > 0$. Hence, to obtain an estimate of (3-50) in the limit of small k, one may replace p and q by k_o, and

$$\sum_p n_p(1 - n_{p+k}) \sim Nk/k_o \sim \sum_q n_q(1 - n_{q+k})$$

On changing the sum over k to an integral, we then find

$$\lim_{k \to 0} E_2^{(a)} \sim - \int dk\, k^2 \left(\frac{4\pi e^2}{k^2}\right)^2 \left(\frac{k^2}{k_o}\right) \frac{m}{\hbar^2 k k_o}$$

$$\sim - \int \frac{dk}{k} \sim - \ln k \qquad (3\text{-}53)$$

This logarithmic divergence may be traced directly to the long range of the Coulomb interaction. As is at once clear, if the interaction fell off rapidly with distance, then V_k for small k could approach a constant, and no divergence would ensue. It can be said that the appearance of this divergence set back the systematic application of perturbation theory to the electron gas for some 20 years.

Wigner Calculation of Correlation Energy at High Densities

The difficulties that we have encountered in the second-order perturbation-theoretic calculations, as well as those encountered in the treatment of the Hartree-Fock single-particle energies, reflect a definite inconsistency in the straightforward perturbation-theoretic approach to the electron gas. Despite the great successes in the Sommerfeld-Hartree independent electron model, the electron interaction cannot be treated as weak, since the next terms beyond the Hartree for single-particle energies, or Hartree-Fock for ground-state energies, give rise to unphysical or divergent results. It is clear, therefore, that a better account of the long-range nature of the Coulomb interactions is required in order that one might (1) understand the success of the one-electron model; (2) calculate the correlation energy to a good degree of accuracy.

One approach to this twin problem was developed by Wigner in the 1930s,[12] and we shall now discuss that briefly. A second approach was developed by Bohm and the writer in the early 1950s, and will be considered next.

Wigner wrote the wave function of the electrons as a product of Hartree-Fock determinants formed from single-particle wave functions for up and down spin.

$$\Psi = |\varphi_{\uparrow}| \cdot |\varphi_{\downarrow}|$$

The correlations due to the Coulomb interaction between electrons of antiparallel spin is explicitly included by assuming that the individual electron wave functions of spin-up electrons depend on the position of all the spin-down electrons

$$\Psi = \frac{1}{n!}\begin{vmatrix} \psi_1(x_1, y_1, \ldots, y_n) & \cdots & \psi_1(x_n, y_1, \ldots, y_n) \\ \vdots & & \vdots \\ \psi_n(x_1, y_1, \ldots, y_n) & \cdots & \psi_n(x_n, y_1, \ldots, y_n) \end{vmatrix}$$

$$\times \begin{vmatrix} \psi_1(y_1) & \cdots & \psi_1(y_n) \\ \vdots & & \vdots \\ \psi_n(y_1) & \cdots & \psi_n(y_n) \end{vmatrix}$$

Wigner proceeded to calculate the expectation value of the energy with this expression for Ψ, and then determined the y's and E, in such a way as to minimize the energy E. In so doing, he used second-order Rayleigh-Schrödinger perturbation theory to calculate the $\psi_\gamma(x; y)$. He further neglected the normalization correction, (Ψ^*, Ψ). The resultant expressions were quite complicated; Wigner carried out a numerical calculation of the correlation energy, and concluded that for $r_s = 1$, the correlation energy per electron would be

$$E = -\frac{0.88}{7.8} \text{ rydbergs} = -0.11 \text{ rydberg } (\sim -1.5 \text{ ev}) \tag{3-54}$$

Because of Wigner's use of perturbation theory, $r_s = 1$ is probably an upper limit for the accuracy of a calculation of this kind. It could be expected to be meaningful there, since at this density the constant term obtained by Wigner is indeed small compared to either the kinetic energy (the zeroth-order result) or the exchange energy (the first-order result).

On the other hand, metallic electron densities are such that

$$1.8 \leq r_s \leq 5.5$$

In order to obtain a meaningful expression for the correlation energy in this region, Wigner next obtained an expression for the correlation in the low-density region ($r_s \gtrsim 20$, say); he then interpolated between these regions to obtain the correlation energy at metallic densities.

Low-Density Electron Solid and Wigner Interpolation Formula

Wigner pointed out that for sufficiently low densities, the electrons in a uniform background of positive charge would be found in an ordered array. This low-density electron solid is stable because the potential energy of interaction between the electrons, which favors formation of an ordered array, goes as $1/r_s$; kinetic-energy effects, as we have seen, go as $1/r_s^2$ and are hence ineffective in opposing the localization of the electrons if r_s is sufficiently large. In fact, as we might anticipate from our discussion of the melting of a solid, what is relevant to the stability of the electron solid is the amplitude of the vibration of an electron about its equilibrium position. We shall see that the zero-point oscillations appropriate to the phonons in the electron solid vary as $1/r_s^{3/2}$, so that these are likewise ineffective at sufficiently low densities.

One may obtain a rough estimate of the binding energy of the electron solid in the following way. First, make the Wigner-Seitz approximation of replacing the actual cell surrounding each electron by the appropriate inscribed sphere. The error involved in so doing turns out to be very small indeed. Next, assume that the different cells do not interact with one another—an approximation equivalent to using an Einstein model for the frequency of the phonons. Then assuming the ionic charge distribution to be uniform, the potential at a distance r from the center of the sphere due to a uniform positive charge in the sphere is given by

$$V(r) = \left[e \int_{r'>r} \frac{d^3r'}{|r' - r|} + e \int_{r'<r} \frac{d^3r}{|r' - r|} \right] \left(\frac{3}{4\pi r_o^3} \right)$$

$$= \frac{3}{2} \frac{e}{r_o} - \frac{er^2}{2r_o^3} \qquad (3\text{-}55)$$

The potential energy of a single electron at a distance r from the center of the sphere is then

$$PE = -\frac{3}{2} \frac{e^2}{r_o} + \frac{e^2 r^2}{2r_o^3}$$

This is a harmonic oscillator potential which is stable for small $p^2/2m$:

$$H = \frac{p^2}{2m} + \frac{e^2}{2r_o^3} r^2 - \frac{3}{2} \frac{e^2}{r_o}$$

From the Hamiltonian we see that the frequency of oscillation is

$$\omega^2 = \frac{e^2}{r_o^3 m} = \frac{\omega_p^2}{3}$$

where

$$\omega_p^2 = \frac{4\pi n e^2}{m}$$

and n is the density of electrons:

$$n = \frac{1}{\frac{4}{3}\pi r_o^3}$$

The energy of the lowest state is then

$$E_{solid} = -\frac{3}{2} \frac{e^2}{r_o} + \frac{\sqrt{3}\hbar \omega_p}{2}$$

since there are three directions of oscillation. E_{solid} may be calculated by using

$$\hbar \omega_p = \left(\frac{12}{r_s^3} \right)^{1/2} \quad \text{rydbergs}$$

as

$$E_{solid} = -\frac{3}{r_s} + \frac{3}{2}\sqrt{\frac{12}{r_s^3}}\frac{1}{\sqrt{3}}$$

$$= -\frac{3}{r_s} + \frac{3}{r_s^{3/2}} \quad \text{rydbergs}$$

We wish to compare this with the energy of interaction for the Hartree-Fock calculation. In the latter case the electrons are not localized but are uniform over the sphere. This gives a self-energy of the electron:

$$PE = -\frac{1}{2}\int_0^{r_o} eV(r)\frac{3}{4\pi r_o^3}\, d^3r$$

$$= \frac{1}{2}\int\left(\frac{3}{2}\frac{e^2}{r_o} - \frac{e^2 r^2}{2r_o^3}\right)\frac{3}{4\pi r_o^3}\, d^3r$$

$$= \frac{3}{2}\frac{e^2}{r_o} - \frac{9}{10}\frac{e^2}{r_o} = 0.6\frac{e^2}{r_o} = \frac{1.2}{r_s} \quad \text{rydbergs} \tag{3-56}$$

The 1/2 enters the expression for the self-energy of the electron distribution in order not to count each electron twice. Hence the self-energy is $1.2/r_s$ rydbergs per electron. The interaction energy with a uniform positive charge is negative and twice the self-energy: $-2.4/r_s$. Finally the exchange energy was given before to be $-0.92/r_s$ rydbergs [cf. (3-26)].

Adding these gives an energy for Hartree-Fock calculation,

$$E_{HF} = -\frac{2.12}{r_s} \quad \text{rydbergs}$$

On comparing this with the leading term in the ground-state energy computed by the above model,

$$E = -3/r_s \quad \text{rydbergs}$$

we find a correlation energy which is

$$E_{corr} = -\frac{0.88}{r_s} \quad \text{rydbergs} \tag{3-57}$$

up to terms of order $r_s^{-3/2}$.

Next, we follow Wigner, and obtain a formula which interpolates between the high- and low-density regimes by requiring that the "interpolation-determined" correlation energy reduce to (3-54) and (3-57) in the appropriate limits. The desired expression is[15a]

$$E_{corr} = -\frac{0.88}{r_s + 7.8} \text{ rydbergs} \tag{3-58}$$

The improvement this method brings to the cohesive energy is shown in Table 3-7.

Table 3-7
Table of Cohesive Energies
(energies in kcal/mole)

E_{exp}	E_{HF}	E_{Wig}
Li - 36.5	-17.0	-41.4
Na - 26.0	-6.8	-30.3
K - 22.6	-4.3	-25.9
Rb - 18.9	-3.4	-24.4
Cs - 18.8	-2.9	-23.3

Wigner also pointed out how the correlation energy counteracts the tendency for spins to align themselves since when they do, that part of the correlation energy associated with the interaction between electrons of antiparallel spin is lost. Finally he suggested that the difficulties in the Hartree-Fock state density-of-states calculation would likewise be resolved by taking electron correlation into account.

The low-density electron solid has been the object of further theoretical concern recently, and we mention here two subsequent developments. First, we remark that the Einstein model we have used for the phonon frequencies is unnecessarily rough. The problem of calculating the relevant phonon frequencies is identical to that we have discussed in the previous chapter for a solid composed of ions in a uniform background of positive charge, so that the results mentioned there are directly applicable to the present considerations. Carr and his collaborators[16] have used these results to estimate the zero-point energy of the phonons; they find, per electron

$$\frac{2.66}{r_s^{3/2}} \text{ rydbergs}$$

in place of the Einstein model result, $3/r_s^{3/2}$ rydbergs. They have also estimated the next term in the series expansion for the energy, which is of order $1/r_s^2$, and which arises from "anharmonic" terms in the coupling between the electron displacement from equilibrium.

Nozières and the writer[17] have considered the stability of the electron solid with the aid of the Lindemann melting criterion discussed in Sec. 2-4. The argument in that section was that any solid would melt when the mean vibration amplitude $\langle \delta R^2 \rangle^{1/2}$ reaches a certain critical fraction of the interatomic spacing R_o,

$$\langle \delta R^2 \rangle / R_o^2 = \gamma_m$$

The constant γ_m varies somewhat from one solid to another but, as we saw, is of the order of 1/16 for most simple lattice types. For the electron solid at T = 0, $\langle \delta R^2 \rangle$ is determined solely by the zero-point vibrations of the electrons. We shall underestimate $\langle \delta R^2 \rangle$ if we assume that the phonons of importance are longitudinal phonons at frequency ω_p. [This assumption is consistent with the extension of the extension of the phonon sum rule (2-53) to the electron solid.] We then have

$$\frac{\langle \delta R^2 \rangle^{1/2}}{R_o} = \left(\frac{\hbar}{2m\omega_p} \right)^{1/2} \frac{1}{r_s} = \left(\frac{1}{12 r_s} \right)^{1/4} \tag{3-59}$$

and we expect that below $r_s \sim 20$ the electronic solid will not be stable.

The Electron Gas as a Quantum Plasma: Screening and Plasma Oscillations

Some 10 years ago Bohm and the writer[13-15] were led to develop a theory for the interacting electron gas which was based on its close resemblance to a classical plasma. Classical plasmas are highly ionized collections of electrons and positive charges; they possess comparatively high temperatures and low densities; physical examples include hot gaseous discharges and the ionosphere. A typical model for the study of the electronic behavior in a classical plasma involves the replacement of the positive ions by a uniform background of positive charge. Our free-electron gas model for a metal differs from that used for a classical plasma only in that we deal with a system in which the electron density is very high, and the temperature quite low, so that quantum, rather than classical, statistics for the electrons must be employed. It is natural, then, to regard the free-electron gas at low temperatures and metallic densities as a quantum plasma.

Bohm and the writer found that quantum plasmas, like classical plasmas, displayed considerable organized, or collective, behavior of just the kind one might have expected from the long range of the Coulomb interaction between the electrons. Such collective behavior manifests itself in two ways: screening and collective oscillation. Let us consider first the phenomenon of screening.

Suppose there exists an imbalance in the charge distribution at some point in the plasma—say an excess of positive charge. As a result, the electrons will tend to concentrate in that region, since they are in fact quite mobile and respond readily to the attractive potential represented by the positive charge excess. In so doing the electrons act to *screen* the influence of the charge imbalance and to restore charge neutrality in the plasma. Such screening was first studied for classical plasmas by Debye and Hückel in connection with their theory of electrolytes. We may obtain an estimate of its importance for quantum plasmas by a calculation in the Fermi-Thomas approximation of the electron response to a static charge q in the plasma.[18]

Let the charge be at the origin. We may then write Poisson's equation as

$$\nabla^2\varphi(\mathbf{r}) = -4\pi q\,\delta(\mathbf{r}) + 4\pi e\,\delta\rho(\mathbf{r}) \tag{3-60}$$

where $\varphi(\mathbf{r})$ is the net potential in the plasma, and $\delta\rho(\mathbf{r})$ is the change in electronic density brought about by the introduction of the point charge q. According to the Fermi-Thomas approximation, one can in the case of a spatially inhomogeneous disturbance, which varies little over an atomic spacing, regard the Fermi energy as likewise slowly varying in space. One has then

$$\frac{\hbar^2 k_o^2(r)}{2m} = \varepsilon_F + e\varphi(r)$$

where ε_F is the energy at the Fermi surface in the absence of the potential $\varphi(r)$. Moreover, we can write for the electron density,

$$\rho(r) = \frac{[k_o(r)]^3}{3\pi^2} = \frac{1}{3\pi^2}\left\{\frac{2m}{\hbar^2}\,[\varepsilon_F + e\varphi(r)]\right\}^{3/2} = n + \delta\rho(r) \tag{3-61}$$

where n is the average electron density. If we now linearize (3-60) by regarding the local shift in energy $e\varphi(r)$ as small compared to ε_F, we find

$$\delta\rho(r) = \frac{3}{2}\,n\,\frac{e\varphi(r)}{\varepsilon_F} \tag{3-62}$$

We now make use of (3-62) to rewrite (3-60) as

$$\left(\nabla^2 - \frac{6\pi n e^2}{\varepsilon_F}\right)\varphi(r) = -4\pi q\,\delta(r)$$

which may be readily solved by taking its Fourier transform,

$$\varphi(r) = \sum_k \varphi_k e^{ik\cdot r} = \sum_k \frac{4\pi q e^{ik\cdot r}}{k^2 + 6\pi n e^2/\varepsilon_F} = \frac{q}{r} \exp(-k_{FT} r) \tag{3-63}$$

where k_{FT} is the Fermi-Thomas screening wave vector,

$$k_{FT} = \left(\frac{6\pi n e^2}{\varepsilon_F}\right)^{1/2} \tag{3-64}$$

Thus the polarization induced by the charge acts to screen out its field within a distance $\lambda_{FT} = k_{FT}^{-1}$. For metallic electron densities, λ_{FT} is of the order of the interparticle spacing, so that such screening is quite effective.

How might we expect to relate this simple calculation to the behavior of the quantum plasma? First, we could regard each electron as a source of local charge imbalance, and expect that it will polarize the other electrons in its immediate vicinity in such a way that they tend to avoid the electron in question. Thus we expect electrons to avoid another as best they can; to the extent that they are able to do this the field of a given electron will tend to be neutralized by the background of positive charge within a distance of something like the interparticle spacing. Second, we might hope that the Fermi-Thomas calculation would yield a satisfactory estimate of such screening provided:

a. the electron in question was slowly moving, so that it could be regarded as giving rise to a nearly static disturbance

b. the linearization procedure we have followed can be shown to be valid

c. one looks only at the long-wavelength behavior, for which the assumption of a slowly varying potential was valid

Requirement (b) is equivalent to saying that

$$\frac{e^2}{r_o} \ll \varepsilon_F$$

since e^2/r_o, where r_o is the interparticle spacing, is the potential energy of interest. This requirement can be written

$$\frac{e^2}{a_o r_s} \ll \frac{3.62}{r_s^2}\left(\frac{e^2}{2a_o}\right) \quad \text{or} \quad r_s \ll 1$$

on introducing

$$r_s = r_o/a_o$$

the interelectron spacing measured in units of the Bohr radius, and using the identity

$$\varepsilon_F = \frac{\hbar^2 k_o}{2m} = \frac{3.62}{r_s^{\,2}} \quad \text{rydbergs}$$

In order to satisfy (b) one must therefore deal with a very high density electron gas; metallic electron densities tend to fall between $r_s = 2$ and $r_s = 5.5$. (Note that

$$n = \frac{1}{4\pi r_o^{\,3}/3} = \frac{3}{4\pi r_s^{\,3} a_o^{\,3}}\Bigg)$$

The condition (c) would lead one to expect that, for example,

$$\varphi_k = \frac{4\pi q}{k^2 + k_{FT}^2}$$

provided k is sufficiently small—but that such a simple relationship need not be expected for larger k, since for k's of the order of the inverse of the interparticle spacing, one is surely not justified in regarding a "disturbance" as slowly varying.

Finally, since most electrons are not in fact slowly moving, in order to develop an adequate picture of the polarization processes in an electron gas it is necessary that one develop a method to describe the response of the electrons to a time-varying disturbance.

The existence of organized oscillations in the plasma may be understood in the following way. When the electrons move to screen a charge disturbance in the plasma, they will, in general, overshoot their mark somewhat. They are consequently pulled back toward that region, overshoot again, etc., in such a way that an oscillation is set up about the state of charge neutrality. For a preliminary survey of this oscillatory behavior, it is particularly fruitful to study the equation of motion of the density fluctuations in the electron gas.[13]

As we have seen, the density fluctuation ρ_k is given by

$$\rho_k = \sum_i e^{-i\mathbf{k}\cdot\mathbf{r}_i}$$

We may compute its equation of motion with the aid of the familiar identity

$$\dot{\rho}_k = [\rho_k, H]/i\hbar$$

Recalling that

$$H = \sum_i p_i^2/2m + \sum_{k \neq 0} \frac{2\pi e^2}{k^2} (\rho_k^+ \rho_k - N)$$

one finds readily:

$$\dot{\rho}_k = -i \sum_i \left(\frac{\mathbf{k} \cdot \mathbf{p}_i}{m} + \frac{\hbar k^2}{2m} \right) e^{-i\mathbf{k} \cdot \mathbf{r}_i}$$

and

$$\ddot{\rho}_{\mathbf{k}} = -\sum_i \left(\frac{\mathbf{k} \cdot \mathbf{p}_i}{m} + \frac{\hbar k^2}{2m} \right)^2 e^{-i\mathbf{k} \cdot \mathbf{r}_i} - \sum_q \frac{4\pi e^2}{mq^2} \mathbf{k} \cdot \mathbf{q}\, \rho_{k-q} \rho_q \tag{3-65}$$

The first term on the right-hand side represents the influence of the kinetic energy of the particles; the second arises from their mutual interaction. We may rewrite (3-65) separating out the term with $\mathbf{q} = \mathbf{k}$ in the second term on the right-hand side; we then have

$$\ddot{\rho}_{\mathbf{k}} + \omega_p^2 \rho_{\mathbf{k}} = -\sum_i \left(\frac{\mathbf{k} \cdot \mathbf{p}_i}{m} + \frac{\hbar k^2}{2m} \right)^2 e^{-i\mathbf{k} \cdot \mathbf{r}_i}$$

$$- \sum_{q \neq k} \frac{4\pi e^2}{mq^2} \mathbf{q} \cdot \mathbf{k}\, \rho_{k-q} \rho_q \tag{3-66}$$

where

$$\omega_p = (4\pi n e^2/m)^{1/2} \tag{3-67}$$

is the so-called plasma frequency of the electron gas.

We see that the ρ_k oscillate at a frequency ω_p provided we can neglect the two terms on the right-hand side of (3-66). Let us see under what circumstances we may do so. We may estimate the first term as being of order $k^2 v_o^2 \rho_k$, where v_o is the velocity at the top of the Fermi distribution. The second term involves a product of two density fluctuations. Since the density fluctuation

$$\rho_q = \sum_i e^{i\mathbf{q} \cdot \mathbf{r}_i}$$

for $q \neq 0$ is a sum of exponential terms with randomly varying phases (and since the expectation value $\langle \rho_q \rangle$ vanishes for a translationally invariant system), one might hope that this term represents a small correction to the equation of motion of ρ_k and may be neglected in first approximation. Such an approximation we called the *random phase approximation*, in view of the randomly varying phases of terms which contribute to a given ρ_k, as distinguished from the coherent addition of terms for $\rho_o = N$.

Within the RPA (as we shall henceforth refer to the random phase approximation), we see that the condition for collective oscillatory behavior of the ρ_k, and hence of the entire electron gas, is that

$$\frac{k^2 v_o^2}{\omega_p^2} \ll 1 \quad \text{or} \quad k^2 \ll k_c^2$$

where k_c^2 is of the order of ω_p^2/v_o^2. Thus in general we may expect that the quantum plasma behaves collectively for $k \ll k_c$, in that it will exhibit oscillations at a frequency near ω_p. On the other hand, for short-wavelength phenomena, for which $k \gg k_c$, the plasma behaves like a system of free individual particles, since then the first term on the right-hand side of (3-66) governs the system behavior. In the region of k near k_c the behavior will be more complicated, since we deal with a transition from single particle to collective behavior.

Let us put in some numbers. For an electron gas at a typical metallic density, $n \sim 10^{23}$ electrons/cm^3 and the frequency of a plasma oscillation is $\sim 2 \times 10^{16}$. The energy in a plasmon, a single quantum of plasma oscillation, is

$$\hbar\omega_p \sim 12 \text{ ev}$$

It is clear then that there will be no thermal excitation of plasmons. However, what about plasmon excitation by single electrons in the metal? In order that an electron of momentum $\hbar p$ excite a plasmon of momentum $\hbar k$, with conservation of momentum and energy, one must have

$$\frac{\hbar^2 p^2}{2m} - \frac{\hbar^2 (p - k)^2}{2m} = \hbar\omega_p$$

since the final electron momentum is $\hbar(p - k)$. Hence,

$$\frac{\hbar^2 \mathbf{k} \cdot \mathbf{p}}{m} - \frac{\hbar^2 k^2}{2m} = \hbar\omega_p \tag{3-68}$$

Since p is at most k_o, it is clear that for small k such a process cannot occur. As one considers larger values of k, plasmon excitation by a single electron can first occur at

$$k \cong k_{min} = \omega_p/v_o \tag{3-69}$$

This is likewise essentially the condition for a plasmon of momentum k to disappear via the direct excitation of an electron from a state of momentum $\hbar p$ to momentum $\hbar(p+k)$. The frequency kv_o is the frequency that characterizes single-particle transitions out of the Fermi sea; what we are saying is that for small k there is no match between this and the plasma frequency, so that within the RPA no direct coupling between the two kinds of excitations can take place.

The plasmon energy, $\hbar\omega_p$, is so large compared to the single-particle energy, $\hbar k v_o$, because a plasma oscillation at long wavelengths involves the correlated motion of a very large number of electrons. No single electron is greatly perturbed, but because a large number of electrons are moving together in coherent fashion, the resultant energy of the collective mode is quite substantial.

The plasma oscillations resemble sound waves, in that they represent an oscillation in particle density. However, their dispersion relation and the physical mechanism responsible for their existence are quite different. Ordinary sound waves exist in consequence of frequent collisions between the particles; these act to bring about local thermodynamic equilibrium. If one attempts to change the density at a given point, the frequent collisions act as a restoring force opposing any such change. Thus the condition for the existence of a sound wave is that there be *many* collisions between the particles during the period of an oscillation. If we characterize short-range particle collisions by a relaxation time τ, we may write this condition as

$$\omega\tau \ll 1$$

For the plasma oscillations, it is the averaged force field of many other particles which acts as a restoring force, as we shall see explicitly in a subsequent section. Collisions, therefore, act to disrupt the influence of the average field, and so tend to damp the collective mode. Indeed, the condition for the existence of collective plasma modes is

$$\omega\tau \gg 1$$

if τ is a relaxation time appropriate to a short-range collision.

We remark that if one considers the passage of an external charge particle through the plasma, then the condition (3-68) for plasmon excitation can be satisfied without difficulty. This excitation resembles closely the Ĉerenkov excitation of light waves by fast electrons moving at a velocity greater than the light-wave phase velocity in a dielectric medium. Here an electron moving fast compared to the phase velocity of a plasma wave, ω_p/k, will emit plasmons in a narrow wake behind itself. Such plasmon excitation plays an important role in the passage of fast particles through solid films, and will be considered in Chapter 4.

Let us now see qualitatively how the two concepts, screening and plasma oscillation, enable one to overcome the difficulties and divergences of the contribution made by $E^{(2)}_{\text{direct}}$ to the correlation energy. Suppose we write the Hamiltonian for the electron gas in the following way:

$$H = \sum_i \frac{p_i^2}{2m} + \sum_{k>k_c} \frac{2\pi e^2}{k^2}\left(\rho_k^+ \rho_k - N\right) + \sum_{k<k_c} \frac{2\pi e^2}{k^2}\left(\rho_k^+ \rho_k - N\right)$$

In this expression the second term represents a screened interaction between the electrons, of range k_c^{-1}; the third term is the long-range part of the Coulomb interaction, which gave rise to the aforementioned divergences. However, on the basis of our study of the equations of motion, we have seen that for a suitable choice of k_c, the ρ_k for $k \leq k_c$ display essentially collective behavior, and oscillate at a frequency near ω_p. Hence they can be regarded as proportional to some collective coordinates (q_k, say) which describe harmonic oscillators possessing frequency ω_p.

At $T = 0$, the oscillators will be in their ground state, and contribute only a zero-point energy term to the ground-state energy. (We have seen that for $k \leq \omega_p/V_o$, no electron can excite a plasmon.) One can regard the term

$$\frac{2\pi e^2}{k^2} \rho_k^+ \rho_k$$

as corresponding to, say, a potential energy term,

$$\frac{\omega_p^2 q_k^+ q_k}{2}$$

which contributes a term to the ground-state energy which is $\hbar\omega_p/4$ for each oscillator, since half the zero-point energy is potential energy. The other half of the zero-point energy will come from the expectation value of the kinetic energy taken with the plasmon wave functions.

As a result of the plasma oscillations, then, the long-range part of the Coulomb energy is essentially frozen out; that is, it is completely tied up in the zero-point oscillations of the plasmons. The contribution to the ground-state energy from this long-range part is simply

$$E_{p\ell}^{\ell.r.} = \sum_{k<k_c} \frac{h\omega_p}{2} - \frac{2\pi Ne^2}{k^2}$$

Where $E_{p\ell}^{\ell.r.}$ is less than the corresponding Hartree-Fock value,

$$E_{HF}^{\ell.r.} = \sum_{k<k_c} \frac{2\pi Ne^2}{k^2} \{S_{HF}(k) - 1\}$$

the ground-state energy is reduced by a calculation which takes account of the plasmon modes, and one finds thereby a long-range contribution to the correlation energy.

What is left is a collection of electrons interacting via a short-range interaction, of range k_c^{-1}. As we have already remarked, the description of the quasi-particle behavior for such a system is divergence-free; one might hope for a consistent account of the quasi-particles in the approximation in which

$$H_{sr} = \sum_{\substack{k>k_c \\ i\neq j}} \frac{2\pi e^2}{k^2} \exp\left[ik\cdot(x_i - x_j)\right]$$

is regarded as a small perturbation. A first-order calculation (which included only the exchange contribution of the quasi-particle energy was carried out some time ago.[7] An improved calculation of quasi-particle properties, in which the effects of H_{sr} were included within second-order perturbation theory, was later carried out by Fletcher and Larson.[19] The results of these calculations showed that with a screened Coulomb interaction between the electrons, the quasi-particles' properties were not appreciably modified from their Sommerfeld-Hartree values, so that one could hope to make a detailed comparison between theory and experiment.

Let us emphasize that the screening had to accompany the introduction of the plasma waves, for it was only in this way that one did not lose a substantial contribution to the cohesive energy, namely, the long-range part of the exchange energy. Indeed, with an appropriate choice of k_c, one even gains correlation energy upon introducing plasmons. (The correlation energy is further increased when one includes the results of the second-order perturbation theoretic estimate of H_{sr}, as we shall see presently.)

The foregoing picture is somewhat qualitative. It assumes the validity of the RPA, and neglects altogether the coupling between individual electron motion and the plasma waves. Both approximations may be studied with the aid of a collective description of the electron gas, a method which we consider now.

The Collective Description of the Electron Gas

In this section we should like to sketch the way in which one may introduce an explicit set of collective variables to describe the plasmons, and then carry out a series of canonical transformations to a representation in which (within the RPA) the plasmons are an independent elementary excitation of the interacting electron system.[14] The approach is known as the *collective description* because the primary emphasis is placed on identifying and isolating the new phenomenon of collective oscillation brought about by the Coulomb interaction between the electrons. The collective description is somewhat old-fashioned now; we have nonetheless decided to discuss it, because it leads to a particularly simple example of a coupled field-particle system and because it offers certain insights into the behavior of the electron gas which are not readily obtained using other methods.

The essential idea behind the collective description is to introduce at the outset a set of field coordinates which are intended to describe the plasmons. From a physical point of view, one expects that such a description should exist. The plasmons are, in fact, a better-defined excitation than phonons in a free-electron gas model of a metal, in the sense that the lifetime for a long-wavelength plasmon is longer than that for a long-wavelength phonon. However, when one seeks an explicit description for the plasmons, complications arise which are not present in the case of the phonons. For the phonons one simply redescribes the ionic motion in terms of the phonon coordinates and momenta, as we have seen in Chapter 2; in place of 3N particle coordinates and momenta (for a monoatomic system) one has 3N phonon coordinates and momenta. On the other hand, for the electron gas, even if one could find such a complete redescription of the electrons in terms of field coordinates, it would not be useful. The only well-defined collective modes are the long-wavelength plasmons, some N' in number, where $N' = k_c^3/6\pi^2$; since these describe only longitudinal collective modes, and since $N' \ll N$ for electrons in metals, it is obviously not fruitful to attempt a complete redescription of the single-particle motion in terms of collective coordinates only.[20]

The method that Bohm and the writer adopted involved, therefore, the introduction of only a limited number of collective coordinates to describe the plasmons. This was accomplished by considering a new model Hamiltonian for the electron system, one which describes a boson field (like the phonon field) in interaction with the electrons. One chooses as the model Hamiltonian

$$H = \sum_i \frac{p_i^2}{2m} + \sum_k \frac{2\pi e^2}{k^2}\left(\rho_k^+\rho_k - N\right) + \sum_{k<k_c} \frac{\Pi_k^+\Pi_k}{2} + \left(\frac{4\pi e^2}{k^2}\right)^{1/2} \Pi_k^+\rho_k \tag{3-70}$$

The last two terms are the new ones; they represent the kinetic energy of a set of field oscillators, with momenta variables Π_k, and a coupling of this field to the electron density fluctuations. There are a total of n' field variables, where

$$n' = k_c^3/6\pi^2$$

k_c here represents the maximum wave vector for which it is useful to introduce an explicit description of the plasmons.

The new Hamiltonian will be identical to our original one if one imposes a set of subsidiary conditions on the Π_k, viz,

$$\Pi_k \Psi = 0 \tag{3-71}$$

where Ψ represents the wave function for the coupled field-electron system. In general such subsidiary conditions are necessary, since we have in (3-70) a system with 3n + n' degrees of freedom. However, and here is the power and utility of the model Hamiltonian we have chosen, one can show that the ground-state energy of the model Hamiltonian (3-70) is identical to that for the original problem[21]; hence one can ignore the subsidiary conditions (3-71) in calculating the ground-state energy of (3-70).

The model Hamiltonian is only useful if it leads to a problem which is easier to solve than that we originally had. Let us now see how this comes about. We first carry out the canonical transformation,

$$\Psi_{old} = e^{iS/\hbar}\,\Psi_{new}$$

generated by the Hermitian operator S defined by

$$S = \sum_{k<k_c} M_k Q_k \rho_k$$

where

$$M_k = (4\pi e^2/k^2)^{1/2} \tag{3-72}$$

and Q_k represents a field coordinate conjugate to Π_k; that is, it satisfies the commutation relation:

$$[\Pi_k, Q_{k'}] = -i\hbar\,\delta_{kk'} \tag{3-73}$$

With the aid of (3-73) it is easy to calculate the following commutation relations:

$$[\Pi_k, S] = -i\hbar M_k \rho_k$$

$$\left[S, [S, \Pi_k]\right] = 0 \quad [\rho_k, S] = 0$$

$$[p_i, S] = -\hbar \sum_{k<k_o} M_k Q_k k e^{-ik\cdot r_i} \tag{3-74a}$$

$$\left[p_i, [p_i, S]\right] = 0 \quad [Q_k, S] = 0$$

The relationship between any-old operator O and the corresponding new operator O_{new} is given as

$$O_{new} = e^{-iS/\hbar} O e^{iS/\hbar}$$

$$= O - \frac{i}{\hbar}[S, O] - \frac{1}{2\hbar^2} S, [S, O] + \cdots \tag{3-74b}$$

Introducing (3-74b) in this expression, we see that the new operators are given by

$$(\Pi_k)_{new} = \Pi_k + M_k \rho_k$$

$$(Q_k)_{new} = Q_k$$

$$(p_i)_{new} = -i \sum_{k<k_c} M_k Q_k k e^{-ik\cdot r_i} + p_i \tag{3-75}$$

$$(\rho_k)_{new} = \rho_k$$

From these expressions, we obtain the transformed Hamiltonian (we drop the subscripts "new"):

$$H = \sum_i p_i^2/2m + i \sum_{\substack{k<k_c \\ i}} M_k \left\{ \frac{k\cdot p_i}{2m} Q_k e^{-ik\cdot r_i} + e^{-ik\cdot r_i} \frac{k\cdot p_i}{2m} Q_k \right\}$$

$$- \sum_{\substack{k,k'<k_c \\ i}} Q_k Q_{k'} M_k M_{k'} \frac{k\cdot k'}{2m} e^{-i(k+k')\cdot r_i} + \frac{1}{2} \sum_{k<k_c} \Pi_k^* \Pi_k$$

$$- \sum_{k<k_c} \frac{2\pi n e^2}{k^2} + \frac{1}{2} \sum_{k>k_c} M_k^2 \left(\rho_k^+ \rho_k - n\right) \tag{3-76a}$$

If in the third term on the right-hand side we single out the term $k = -k'$, we may rewrite (3-76a) as

$$H = \sum_i p_i^{\,2}/2m + \sum_{k<k_c} \left\{ \frac{\Pi_k^+ \Pi_k}{2} + \omega_p^{\,2} \frac{Q_k^+ Q_k}{2} - \frac{2\pi n e^2}{k^2} \right\}$$

$$+ H_{sr} + H_{int} + U \tag{3-76b}$$

where

$$H_{sr} = \sum_{k>k_c} \left(2\pi e^2/k^2\right)\left(\rho_k^+ \rho_k - n\right) \tag{3-77}$$

$$H_{int} = i \sum_{\substack{k<k_c \\ i}} \left(\frac{\mathbf{k}\cdot\mathbf{p}_i}{m} + \frac{\hbar k^2}{2m}\right) M_k Q_k e^{-i\mathbf{k}\cdot\mathbf{r}_i} \tag{3-78}$$

$$U = \frac{2\pi e^2}{m} \sum_{\substack{k\neq k' \\ i}} Q_k^+ Q_{k'} \frac{\mathbf{k}\cdot\mathbf{k}'}{kk'} e^{i(\mathbf{k}-\mathbf{k}')\cdot\mathbf{r}_i} \tag{3-79}$$

In (3-76) we encounter our first example of a system of coupled particles and fields. The particles are the electrons, which interact with one another via the short-range interaction, H_{sr}. The fields are the plasmons, which oscillate at a frequency ω_p. The terms that give rise to an interaction between the electrons and plasmons are H_{int} and U.

Suppose we can neglect the electron-plasmon coupling. What we have then in (3-76) is a system of electrons which interact via a screened Coulomb interaction, of range k_c^{-1}, and a set of n' (= $k_c^{\,3}/6\pi^2$) plasmons which are independent elementary excitations of the electron gas. This is the picture we were led to by our considerations of the previous section. The screening of the electron interactions is very nearly what we were led to expect on the Fermi-Thomas model, since H_{sr} resembles closely a Yukawa interaction, $e^2/r \exp(-k_c r)$, as may be seen in Fig. 3-12. The range is somewhat longer than k_{FT}^{-1}; we shall see that it is convenient to take $k_c^{-1} \cong 2k_{FT}^{-1}$. Moreover, the neglect of H_{int} corresponds to neglecting the first term on the right-hand side of (3-66), while the neglect of U is just the random phase approximation. The connection with the equation-of-motion approach is made even more obvious if one remarks that the subsidiary condition (3-71) has been transformed to

$$\left(\Pi_k - \sqrt{\frac{4\pi e^2}{k^2}}\,\rho_k\right) \Psi_{new} = 0 \tag{3-80}$$

Thus the Π_k correspond directly to the density fluctuations.

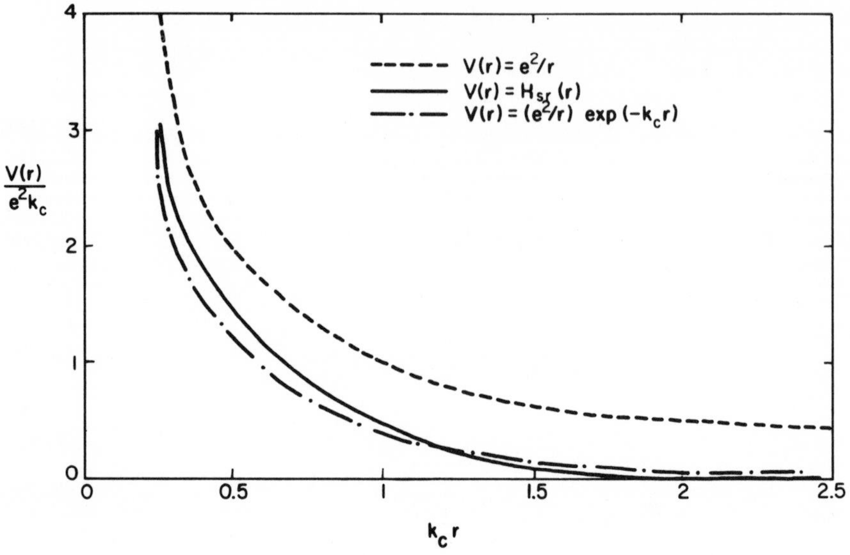

Fig. 3-12

What we have done is to redescribe the long-range part of the Coulomb interaction,

$$\sum_k (2\pi e^2/k^2)\, \rho_k^+ \rho_k$$

in terms of the plasmons. The plasma waves will carry out only zero-point oscillations; hence we have effectively frozen out the long-range part of the Coulomb interaction. We can easily calculate the reduction in system energy associated with this process. The energy of the system is

$$E_o^{(1)} = \left\langle 0 \middle| \sum_i \frac{p_i^{\ 2}}{2m} \middle| 0 \right\rangle + \sum_{k<k_c} \frac{\hbar\omega_p}{2} - \frac{2\pi N e^2}{k^2} + \left\langle 0 \middle| H_{sr} \middle| 0 \right\rangle$$

where the wave function, $|0\rangle$, is that for the unperturbed Fermi sea, that is, a Slater determinant of plane waves. The correlation energy is the difference between this value and that calculated in the Hartree-Fock approximation,

$$E_o^{HF} = \left\langle 0 \middle| \sum_i \frac{p_i^{\ 2}}{2m} \middle| 0 \right\rangle + \sum_{k<k_c} \frac{2\pi e^2}{k^2} \left\langle 0 \middle| \rho_k^+ \rho_k - N \middle| 0 \right\rangle + \left\langle 0 \middle| H_{sr} \middle| 0 \right\rangle$$

We find then, for what we shall call the long-range part of the correlation energy (associated as it is with wave vectors $< k_c$),

$$E_c^{\ell.r.} = \frac{E_o^{(1)} - E_o^{HF}}{N} = \frac{1}{N}\sum_{k<k_c}\left\{\frac{\hbar\omega_p}{2} - \frac{2\pi e^2}{k^2}\langle 0|\rho_k^+\rho_k|0\rangle\right\} \tag{3-81}$$

On using the result (3-25) for $S_{HF}(k)$, we find

$$E_c^{\ell.r.} = \sum_{k<k_c}\left\{\frac{\hbar\omega_p}{N} - \left(\frac{3}{4}\frac{k}{k_o} - \frac{3}{48}\frac{k^3}{k_o^3}\right)\frac{2\pi e^2}{k^2}\right\}$$

$$= -0.46\beta^2/r_s + 0.87\beta^3/r_s^{3/2} + 0.019\beta^4/r_s \quad \text{rydbergs} \tag{3-82}$$

on changing the sum to an integral, and expressing the result in rydbergs. Here we have introduced

$$\beta = k_c/k_o$$

as the maximum wave vector (measured in units of k_o), for which we have introduced the plasmons.

The gain in energy has come about because the mean-square density fluctuation associated with the zero-point oscillations of the plasmons is less than that calculated in the Hartree-Fock approximation. This reduction is expressed by the new form factor,

$$S_{pl}(k) = \frac{\hbar k^2}{2m\omega_p}$$

which replaces the Hartree-Fock value (3-25). It may be remarked that for $\beta \lesssim 0.5\, r_s^{1/2}$ it is energetically favorable to introduce the plasmons.

It is interesting to consider what the system wave function we have been considering looks like in configuration space. We have taken as our system wave function

$$\Psi = \psi_{osc}|0\rangle$$

where ψ_{osc} represents the wave function appropriate to the n' field oscillators in their ground state. We may write

$$\psi_{osc} = \exp\left[-\sum_{k<k_c}\frac{\Pi_k^+\Pi_k}{2\hbar\omega_p}\right]$$

by using a momentum representation for each oscillator. If we now make use of the fact that the Π_k are related to the density fluctuations ρ_k through the subsidiary conditions (3-80) (and this we may do for the ground state), we have

$$\psi_{osc} = \exp\left[-\sum_{k<k_c} \frac{2\pi e^2}{k^2} \frac{\rho_k^+ \rho_k}{\hbar\omega_p}\right]$$

and hence

$$\Psi = \left\{\exp\left[-\sum_{\substack{k<k_c \\ i,j}} \frac{2\pi e^2}{k^2} \frac{e^{ik\cdot(r_i - r_j)}}{\hbar\omega_p}\right]\right\}\Big|0\Big\rangle \tag{3-83}$$

The electronic correlations are expressed in the exponential factor multiplying the Slater determinant in (3-83); this factor allows only for long-range correlations in the positions of the electrons, and yields the result that the probability of finding two electrons some distance r apart is reduced over that calculated in the Hartree-Fock theory.

We now consider the influence of the terms we have neglected, H_{int} and U. On introducing the plasmon creation and annihilation operators, by means of the transformation [compare (2-25)]

$$Q_k = \sqrt{\frac{\hbar}{2\omega_p}}\left(A_k + A_{-k}^+\right)$$

we see that

$$H_{int} = i \sum_{\substack{k<k_c \\ p}} \left(\frac{k\cdot p}{m} + \frac{\hbar k^2}{2m}\right)\left(\frac{4\pi e^2}{k^2}\right)^{1/2}\left(\frac{\hbar}{2\omega_p}\right)^{1/2}$$

$$\times \left(A_k + A_{-k}^+\right) c_{p+k}^+ c_p \tag{3-84}$$

H_{int} thus describes excitation of a plasmon of momentum **k** by an electron which is scattered from a state **p** to **p** - **k**, or the decay of a plasmon into a hole of momentum **p** and an electron of momentum **p** + **k**. Such processes can only be real physical processes if energy can be conserved; as we have seen earlier in this section for plasmons of wave vector **k** such that

$$k \lesssim k_{max} = \frac{\omega_p}{v_o} = 0.47\, r_s^{1/2} k_o \tag{3-85}$$

such real processes will not take place. We shall henceforth assume that $k_c \lesssim k_{max}$; under these circumstances, H_{int} will give rise only to *virtual* plasmon processes, which act to

1. shift the plasmon energy from $\hbar\omega_p$ to a new energy $\hbar\omega_k$
2. introduce an effective interaction between the electrons, corresponding to an exchange of virtual plasmons between the electrons
3. increase slightly the effective mass of each electron

The coupling between electrons and plasmons introduced by H_{int} may be measured by the coupling constant

$$g^2 = \left\langle \left(\frac{\mathbf{k} \cdot \mathbf{p}_i}{m\omega_p} \right)^2 \right\rangle_{av} = \frac{\beta^2}{r_s}$$

For $\beta < \beta_{max} = 0.47 r_s^{1/2}$, such corrections are not large, and may be taken into account by means of a suitable perturbation-theoretic canonical transformation, as we shall see shortly.

On the other hand, U gives rise to terms which involve the emission or absorption of two plasmons, or to plasmon scattering. As we have mentioned, it is a term that we would neglect in the RPA. We can use second-order perturbation theory to obtain a measure of how good is the RPA neglect of U. The change in energy per electron is

$$\Delta E = -\frac{1}{N} \sum_n \frac{|(U)_{no}|^2}{E_n - E_o} \cong \frac{\beta^7}{48} \hbar\omega_p \qquad (3\text{-}86)$$

This result may be compared to the plasmon zero-point energy, which is

$$E_{pl} = \frac{\beta^3}{4} \hbar\omega_p$$

The ratio is

$$\Delta E / E_{pl} = \frac{\beta^4}{12}$$

One sees, then, that U represents a minor correction to the plasmon zero-point energy; the correction is no more than 10 percent for $\beta = 0.47 r_s^{1/2}$ and $r_s = 5.5$ (Cs)—so that the neglect of U is well-justified.

It is straightforward to take into account the influence of H_{int} by carrying out a canonical transformation which eliminates H_{int} from the basic Hamiltonian (3-76) to order g^2. (One obtains more information from a canonical transformation than is readily found using, for example, second-order Rayleigh-Schrödinger perturbation theory.)

The game one plays is the following: Find a transformation S such that

$$\Psi = e^{iS/\hbar}\chi$$

where

$$-\frac{i}{\hbar}[S, H_o] = -H_{int} \tag{3-87}$$

In these equations H_o is taken to be the Hamiltonian for noninteracting electrons and plasmons of frequency ω, the new plasmon frequency being determined in self-consistent fashion. I refer you to the original literature for the details of the choice of S and the calculation of the results.[14] (A simplified version of the transformation is given as a problem at the end of the chapter.) One finds thereby a new Hamiltonian, which has the following schematic form:

$$H = H_{el} + H_{pl} + H_{rp} + H_{sr} + U + i[S, H_{sr}] \tag{3-88}$$

H_{el} is, as before, the electronic kinetic energy. H_{pl} describes a collection of independent plasmons, of frequency ω_k;

$$H_{pl} = \sum_k \left[\frac{\Pi_k^+ \Pi_k}{2} + \omega_k^2 \frac{Q_k^+ Q_k}{2} - \frac{2\pi N e^2}{k^2}\right] \tag{3-89}$$

ω_k is given by the dispersion relation

$$1 = \frac{4\pi e^2}{m} \sum_i \frac{1}{\left(\omega_k - \frac{k \cdot p_i}{m}\right)^2 - \frac{\hbar^2 k^4}{4m^2}} \tag{3-90a}$$

The indicated summation in (3-90a) can be carried through without difficulty provided

$$\frac{k \cdot p_i}{m} + \frac{\hbar k^2}{2m} < \omega_k$$

for all wave vectors k and momenta p_i considered. This condition is just the requirement that none of the electrons in the system possess a momentum sufficiently large to excite a plasmon of momentum, $\hbar k$, energy $\hbar\omega_k$ [compare (3-68)]. If we average the dispersion relation (3-90a) over the unperturbed Fermi distribution, we find

$$1 = \frac{4\pi e^2}{m} \sum_{p\sigma} \frac{n_{p\sigma}}{\left(\omega_k - \mathbf{k}\cdot\mathbf{p}/m\right)^2 - \hbar^2 k^4/4m^2} \tag{3-90b}$$

and plasmon excitation by single electrons (or plasma damping by single excitation) will not occur as long as the plasmon vector k is such that

$$\frac{kp_o}{m} + \frac{\hbar k^2}{2m} < \omega_k \tag{3-91}$$

(We discuss this condition further in Sec. 3-5.)

For small values of k one may easily carry out a systematic expansion of (3-90b) in powers of k^2; one finds

$$\omega_k{}^2 = \omega_p{}^2 + \frac{3}{5} k^2 v_o{}^2 + \frac{\hbar k^4}{4m^2} + \cdots \tag{3-90c}$$

Thus the plasmon energies are shifted by a term of order k^2, as our simple equation-of-motion estimate would have led us to expect.

H_{rp} represents the long-range part of an effective screened interaction between the electrons brought about by an exchange of virtual plasmons; it is, approximately,

$$H_{rp} = - \sum_k \frac{2\pi e^2}{k^2} \frac{1}{\omega_p{}^2} \frac{\mathbf{k}\cdot\mathbf{p}}{m} \frac{\mathbf{k}\cdot\mathbf{q}}{m} c^+_{p-k} c^+_{q+k} c_q c_p \tag{3-92}$$

Note that the correction to ω_p is of order g^2, while H_{rp} is likewise of order g^2 times the original long-range Coulomb interaction.

Before going any further, let us make more precise what we mean by the RPA. In the derivation of the equations of motion for ρ_k, we said that the RPA corresponded to neglecting the influence of the coupling between different wavelength density fluctuations. Hence, as we have seen, it corresponds to neglecting the coupling between long-wavelength plasmons (which are, after all, density fluctuations) or between plasmons and H_{sr}, since H_{sr} represents short-wavelength density fluctuations. More precisely, we could say that *in the RPA one determines a given property of the system* [contribution to the correlation energy, S(k), etc.] *which depends upon a particular momentum transfer* k, *by keeping only that component of the Coulomb interaction which involves the momentum transfer* k. Thus in making the RPA one neglects the coupling between different momentum transfers for either the electron-plasmon or electron-electron interaction.

The term $i\,[S, H_{sr}]$ describes a coupling between the plasmons and the electrons which lies outside the RPA; it gives rise to a shift in the plasmon frequency which is[17]

$$- \frac{3}{40} \frac{k^2}{k_o^2} \omega_p \tag{3-93}$$

and hence contributes a term to the ground-state energy which is

$$E^{(3)} = - \frac{9}{400} \beta^5 h\omega_p$$

The ratio of this term to the plasmon zero-point energy is

$$\frac{E^{(3)}}{E_{pl}} = \frac{9}{100} \beta^2$$

One sees that this correction is likewise negligible for $\beta < \beta_{max}$, and all metallic densities. It might be added that this term also gives rise to a damping of long-wavelength plasmons which is order k^2 in the limit $k \to 0$ (DuBois[22]). Thus only in the long-wavelength limit is the plasmon a truly long-lived excitation. This is just what one should expect—because the single-particle excitations of the electron gas lie lower than the plasmons, there must be a way to couple the plasmon to these in such a way that the plasmons decay. Coherence effects play a role in such a coupling, hence the plasmon lifetime is inversely proportional to k^2, and becomes infinite as $k \to 0$.

Let us look anew at the long-range correlation energy in the RPA. There will be two kinds of corrections to our earlier value, which arise from H_{int}. One kind arises from the corrections to the zero-point energy of the plasmons, owing to the shift in frequency described by (3-92). One finds, from the correction, $(3/10)\,(k^2 v_o^2)/\omega_p$, to ω_p, a contribution which is

$$0.70\,\beta^5/r_s^{5/2} \quad \text{rydbergs}$$

The higher-order corrections $\left[\beta^7/r_s^{7/2}, \text{ etc.}\right]$ are negligible for metallic electron densities and $\beta \lesssim \beta_{max}$. The second class of corrections come from H_{rp}, and may be treated by ordinary perturbation-theoretic methods. Thus one finds for the "exchange energy" arising from this long-ranged screened interaction

$$\frac{\langle 0 | H_{rp} | 0 \rangle}{N} = - 0.52 \frac{\beta^4}{r_s^2} \quad \text{rydbergs}$$

There are, moreover, a set of higher-order terms which likewise need to be considered if one is making a consistent RPA treatment. The method of Gell-Mann and Brueckner,[23] which we shall consider in the next section, may be applied to take these into account; one then finds (Nozières and Pines[17]) that H_{rp} gives rise to the following term of order β^4/r_s^2 in the long-range correlation energy:

$$\Delta E_{rp} = -0.98\beta^4/r_s^2 \quad \text{rydbergs}$$

There will, in addition, be terms of order β^6/r_s^3, etc., which are negligible at metallic electron densities for $\beta \lesssim \beta_{max}$.

We conclude, then, that the long-range part of the correlation energy may be written

$$E^{\ell.r.}_{corr}(\beta) = -0.46\frac{\beta^2}{r_s} + 0.87\frac{\beta^3}{r_s^{3/2}} - 0.98\frac{\beta^4}{r_3^{\,2}} + 0.070\frac{\beta^5}{r_s^{5/2}} + \cdots \tag{3-94}$$

to an accuracy of something like 10 per cent, provided we keep to metallic electron densities and choose $\beta \lesssim 0.47\, r_s^{1/2}$. In fact, we might now simply choose $\beta = 0.47\, r_s^{1/2}$. With this choice, we have no plasmon decay within the RPA, and a sufficiently accurate account by means of the RPA of the long-range contribution to the correlation energy. We find, therefore,

$$E^{\ell.r.}_{corr}\left(\beta = 0.47\, r_s^{1/2}\right) \cong -0.043 \text{ rydberg} \tag{3-95}$$

There remains the problem of treating the influence of the short-range screened interaction, H_{sr}, on the correlation energy, and the calculation of various other quantities of physical interest—specific heat, spin susceptibility, and the like. The essential point is that perturbation-theoretic methods can now be used for such calculations because no divergences occur; as we have remarked, a system of electrons interacting via a screened Coulomb interaction is essentially well behaved. For example, one can calculate the contributions of the second-order direct and exchange terms, (3-50) and (3-51), to the correlation energy. One finds for the short-range part of $E_2^{(a)}$ [15]

$$E_2^{(a)} = -\{0.050 - 0.0125\, \ell n\, \beta + 0.0128\beta^2\} \quad \text{rydbergs} \tag{3-96}$$

However, there is no guarantee that second-order perturbation theory furnishes a good estimate of the effects of H_{sr}, and, indeed, in general, it does not. Thus it is necessary to examine the structure of the perturbation-series expansion—and this brings us to the work of Gell-Mann and Brueckner.

The Method of Gell-Mann and Brueckner[23]

The next major development in the theory of the interacting electron gas occurred in 1957, when Gell-Mann and Brueckner showed that perturbation-theoretic methods could be applied *ab initio* to the electron gas, provided one did not stop at the first divergent term one encountered but instead summed the entire series of most divergent terms, one from each order, to obtain thereby a convergent answer. (A similar calculation had been carried out by Macke[24] with somewhat less conclusive results.)

As we have seen, the perturbation-theoretic calculation of the ground-state energy gives a logarithmic divergence in the second order. The higher-order terms in the perturbation expansion exhibit even stronger divergences associated with the long range of the Coulomb interaction. The structure of the terms may be made clear in the following way. In second order we have seen that for a "direct" process, in which one goes up and back with the same momentum transfer k, one gets a divergent answer because of the "piling up" of factors $1/k^2$. On the other hand, for an exchange process, there is no divergence because one has one factor of $1/k^2$, and one of $(p+q+k)^{-2}$, the latter being well behaved as $k \to 0$. What about third order? The most divergent term then will be that in which the electrons simply pass on the momentum transfer k—as shown in Fig. 3-13a. For this term one has initially the excitation of two electron-hole pairs, associated with a momentum transfer k; one of these pairs is then annihilated—and created anew—again by the interaction $V_k = 4\pi e^2/k$; finally the two pairs annihilate, to return the system to a state of no-pair excitation. The size of this term may be simply estimated in the limit of $k \to 0$. Compared to $E_2^{(a)}$, one has an additional factor of $4\pi e^2/k^2$, an additional energy denominator, which goes as hkp_F, and a reduction in the available phase space, due to Pauli principle restrictions, which goes as k/k_F. Hence, the contribution from Fig. 3-13 is quadratically divergent,

$$E_3^{(a)} \propto \int_\beta \frac{dk}{k} \frac{4\pi e^2}{k^2} \frac{k}{k_F} \frac{1}{\hbar k p_F} \propto \frac{r_s}{\beta^2} \quad \text{rydbergs}$$

where we have put in a cutoff β. On the other hand, if we had permitted one of the electron-hole pairs to scatter via an exchange process, we would find

$$E_3^{(b)} \propto \int_\beta \frac{dk}{k} \frac{4\pi e^2}{(k+p+q)^2} \frac{k}{k_F} \frac{1}{\hbar k p_F} \propto r_s \ln \beta \quad \text{rydbergs}$$

a result which is still divergent, but not so strongly so as is $E_3^{(a)}$. Similarly terms which involve *two* exchange scattering processes yield

$$E_3^{(c)} \propto r_s \quad \text{rydbergs}$$

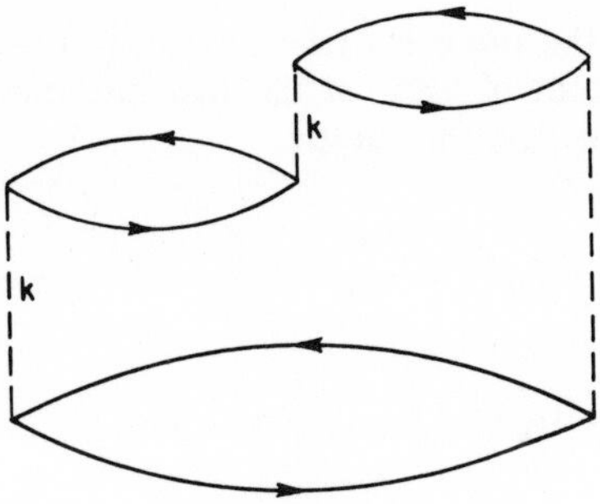

(a)

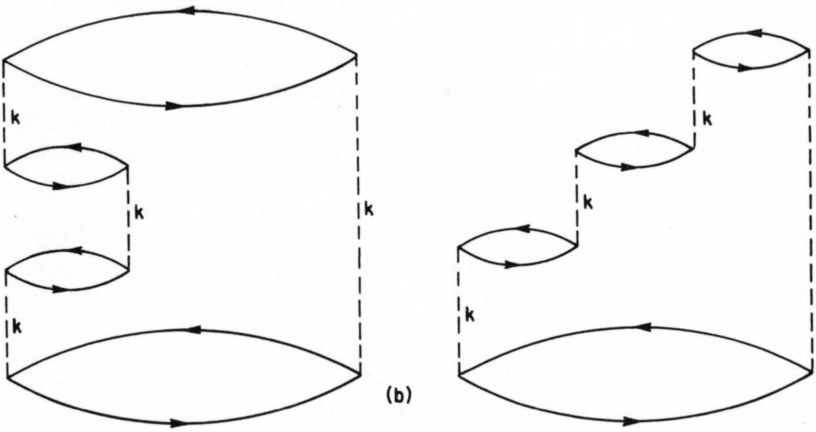

(b)

Fig. 3-13

Again, one can look at the fourth order. One then finds, from ring diagrams such as those shown in Fig. 3-13b a quartically divergent contribution:

$$E_4^{(2)} \propto \int_\beta \frac{dk}{k}\left(\frac{4\pi e^2}{k^2}\right)^2\left(\frac{k}{k_F}\right)^2 \frac{1}{(\hbar k p_F)^2} \propto \frac{r_s^2}{\beta^4} \quad \text{rydbergs}$$

from those terms which involve *only* the momentum transfer k. On the other hand, from terms which involve one exchange scattering for an excited electron-hole pair, one has $E_4^{(b)} \propto r_s^2/\beta^2$; terms which involve two such exchange scatterings are of order $r_s^2 \ln \beta$; terms which involve three such exchange scatterings, of order r_s^2.

The structure of the perturbation series is therefore clear. When analyzed from the point of view of the low momentum behavior of the matrix elements, one finds a series:

$$E_{corr} = a + b \ln \beta + c \frac{r_s}{\beta^2} + d \frac{r_s}{\beta^4} + e \frac{r_s^3}{\beta^6} + \cdots$$
$$+ a_1 + b_1\beta^2 + c_1 r_s^2/\beta^2 + \cdots$$
$$+ a_2 r_s \ln \beta + b_2 r_s^2 \ln \beta + c_2 r_s^2 + \cdots \qquad (3\text{-}97)$$

If now, following the results of the previous section, we take β, the screening wave vector, proportional to $r_s^{1/2}$, we see that the first set of terms, which arise from contributions which involve *only* the momentum transfer k, give rise to a term proportional to $\ln r_s$ and to a constant term in the correlation energy. The second set give rise to a constant, and terms of order r_s; the third to terms of order $r_s \ln r_s$, r_s^2 etc. Thus if one could sum the most divergent terms in the perturbation series, one would find both a $\ln r_s$ and a constant contribution to the correlation energy (measured in rydbergs); the next most divergent terms yield terms of order r_s and $r_s \ln r_s$, etc.

What Gell-Mann and Brueckner did was just that; they used a Feynman propagator approach to work out a simple way for carrying out such series summations; they then summed the most divergent terms and obtained the result

$$E_{corr}^{RPA} = 0.062 \ln r_s - 0.142 + 0(r_s) \qquad (3\text{-}98a)$$

This result is just the RPA contribution to the correlation energy, since each momentum transfer k appearing in the Coulomb interaction is treated independently. There is a further constant term in the correlation energy, which comes from the second-order "exchange" term, $E_2^{(b)}$ [Eq. (3-51)], which GB have obtained by a numerical calculation:

$$E_2^{(b)} = 0.046 \quad \text{rydberg}$$

These results, together with the arguments presented above, led Gell-Mann and Brueckner to write the ground-state energy of the electron gas in the form

$$E_o = \frac{2.21}{r_s^2} - \frac{0.916}{r_s} + 0.062 \ln r_s - 0.096 + ar_s + br_s \ln r_s$$
$$+ cr_s^2 + \cdots \quad \text{rydbergs} \qquad (3\text{-}98b)$$

Thus they showed that at high densities ($r_s \ll 1$), the RPA yields a rigorous result for the correlation energy, and that moreover at such densities the ground-state energy possesses a series expansion of the form (3-98b).

Looked at *ab initio*, their procedure of summing the most divergent terms first, and then carrying out the appropriate integration, was a most daring procedure, and one which was not obviously correct. On the other hand, if we look at their calculation as a way of treating H_{sr} only, then it is clearly all right. For there are no divergences, and such a series summation is indeed well behaved. In this second point of view, based on the BP collective coordinate method, one then needs to discuss the structure of the higher-order terms caused by the intermingling of the long-range and short-range effects—and we have already considered some of these in our consideration of the validity of the RPA calculation of the long-range part of the correlation energy. It may easily be seen that these, and others, give rise to terms of order r_s, r_s^2, etc.—all of which are well behaved, and indeed negligible, in the limit of $r_s \to 0$; hence one can simply smoothly join the BP procedure for calculating the long-range part of the correlation energy to the GB method for calculating the short-range part, to whatever accuracy one desires.

This was *not* the procedure which GB followed. They considered only individual-particle-like behavior, used perturbation theory for all momentum transfers, and nowhere in their theory did plasmons appear. How therefore can one reconcile the two approaches to the treatment of the long-range part of the Coulomb interaction? Historically, a further field-theoretic calculation by Hubbard[25] played an essential role in establishing the connection between the two approaches to the long-range part of the interaction—and to showing that they lead to identical results for the ground-state energy. However, we do not, in this book, need to delve that deeply into field-theoretic matters, because one can in fact establish the desired connections and interrelationships between the collection description and the perturbation-theoretic approach through a calculation of the frequency and wave-vector-dependent dielectric constant for the electron gas. Such a calculation can be carried out in the RPA without invoking field theory, as we shall see in Sec. 3-4.

Brief Summary

The GB result is perhaps not surprising—that once one has developed a method of dealing with the long range of the Coulomb interaction, at sufficiently high densities the interaction turns out to be comparatively weak. For at high densities ($r_s \ll 1$) the kinetic energy of the electrons is the dominant term in determining their behavior; the Hartree-Fock exchange energy is already a small correction, and the correlation energy terms, over which we have labored so mightily, yield smaller corrections yet. The form of the series expansion which contains both powers of r_s and $\ln r_s$ is perhaps surprising (as might be the fact that such a series exists at all), but, as we have seen, the appearance of the logarithmic terms is a simple consequence of the long range of the Coulomb force. We return later to the question of the range of r_s over which such a series is meaningful; here we remark that for $r_s << 1$ it would seem obviously all right, and that one could perhaps use it up to values of r_s of the order of unity.

On the other hand, we have seen that a quite different situation exists at low densities ($r_s > 20$, say); here the correlations brought about by the Coulomb interaction dominate kinetic-energy effects, and the electrons form a stable lattice. We can say, therefore, that we deal here with a strong coupling situation; the series expansion takes the quite different form

$$E = \frac{a}{r_s} + \frac{b}{r_s^{3/2}} + \frac{d}{r_s^2} + \cdots$$

Between those two extremes there is situated a large intermediate coupling region. It is in this region that the densities of actual metals ($2 < r_s < 5.5$) are located. Kinetic energy and potential energy are of the same order, so that one can expand neither in powers of the potential energy over the kinetic energy or vice versa. It is perhaps to be expected that the kinetic and potential energies are of the same order of magnitude for electrons in metals, since cohesion arises out of a delicate interplay between the two. If, for example, kinetic effects were a bit larger, one would no longer have any binding; or, to put it another way, potential energy effects are *just* large enough to bring about metallic cohesion.

It is perhaps most appropriate to speak of an electron liquid in this intermediate coupling region, with the liquid-like behavior becoming more pronounced as one gives to larger values of r_s.[26] Thus, for example, for $r_s \cong 7.3$, one has already N plasmon degrees of freedom (for a choice of $\beta = 0.47\, r_s^{1/2}$), so that the number of independent longitudinal collective modes has reached its maximum value here. Another way of looking at the extent of the liquid-like behavior is to compare the kinetic energy tied up with the zero-point oscillations of the plasmons with that due to the Fermi sea. Using $\beta \cong 0.47\, r_s^{1/2}$, one has $(\beta^3/12)\hbar\omega_p \cong 2.21/r_s^2$ rydbergs at about $r_s = 5.4$. In any event, it is clear that at metallic densities, neither the series (3-98), nor (3-59), is appropriate, and, indeed, no series expansion can exist. One must therefore devise a different method of dealing with this intermediate coupling domain, a question to which we return in Sec. 3-6.

3-4 DIELECTRIC RESPONSE OF AN ELECTRON SYSTEM

Defining Equations

In our discussion of the Fermi-Thomas approximation, we have considered the screening action of an electron gas for a point impurity. As was remarked there, if one wants to consider the screening of the interaction between the rapidly moving electrons in a metal, it is necessary that one develops a formulation capable of describing the screening of a longitudinal field which varies in both space and time (longitudinal because the motion of particles gives rise to density fluctuations in the system). What we are interested in is the dielectric response of the electron gas to such a field; this may be specified in terms of a longitudinal wave vector and frequency-dependent dielectric constant, $\varepsilon(k\omega)$.[27,28]

A knowledge of $\varepsilon(k\omega)$ provides us with a good deal more in the way of information about the properties of the electron gas than simply the dielectric response. In fact, it may be said that $\varepsilon(k\omega)$ serves as a simple unifying concept for the theories of the electron gas. To be specific, a knowledge of $\varepsilon(k\omega)$ permits one to obtain directly the following properties of an interacting electron system:

1. The response of the system to weak external longitudinal fields which vary in space and time.
2. The density-fluctuation excitation spectrum (both the single-particle and collective modes) as measured by an incident fast charged particle.
3. The time-dependent correlations between the density fluctuations.
4. The ground-state energy.

We begin by considering the time-dependent response of the electron gas to a weak external test charge.[28] Let the external *charge* density be such that its Fourier transform in space and time is $z\rho_{ext}(k\omega)$; that is,

$$z\rho_{ext}(\mathbf{r}, t) = \sum_{k\omega} z\rho_{ext}(k\omega)\, e^{i(\mathbf{k}\cdot\mathbf{r}-\omega t)} \tag{3-99}$$

The corresponding Fourier transform of the macroscopic Poisson equations then reads

$$ik \cdot \mathbf{D}(k\omega) = 4\pi z\rho_{ext}(k\omega) \tag{3-100a}$$

$$ik \cdot \mathbf{E}(k\omega) = 4\pi\,[-e\langle\rho(k\omega)\rangle + z\rho_{ext}(k\omega)] \tag{3-100b}$$

In Equations (3-100) $\mathbf{D}(k\omega)$ and $\mathbf{E}(k\omega)$ are the Fourier transforms of the displacement-field and electric-field vectors, respectively, and

$-e < \rho(k\omega) >$ is the Fourier transform of the charge density induced in the electron system by the external test charge. The average is understood to be an average over the states of the system, electrons plus test charge; in the absence of the external charge, $< \rho(k\omega) > = 0$ by translational invariance.

Both **D** and **E** are purely longitudinal fields; we can therefore define a scalar longitudinal dielectric constant by means of the relation

$$\mathbf{D}(k\omega) = \varepsilon(k\omega)\,\mathbf{E}(k\omega) \tag{3-101}$$

Let us introduce the total scalar field potential, $\varphi(k\omega)$, defined by

$$\mathbf{E}(k\omega) = -i\,\mathbf{k}\,\varphi(k\omega) \tag{3-102}$$

and the potential associated with the test charge,

$$\varphi_{ext}(k\omega) = \frac{4\pi}{k^2}\, z\rho_{ext}(k\omega) \tag{3-103}$$

In terms of these potentials, we may write (3-100a) as

$$\varphi(k\omega) = \frac{\varphi_{ext}(k\omega)}{\varepsilon(k\omega)} \tag{3-104}$$

We see from (3-104) that $\varepsilon(k\omega)$ is a direct measure of the reduction in strength of the potential associated with the external test charge, $\varphi_{ext}(k\omega)$, and thus measures the effectiveness of the screening of an external charge distribution by the electron gas. For example, suppose we consider an impurity of charge Z located at the origin of the electron gas. The potential which it produces at a point r is then given by

$$\varphi_{imp}(\mathbf{r}) = \sum_{\mathbf{k}} \frac{4\pi Ze}{k^2\varepsilon(k0)}\, e^{i\mathbf{k}\cdot\mathbf{r}}$$

where $\varepsilon(k0)$ is the static dielectric constant.

Other useful forms which equations (3-100) take are

$$\frac{1}{\varepsilon(k\omega)} - 1 = -\frac{e< \rho(k\omega)>}{z\rho_{ext}(k\omega)} \tag{3-105a}$$

and

$$\varepsilon(k\omega) - 1 = (4\pi e/k^2)\,[< \rho(k\omega)>/\varphi(k\omega)] \tag{3-105b}$$

Either of these permit a direct determination of $\varepsilon(k\omega)$, once one has calculated $<\rho(k\omega)>$.

There is a simple connection between $\varepsilon(k\omega)$ and the wave-vector and frequency-dependent electrical conductivity $\sigma(k\omega)$. The latter is defined by the familiar relation:

$$-e < j(k\omega) > = \sigma(k\omega)\, \mathbf{E}(k\omega) \tag{3-106}$$

Here $< j(k\omega) >$ is the Fourier transform of the particle current density averaged over the states of the electrons in the presence of a weak external longitudinal field; $\mathbf{E}(k\omega)$ is the sum of that external field, plus the induced field, according to (3-100b). If we take the divergence of (3-106), make use of the current-conservation or continuity equation,

$$i\mathbf{k} \cdot < j(k\omega) > = i\omega < \rho(k\omega) >$$

together with (3-105b), we find

$$\varepsilon(k\omega) = 1 + \frac{4\pi i \sigma(k\omega)}{\omega} \tag{3-107}$$

To complete our definition of $\varepsilon(k\omega)$ we must specify the boundary conditions which apply in the determination of the response of the electron system to the test charge. We shall employ causal boundary conditions; we thus choose the retarded solution to Equations (3-105), in which the response of the electron system follows (in time) the introduction of the test charge.

One may calculate $<\rho(k\omega)>$ by straightforward application of ordinary time-dependent perturbation theory to the problem of electrons interacting with each other and with the test charge. Perturbation theory suffices because the test charge is regarded as arbitrarily weak. The basic Hamiltonian is

$$H_{tot} = H + H_{int} \tag{3-108}$$

where H is, as before, the Hamiltonian for the system of electrons in a uniform background of positive charge,

$$H = \sum_i \frac{p_i^{\,2}}{2m} + \sum_k \frac{2\pi e^2}{k^2}\left(\rho_k^+ \rho_k - N\right) \tag{3-109a}$$

and H_{int} describes their weak interaction with the test charge, specified by (3-99). Because this interaction contains frequencies which are in general equal to the resonant frequencies of the electron system, there will be a transfer of energy from the test charge to the electrons. If the transfer is permitted to take place for an arbitrarily long time, the electron system will heat up, and we can no longer regard the charge as representing a weak perturbation. Such difficulties can be avoided by a suitable choice of boundary conditions. If we switch on the interaction between the electrons and the test charge *adiabatically*, that is, *very* slowly, then real transitions between the electron states are not introduced over a long period of time. The mathematical statement of this boundary condition takes the following form:

$$H_{int} = - \lim_{\delta \to 0} \sum_{k\omega} \frac{4\pi e z}{k^2} \rho_k^+ \rho_{ext}(k\omega)\, e^{-i\omega t} e^{\delta t} \qquad (3\text{-}109b)$$

The device of introducing δ, and then passing eventually to the limit $\delta = 0$, means that the interaction is turned on at $t = -\infty$ and builds up gradually to its full strength at $t = 0$, during which time the electrons adiabatically follow the interaction. We note too that with this boundary condition the electron response to the perturbation is necessarily causal, in that the response follows (in time) the switching on of the perturbation.

Our derivation of an exact expression for $\varepsilon(k\omega)$ follows closely that of Ref. 28. We use time-dependent perturbation theory to compute the change in the system wave function brought about by H_{int}, under the assumption that the system is initially in its ground state. Thus we consider the time-dependent Schrödinger equation

$$i\hbar \frac{\partial}{\partial t} \Psi(t) = (H + H_{int})\, \Psi(t)$$

We expand $\Psi(t)$ in terms of the exact many-body eigenstates, Ψ_n, of the unperturbed electron system

$$H\Psi_n = E_n \Psi_n$$

the E_n being the corresponding *exact* system energies:

$$\Psi(t) = \sum_n \Psi_n a_n(t)\, e^{-iE_n t/\hbar}$$

Our boundary conditions tell us that

$$a_o(t = -\infty) = 1$$

$$a_n(t = -\infty) = 0$$

since the system is initially in its ground state. We are interested in calculating $<\rho(k\omega)>$, that is, the expectation value of the density fluctuation of momentum k and frequency ω in the presence of the test charge. Because we assume that the test charge, and hence H_{int}, represents a *weak* perturbation on the electron system, the response of the electrons will be *linear*, that is proportional to H_{int}. Thus in calculating $<\rho(k\omega)>$ it suffices to keep only those terms in H_{int} which vary with a frequency ω; the other Fourier components of the test charge do not contribute in first order. (The skeptical reader may easily verify this by direct calculation.)

The calculation is then of the classic first-order variety; one substitutes the expansion for $\Psi(t)$ into the Schrödinger equation, keeps only the relevant linear terms in H_{int}, and obtains

$$a_n(t) = -\frac{4\pi ez}{\hbar k^2}\left\{\frac{\rho_{ext}(k\omega)\,(\rho_k^+)_{no}\,e^{-i(\omega-\omega_{no}+i\delta)t}}{\omega-\omega_{no}+i\delta} - \frac{\rho^+_{ext}(k\omega)\,(\rho_k)_{no}\,e^{i(\omega+\omega_{no}-i\delta)t}}{\omega+\omega_{no}-i\delta}\right\}$$

where the $(\rho_k)_{no}$ are the *exact* matrix elements of the density fluctuation between the ground state and the excited state, Ψ_n, and the ω_{no} are the corresponding *exact* excitation frequencies of the electron system, $\omega_{no} = (E_n - E_o)/\hbar$. Next one calculates the expectation value of ρ_k, keeping only terms linear in a_n,

$$<\rho_k(t)> = \sum_n <0|\,\rho_k\,|\,n>\,a_n(t)\,e^{-i\omega_{no}t} + <n|\,\rho_k\,|\,0>\,a_n^+(t)\,e^{i\omega_{no}t}$$

The calculation is simplified if one notes that when an intermediate state $|\,n>$ is coupled to the ground state by ρ_k, then that same state cannot be coupled to the ground state by ρ_k^+. One finds, by direct substitution,

$$<\rho_k(t)> = -\frac{4\pi ez}{\hbar k^2}\,\rho_{ext}(k\omega)\,e^{-i(\omega+i\delta)t} \times\left\{\sum_n \frac{|(\rho_k^+)_{no}|^2}{\omega-\omega_{no}+i\delta} - \frac{|(\rho_k)_{no}|^2}{\omega+\omega_{no}+i\delta}\right\}$$

This result can be further simplified. The spectrum of states available to a density fluctuation of momentum k, (ρ_k^+), and one of momentum

$-\mathbf{k}$, (ρ_k), are in fact identical, as are the corresponding matrix elements, if one assumes the system is invariant under the transformation $t \to -t$.[28a] If we make use of this fact, recall that

$$< \rho_k(t) > = < \rho(k\omega) > e^{-i\omega t}$$

and substitute the resulting expression into our definition, (3-105a), of the dielectric constant, we obtain finally

$$\frac{1}{\varepsilon(k\omega)} - 1 = \frac{4\pi e^2}{\hbar k^2} \sum_n \left| \left(\rho_k^+\right)_{no} \right|^2 \left\{ \frac{1}{\omega - \omega_{no} + i\delta} - \frac{1}{\omega + \omega_{no} + i\delta} \right\} \tag{3-110a}$$

which is our desired result.

We see in (3-110a) that the causal boundary conditions do indeed serve to specify the resonant response of the system, that is, how one describes the response to an excitation whose frequency ω is equal to a "natural" excitation frequency ω_{no} of the electron gas. We can separate out the real and imaginary parts of $1/\varepsilon(k\omega)$ by making use of the result (which becomes strictly valid under an integral sign)

$$\frac{1}{x - a + i\delta} = \text{principal part } \frac{1}{x - a} - i\pi\delta(x - a)$$

in the summation, (3-110a). Thus one has

$$\text{Re } \frac{1}{\varepsilon(k\omega)} = 1 + \frac{4\pi e^2}{\hbar k^2} \sum_n{}' \left| \left(\rho_k^+\right)_{no} \right|^2 \left\{ \frac{2\omega_{no}}{\omega^2 - \omega_{no}^2} \right\} \tag{3-110b}$$

$$\text{Im } \frac{1}{\varepsilon(k\omega)} = -\frac{4\pi^2 e^2}{\hbar k^2} \sum_n \left| \left(\rho_k^+\right)_{no} \right|^2 \left\{ \delta(\omega - \omega_{no}) - \delta(\omega + \omega_{no}) \right\} \tag{3-110c}$$

where the prime in (3-110b) denotes the fact that principle parts are to be taken. The real part of $1/\varepsilon(k\omega)$ describes the polarization processes which are in phase with the external field; the imaginary part represents the out-of-phase part, and is therefore related to the transfer of energy from the test charge to the system.

Energy Loss of a Fast Charged Particle

Let us consider now the way in which a fast particle of charge Z_e, momentum $\mathbf{P}_e$, energy $E_e = P_e^2/2M_e$, transfers energy and momentum to the electron gas. The interaction is given by

$$-\sum_{\mathbf{k}} \frac{4\pi Ze^2}{k^2} \rho_k^+ e^{i\mathbf{k}\cdot\mathbf{R}_e}$$

where R_e is the position of the particle. If the particle moves sufficiently rapidly ($\mathbf{P}_e/M_e >> v_o$) the Born approximation may be applied to the description of the scattering act; indeed, the physical problem becomes identical with that we have just considered, with the charged particle playing the role of a time-varying external test charge. The "golden rule" of second-order perturbation theory may be applied to obtain the probability per unit time $W(k\omega)$ that the particle transfer momentum $\hbar\mathbf{k}$ and energy, $\hbar\omega$, to the electron gas; one has

$$W(\mathbf{k}\,\omega) = \frac{2\pi}{\hbar^2}\left(\frac{4\pi Ze^2}{k^2}\right)^2 \sum_n \left|\left(\rho_{\mathbf{k}}^+\right)_{no}\right|^2 \delta(\omega - \omega_{no}) \tag{3-111}$$

where $(\rho_k^+)_{no}$ and ω_{no} have the meaning specified above. The geometry of the scattering act is shown in Fig. 3-14.

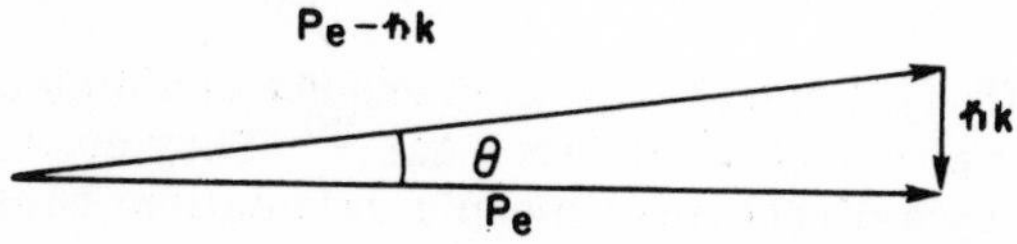

Fig. 3-14

The momentum transfers of interest are generally such that $k < k_o$, in which case it follows from conservation of energy that k is very nearly perpendicular to $\mathbf{P}_e$.

If we compare (3-111) with (3-110c), we see that one can also write

$$W(\mathbf{k}\omega) = -\frac{8\pi e^2}{\hbar k^2} \operatorname{Im} \frac{1}{\varepsilon(k\omega)} \tag{3-112}$$

so that the energy transfer from the particle to the electron gas is determined by Im $1/\varepsilon(k\omega)$, which we might call the energy-loss function. We can obtain the total energy transfer per unit time by integrating (3-112) over all energies $\hbar\omega$ and summing over all momentum transfers $\mathbf{k}$. In so doing, one must recall that ω and k are not independent; by conservation of energy and momentum, one has

$$\omega_{no} = \omega = \frac{\mathbf{k}\cdot\mathbf{P}_e}{M_e} - \frac{\hbar k^2}{2M_e} \tag{3-113}$$

Where the fast particle momentum $\mathbf{P}_e$ is large compared to the momentum transfer $\hbar\mathbf{k}$ one can neglect the recoil term, $\hbar k^2/2M_e$, in (3-113) and write

$$\omega \cong \mathbf{k} \cdot \mathbf{V}_e$$

where $\mathbf{V}_e$ is the particle velocity. The energy loss per unit time is then

$$W = \sum_{\mathbf{k}} \int_0^\infty d\omega \hbar W(\mathbf{k}\omega)\, \delta(\omega - \mathbf{k} \cdot \mathbf{V}_e)$$

$$= \int \frac{d\mathbf{k}}{(8\pi^3)} \int_0^\infty d\omega \hbar W(\mathbf{k}\omega)\, \delta(\omega - \mathbf{k} \cdot \mathbf{V}_e)$$

$$= -\frac{e^2}{\pi^2} \int \frac{d\mathbf{k}}{k^2} \int_0^\infty d\omega\, \omega \left\{\operatorname{Im} \frac{1}{\varepsilon(\mathbf{k}\omega)}\right\} \delta(\omega - \mathbf{k} \cdot \mathbf{V}_e) \tag{3-114}$$

Equations (3-112) and (3-114) correspond to a dielectric approach to the stopping power of an electron gas.[29] They could, in fact, have been obtained by a direct macroscopic calculation, based on Ohm's law.

The Dynamic Form Factor

It may be seen from (3-111) that where the Born approximation applies, the electron gas determines the energy and momentum transfer in a scattering experiment through the term

$$S(\mathbf{k}\omega) = \sum_n |(\rho_{\mathbf{k}}^+)_{n0}|^2\, \delta(\omega - \omega_{n0}) \tag{3-115}$$

which we shall call the *dynamic form factor*. (The reader may recall our previous introduction of this quantity in connection with the treatment of neutron scattering by lattice vibrations in Chapter 2.) The dynamic form factor furnishes a direct measure of the density fluctuation spectrum of the electron gas. It is the central quantity of interest in an electron scattering experiment, since it represents the maximum information one can hope to gain in such an experiment, information which is gained by measuring the angular distribution of the inelastically scattered electrons.

We have already made use of the relationship between $S(\mathbf{k}\omega)$ and $\operatorname{Im} 1/\varepsilon(\mathbf{k}\omega)$, which may be written explicitly as[29a]

$$\text{Im}\ \frac{1}{\varepsilon(k\omega)} = -\frac{4\pi^2 e^2}{\hbar k^2}\left\{S(k\omega) - S(k - \omega)\right\} \tag{3-116}$$

We remark that

$$S(k\omega) = 0 \quad \omega < 0$$

since for a system in its ground state all the excitation frequencies must be positive. We further note that the general relationship between $S(k\omega)$ and $\varepsilon(k\omega)$ may be expressed with the aid of (3-110a) and (3-115) as

$$\frac{1}{\varepsilon(k\omega)} - 1 = \frac{4\pi e^2}{\hbar k^2}\int_{-\infty}^{\infty} d\omega' S(k\omega')\left\{\frac{1}{\omega - \omega' + i\delta} - \frac{1}{\omega + \omega' + i\delta}\right\} \tag{3-117}$$

We see in (3-117) that $S(k\omega)$ serves to determine completely $\varepsilon(k\omega)$, so that, in principle, one can determine $\varepsilon(k\omega)$ directly from a scattering experiment in which one measures the angular distribution of inelastically scattered particles.

As van Hove[30] first emphasized, a knowledge of $S(k\omega)$ likewise permits one to obtain detailed information concerning the space-time correlations for a many-particle system. In fact, the dynamic form factor, $S(k\omega)$ [precisely speaking, $(2\pi/N)\, S(k\omega)$, because of our particular definitions], is the Fourier transform in space and time of the time-dependent density-density correlation function,

$$p(r, t) = (1/N)\left\langle \Psi_0 \right| \rho_H(r' + r, t' + t)\, \rho_H(r', t') \left| \Psi_0 \right\rangle \tag{3-118}$$

where $\rho_H(r, t)$ is the particle density in the Heisenberg representation, and Ψ_0 is the exact ground-state wave function. Since the expectation value (3-118) is independent of r' and t', according to our assumption of translational invariance for the system, we can write

$$p(r, t) = (1/N)\left\langle \Psi_0 \right| \rho_H(\mathbf{r}, t)\, \rho_H(0) \left| \Psi_0 \right\rangle$$

$$= \sum_{\mathbf{k}} \int_{-\infty}^{\infty} d\omega\ S(k\omega)\, e^{i(\mathbf{k}\cdot\mathbf{r} - \omega t)} \tag{3-119}$$

In order to show that (3-119) follows directly from (3-115), we establish certain properties of operators in the Heisenberg representation.

Thus far we have worked in the Schrödinger representation in which the operators, O_s are time-independent and the wave functions $\Psi_s(t)$ are time-dependent. In the Heisenberg representation, which is useful for a discussion of explicit time-dependent properties of a quantum system, the wave functions Ψ_H are time-independent, while the operators, $O_H(t)$, are time-dependent. The transformation which takes one from the Schrödinger to the Heisenberg representation is generated by

$$\Psi_s(t) = e^{-iH_o t/\hbar}\ \Psi_H \tag{3-120}$$

where H_o is the exact Hamiltonian for the many-electron system. One sees by direct substitution of (3-120) into the Schrödinger equation, $i\hbar\partial\Psi_s/\partial t = H_o\Psi_s$, that Ψ_H is time-independent. The Heisenberg operators are given by [compare (3-74b)]

$$O_H(t) = e^{iH_o t/\hbar}\ O_s e^{-iH_o t/\hbar} \tag{3-121}$$

We now make use of (3-121) to obtain (3-119). We first carry out a spatial Fourier analysis:

$$p(\mathbf{r}, t) = \sum_{\mathbf{k}} p(\mathbf{k}, t)\, e^{i\mathbf{k}\cdot\mathbf{r}} \tag{3-122}$$

where

$$p(\mathbf{k}, t) = \frac{1}{N}\left\langle \Psi_o \mid \rho_k(t)\, \rho_k^+(0) \mid \Psi_o \right\rangle \tag{3-123}$$

Next, in (3-123), we introduce a complete set of intermediate states $|\Psi_n>$, and use (3-121) to obtain

$$p(\mathbf{k}, t) = \frac{1}{N}\sum_n \left\langle \Psi_o \right| e^{iH_o t/h}\ \rho_k e^{-iH_o t/h} \left| \Psi_n \right\rangle \left\langle \Psi_n \mid \rho_k^+ \mid \Psi_o \right\rangle$$

$$= \frac{1}{N}\sum_n |\rho_k^+{}_{no}|^2\, e^{-i(E_n - E_o)t/h}$$

$$= \frac{1}{N}\sum_n |\rho_k^+{}_{no}|^2\, e^{-i\omega_{no}t} \tag{3-124}$$

where $(\rho_k^+)_{no}$ and ω_{no} have the definitions given earlier. On making use of (3-124) and (3-122), one at once obtains (3-119).

The relation between the time-dependent density-density correlation function (3-119) and the time-independent one, $p(\mathbf{r})$, [defined by (3-36)] is simply

$$p(\mathbf{r}, o) = p(\mathbf{r}) \tag{3-125}$$

One likewise has from (3-119)

$$S(k) = \frac{1}{N} \int_{-\infty}^{\infty} d\omega \; S(k\omega) \tag{3-126}$$

for the mean value of $S(k\omega)$.

One may measure S(k) directly in a particle-scattering experiment provided certain experimental conditions are satisfied. Thus the measurement of the number of particles per unit time scattered through an angle θ (compare Fig. 3-14) is equivalent to a measurement of S(k) provided the relation between the momentum transfer k and the scattering angle θ is essentially independent of ω. For under these conditions, the probability per unit time for scattering through an angle θ, $W(\theta)$, is proportional to

$$W(k) = \int_{0}^{\infty} d\omega \; W(k\omega)$$

which is, in turn, by (3-126) proportional to S(k). Consideration of the scattering geometry together with (3-113), which expresses the relation between ω, k, and θ, shows that the above conditions are met as long as

$$P_e^{\,2}/2M_e >> \omega \tag{3-127}$$

a condition not overly difficult to satisfy in practice.

We note that $S(k\omega)$ is actually the fundamental quantity of importance for the description of the "longitudinal" properties of the electron gas, or, indeed, of any many-particle system. It yields directly the density-fluctuation spectrum, and by suitable integrations both the time-dependent density-density correlation function and the pair distribution function. Moreover, for an electron system one obtains $\varepsilon(k\omega)$ directly by application of (3-116). On the other hand, $\varepsilon(k\omega)$ is perhaps more easily related to our physical intuition: it provides essentially the same information [again via (3-116)]. For an electron system it is, moreover, generally easier to calculate $\varepsilon(k\omega)$ directly, rather than to calculate $S(k\omega)$ first.

Density-Fluctuation Excitation Spectrum

From the definition of $S(k\omega)$ and the relationship (3-116) between $S(k\omega)$ and $\varepsilon(k\omega)$, it is now clear that the poles of $1/\varepsilon(k\omega)$, or what is equivalent, the relation

$$\varepsilon(\mathbf{k}\omega) = 0 \tag{3-128}$$

yields the allowed energy spectrum of the density fluctuations. That (3-128) should determine the resonant frequencies associated with the density fluctuations follows also from a simple semiclassical argument based on (3-100a) and (3-100b). We remark that in the absence of a test charge, these equations possess, in general, the solution

$$\varphi(k\omega) = < \rho(k\omega) > = 0$$

However, if $\varepsilon(k\omega) = 0$, it is possible to have a nonvanishing density fluctuation, $< \rho(k\omega) >$, and a nonvanishing potential in the electron gas; the condition (3-128) is thus the dispersion relation for the existence of polarization waves in the system.

The density-fluctuation excitations will be, in general, of two kinds; the collective modes, the plasmons, that we have just considered, which correspond to coherent electron-hole pair excitation; and the individual particle excitations, which represent incoherent single electron-hole pair excitations.

Ground-State-Energy Theorem[28]

In order to obtain the ground-state energy, we remark that the interaction energy in the ground state E_{int} may, with the aid of (3-116) and (3-126), be written

$$E_{int} = \left\langle 0 \left| \sum_{k} \frac{2\pi e^2}{k^2} \left(\rho_k^+ \rho_k - N\right) \right| 0 \right\rangle$$

$$= - \sum_{k} \left\{ \int_0^{\infty} \hbar \left(\frac{d\omega}{2\pi}\right) \mathrm{Im}\left[\frac{1}{\varepsilon(k\omega)}\right] + 2\pi N e^2/k^2 \right\} \qquad (3\text{-}129)$$

We may pass from a knowledge of E_{int} to a determination of E_0 by means of a trick which was apparently first discovered by Pauli, and which has been subsequently "rediscovered" by many others. Let us consider the variation of the ground-state energy with regard to the parameter (here e^2), which measures the strength of the interaction between the electrons. The ground-state energy of the system is given by

$$E_0 = \left\langle \Psi_0 \left| \sum_i \frac{p_i^2}{2m} \right| \Psi_0 \right\rangle + \left\langle \Psi_0 \left| \sum_k \frac{2\pi e^2}{k^2} \left(\rho_k^+ \rho_k - N\right) \right| \Psi_0 \right\rangle$$

where Ψ_0 is the ground-state wave function.

We now differentiate E_0 with respect to the coupling constant e^2. We then have

$$\frac{\partial E_o}{\partial e^2} = \frac{E_{int}}{e^2} + \left\langle \Psi_o | H | \partial\Psi_o/\partial e^2 \right\rangle + \left\langle \frac{\partial \Psi_o}{\partial e^2} | H | \Psi_o \right\rangle$$

The first term on the right-hand side comes from the explicit dependence of E_{int} on e^2; the next two come from the dependence of Ψ_o on e^2. On making use of the relation $H\Psi_o = E_o\Psi_o$ we may write

$$\frac{\partial E_o}{\partial e^2} = \frac{E_{int}}{e^2} + E_o \frac{\partial}{\partial e^2} \left\langle \Psi_o | \Psi_o \right\rangle = \frac{E_{int}(e^2)}{e^2}$$

since the wave function Ψ_o is normalized to unity. Let us take this equation literally; it tells us that if we regard the strength of the coupling between the electrons as some variable, α, we can write

$$\frac{\partial E_o}{\partial \alpha} = \frac{E_{int}(\alpha)}{\alpha}$$

We can, moreover, integrate this equation over all coupling constants ranging from 0 to the actual coupling constant e^2. We find, therefore,

$$\int_0^{e^2} d\alpha \frac{\partial E_o}{\partial \alpha} = E_o(e^2) - E_o(0) = \int_0^{e^2} d\alpha \frac{E_{int}(\alpha)}{\alpha}$$

But $E_o(e^2)$ is the actual ground-state energy, while $E_o(0)$ is the ground-state energy in the absence of any interaction, NE_{kin}. Hence, we obtain

$$E_o = NE_{kin} + \int_0^{e^2} d\alpha \frac{E_{int}(\alpha)}{\alpha} \tag{3-130}$$

Equations (3-129) and (3-130) thus serve to determine the ground-state energy, once the dependence of $\varepsilon(k\omega)$ on e^2 is known. As a simple example of the application of (3-130), we remark that in Sec. 3-4 we have argued that for each plasmon degree of freedom,

$$E_{int}(k) = \frac{2\pi e^2}{k^2}\left(\rho_k^+ \rho_k - N\right) = \frac{\hbar\omega_p}{4} - \frac{2\pi N e^2}{k^2}$$

If one now carries out the integration, (3-130), one obtains the result quoted earlier,

$$E_o^{\ell.r.} = \sum_{k<k_o} \frac{\hbar\omega_p}{2} - \frac{2\pi Ne^2}{k^2} + \frac{3}{5}\frac{\hbar^2 k_o^2}{2m}$$

Kramers-Kronig Relations and Sum Rules

There are several useful relations which $\varepsilon(k\omega)$ satisfies. The first, the Kramers-Kronig relations, follows directly from our choice of retarded boundary conditions in the definition of $1/\varepsilon(k\omega)$. We have thereby ensured that the response of the system be causal: this in turn, as shown in Appendix B, means that $1/\varepsilon(k\omega)$ is analytic in the upper half of the complex ω plane. From this knowledge of $\varepsilon(k\omega)$, one obtains at once the Kramers-Kronig relations [cf. equations (A-38)],

$$\text{Re}\,\frac{1}{\varepsilon(k\omega)} - 1 = \frac{1}{\pi}\,P\int_{-\infty}^{\infty}\left[\text{Im}\,\frac{1}{\varepsilon(k\omega)}\right]\frac{d\omega'}{\omega' - \omega} \tag{3-131}$$

$$\text{Im}\,\frac{1}{\varepsilon(k\omega)} = \frac{1}{\pi}\,P\int_{-\infty}^{\infty}\left[1 - \text{Re}\,\frac{1}{\varepsilon(k\omega)}\right]\frac{d\omega'}{\omega' - \omega} \tag{3-132}$$

Moreover, as discussed in the Appendix, $\varepsilon(k\omega)$ is likewise analytic in the upper half of the complex ω plane, so that a similar set of relations hold for $\varepsilon(k\omega)$. The Kramers-Kronig relations, (3-131) and (3-132), and their analogues for $\varepsilon(k\omega)$ are very useful in analyzing experimental data, since in general one measures only the real or imaginary part of $\varepsilon(k\omega)$ or $\varepsilon^{-1}(k\omega)$; the above relations show how one can pass directly from a knowledge of one to a knowledge of the other.

Both $1/\varepsilon(k\omega)$ and $\varepsilon(k\omega)$ satisfy simple sum rules, which are a direct consequence of a longitudinal version of the famous Thomas-Reich-Kuhn sum rule,

$$\sum_n \frac{2m}{\hbar k^2}\,\omega_{no}\,\left|\left(\rho_k^+\right)_{no}\right|^2 = N \tag{3-133}$$

To establish (3-133) we calculate the expectation value,

$$\left\langle 0 \left| \left[[\rho_k, H], \rho_k^+\right] \right| 0 \right\rangle$$

in two different ways.[31] As we have already remarked in our derivation of the equations of motion satisfied by ρ_k,

$$[\rho_k, H] = i\hbar\dot{\rho}_k = \hbar\sum_i\left(\frac{\mathbf{k}\cdot\mathbf{p}_i}{m} + \frac{\hbar k^2}{2m}\right)e^{-i\mathbf{k}\cdot\mathbf{r}_i} \tag{3-134}$$

this equation is an operator statement of longitudinal current conservation; the current fluctuation j_k is given by

$$j_k = \frac{1}{2} \int dr\, e^{-ik\cdot r} \left[\frac{p_i}{m}\, \delta(r - r_i) + \delta(r - r_i)\, \frac{p_i}{m} \right]$$

$$= \sum_i \left(\frac{p_i}{m} + \frac{\hbar k}{2m} \right) e^{-ik\cdot r_i}$$

Thus (3-134) is equivalent to

$$\dot{\rho}_k + ik \cdot j_k = 0 \qquad (3\text{-}135)$$

and, as is clear from (3-134), longitudinal current conservation will apply as long as there are no velocity-dependent forces. Next, one sees directly that

$$\left[[\rho_k, H], \rho_k^+ \right] = N\hbar^2 k^2/m$$

the only contribution to the commutator coming from $[p_i, \rho_k]$.

Suppose we now write

$$\left\langle 0 \right| \left[[\rho_k, H], \rho_k^+ \right] \left| 0 \right\rangle$$

$$= \sum_n \left\{ \left\langle 0 \right| [\rho_k, H] \left| n \right\rangle \left\langle n \right| \rho_k^+ \left| 0 \right\rangle - \left\langle 0 \right| \rho_k^+ \left| n \right\rangle \left\langle n \right| [\rho_k, H] \left| 0 \right\rangle \right\} \qquad (3\text{-}136)$$

Then, on using the matrix result,

$$[\rho_k, H]_{no} = (\rho\, H)_{no} - (H\rho_k)_{no} = - \hbar\omega_{no} (\rho_k)_{no}$$

where $\hbar\omega_{no} = E_n - E_o$, we have

$$\sum_n \left\{ \omega_{no} (\rho_k^+)_{on} (\rho_k)_{no} + \omega_{no} (\rho_k)_{on} (\rho_k^+)_{no} \right\} = \hbar N k^2/m$$

which for a system invariant with regard to time reflection reduces to the result (3-133).

We now recall the definition, (3-115), of $S(k\omega)$. On comparing (3-115) and (3-133) we see at once that the sum rule, (3-133), is equivalent to the following sum rule for $S(k\omega)$:

$$\int_0^\infty d\omega\; S(k\omega)\, \omega = N\hbar k^2/2m \qquad (3\text{-}137)$$

Moreover, on making use of (3-116) we have the result

$$\int_0^\infty d\omega \left[\text{Im } \frac{1}{\varepsilon(k\omega)}\right] \omega = -\frac{\pi}{2}\,\omega_p^{\,2} \tag{3-138}$$

An alternative derivation of (3-138) is based on the fact that from the defining equation (3-110a), and the sum rule (3-133), one establishes the high-frequency asymptotic behavior of $\varepsilon(k\omega)$ as

$$\lim_{\omega \to \infty} \frac{1}{\varepsilon(k\omega)} = 1 + \frac{\omega_p^{\,2}}{\omega^2} \tag{3-139}$$

With the aid of (3-133) and the analytic behavior of $\varepsilon^{-1}(k\omega)$, one obtains (3-138). In the same way, with the aid of the analytic behavior of $\varepsilon(k\omega)$, and its asymptotic behavior for large frequencies, one can show

$$\int_0^\infty d\omega\ \omega\ \text{Im}\ \varepsilon(\mathbf{k}\omega) = \frac{\pi}{2}\,\omega_p^{\,2} \tag{3-140}$$

or, what is equivalent,

$$\int_0^\infty d\omega\ \text{Re}\ \sigma(\mathbf{k}\omega) = \pi N e^2/2m \tag{3-141}$$

The sum rules are of great help in analyzing, and relating, characteristic energy-loss and optical experiments on $\varepsilon(k\omega)$ in solids, and play a useful role as well in enabling one to check the consistency of a given approximation.

Dielectric Constant in the Hartree-Fock Approximation

The simplest approximation for $\varepsilon(k\omega)$ involves the neglect of the Coulomb interaction between the electrons in the determination of the matrix elements and excitation frequencies which enter into (3-110). Thus one takes the states $|n\rangle$ to be plane-wave functions, appropriate to a determinant of one-electron wave functions. In this case, the transitions introduced by ρ_k^+ are those in which an electron is taken from some state of momentum $\hbar p$ lying within the Fermi sphere (radius: $\hbar k_o$) to a state of momentum $\hbar(p+k)$ lying outside it, this limitation arising from the Pauli principle. The excitation frequency associated with such a transition is

$$\omega(\mathbf{p}, \mathbf{k}) = \hbar(\mathbf{p} + \mathbf{k})^2/2m - \hbar p^2/2m = \hbar(\mathbf{k} \cdot \mathbf{p}/m) + \hbar k^2/2m \quad (3\text{-}142)$$

It is this approximation for $\varepsilon(k\omega)$ which is equivalent to the usual Hartree-Fock approximation in the calculation of the ground-state energy of the electron gas, and we therefore call the corresponding value of $\varepsilon(k\omega)$, $\varepsilon_{HF}(k\omega)$. One has

$$1/\varepsilon_{HF}(k\omega) = 1 - 4\pi\alpha_o(k\omega) \quad (3\text{-}143)$$

where $4\pi\alpha_o(k\omega)$, the free-electron polarizability, is defined as

$$4\pi\alpha_o(k\omega) = \frac{4\pi e^2}{\hbar k^2} \sum_{\substack{p<k_o \\ |\mathbf{p}+\mathbf{k}|>k_o}} \left\{ \frac{1}{\omega + \omega(\mathbf{p}, \mathbf{k}) + i\delta} - \frac{1}{\omega - \omega(\mathbf{p}, \mathbf{k}) + i\delta} \right\}$$

$$= \frac{4\pi e^2}{\hbar k^2} \sum_{p\sigma} n_{p\sigma}(1 - n_{\mathbf{p}+\mathbf{k}\sigma})$$

$$\times \left\{ \frac{1}{\omega + \omega(\mathbf{p}, \mathbf{k}) + i\delta} - \frac{1}{\omega - \omega(\mathbf{p}, \mathbf{k}) + i\delta} \right\} \quad (3\text{-}144)$$

Let us look anew at the dynamic and static form factors in the Hartree-Fock approximation. With the aid of (3-116) we may write

$$S_{HF}(k\omega) = \sum_{\substack{p<k_o \\ |\mathbf{p}+\mathbf{k}|>k_o}} \delta(\omega - \omega(\mathbf{p}, \mathbf{k})) \quad \omega > 0 \quad (3\text{-}145)$$

where we have made use of the fact the $\omega(\mathbf{p}, \mathbf{k})$ always represent positive frequencies. It is now clear from (3-145) that the density-fluctuation excitation spectrum simply consists of electron-hole pairs of momentum $\hbar\mathbf{k}$. This pair excitation spectrum forms a continuum running from zero to $\hbar(kk_o/m) + \hbar k^2/2m$. The form factor $S(k)$ is calculated with the aid of (3-126); apart from the case of $k \equiv 0$, where $S(0)$ always gives a trivial value of N, one obtains

$$S_{HF}(k) = \frac{1}{N} \int_0^\infty S_{HF}(k\omega)\, d\omega = \frac{1}{N} \sum_{\substack{p<k_o \\ |\mathbf{p}+\mathbf{k}|>k_o}} 1$$

$$S_{HF}(k) = \sum_{p\sigma} n_{p\sigma}(1 - n_{p+k\sigma})/N \qquad (k \neq 0) \tag{3-146}$$

Thus we see that the above calculation reproduces the result of (3-20). We leave it as an exercise for the reader to show that $S(k\omega)$ satisfies the sum rule, (3-137).

Let us emphasize that we have called this approximation for $\varepsilon(k\omega)$ the Hartree-Fock approximation because it leads directly to the ground-state energy in that order of approximation. Thus we are labeling the approximations with regard to the corresponding value of the ground-state energy one obtains. Note that $S_{HF}(k\omega)$ in (3-145) is independent of the coupling constant, and is just the free-particle dynamic form factor (with the Pauli principle duly taken into account); the corresponding value of the ground-state energy is proportional to the coupling constant, since the ground-state energy contains one more power of the coupling constant than does $S(k\omega)$. Thus if we were to replace the single-particle excitation energies in (3-145), $\omega(p, k) = (p + k)^2/2m - p^2/2m$, by *their* Hartree-Fock values (3-46), we would obtain a term in the ground state which is of *second order* in the coupling constant (and is divergent, to boot!).

3-5 PROPERTIES OF THE ELECTRON GAS IN THE RPA

Calculation of $\epsilon(k\omega)$ in the RPA

The next approximation for $\varepsilon(k\omega)$ goes under a wide variety of names (random phase approximation, independent-pair approximation, self-consistent field approximation, time-dependent Hartree-Fock approximation, etc.); in fact, there are almost as many names as there are ways of deriving the answer. We shall arbitrarily refer to it as the random phase approximation, or RPA. Let us first discuss the result, and then sketch briefly some of the myriad ways of deriving it. One finds, in the RPA,

$$\varepsilon(k\omega) = 1 + 4\pi\alpha_o(k\omega) \tag{3-147}$$

where $4\pi\alpha_o(k\omega)$ is the free-electron polarizability, defined by (3-144).

The way in which the RPA differs from the Hartree-Fock approximation is seen most easily by referring back to (3-105a), which we write as follows,

$$\frac{1}{\varepsilon(k\omega)} - 1 = -\frac{4\pi e}{k^2}\,\frac{\langle \rho(k\omega) \rangle}{\varphi_{ext}(k\omega)} \tag{3-105c}$$

and to (3-105b), which, for convenience, we reproduce again here.

$$\varepsilon(k\omega) - 1 = \frac{4\pi e}{k^2} \frac{<\rho(k\omega)>}{\varphi(k\omega)} \tag{3-105b}$$

In these equations, $\varphi_{ext}(k\omega)$ is the potential produced by the weak test charge, while $\varphi(k\omega)$ is the *total* scalar field potential; that is,

$$\varphi(k\omega) = \varphi_{ext}(k\omega) + \varphi_{pol}(k\omega) \tag{3-148}$$

where $\varphi_{pol}(k\omega)$ is the polarization potential induced by the external test charge according to

$$\varphi_{pol}(k\omega) = -(4\pi e/k^2) <\rho(k\omega)> \tag{3-149}$$

In the Hartree-Fock approximation, one has

$$<\rho(k\omega)>_{HF} = 4\pi\alpha_o(k\omega)(k^2/4\pi e)\,\varphi_{ext}(k\omega) \tag{3-150}$$

as substitution of (3-150) into (3-105c) shows. On the other hand, in the RPA one has:

$$<\rho(k\omega)>_{RPA} = 4\pi\alpha_o(k\omega)(k^2/4\pi e)\,\varphi(k\omega) \tag{3-151}$$

as may be seen by substitution of (3-151) into (3-105b). We can thus say that RPA differs from the Hartree-Fock approximation in that in the RPA it is the *effective* field, $\varphi(k\omega)$, to which the electrons respond, rather than to the *external* field, $\varphi_{ext}(k\omega)$. In both cases, the response is given by the free-electron polarizability. On making use of the relation (3-104), between $\varphi(k\omega)$ and $\varphi_{ext}(k\omega)$, one can also write (3-151) as

$$<\rho(k\omega)>_{RPA} = \frac{k^2}{4\pi e}\left\{\frac{4\pi\alpha_o(k\omega)}{1 + 4\pi\alpha_o(k\omega)}\right\}\varphi_{ext}(k\omega) \tag{3-152}$$

Yet another way of stating the RPA result is to make a comparison of the calculation with the Lorentz method of calculating the static dielectric constant.[28,31] One then sees that in the RPA the "local field" corrections are neglected; only the polarization of the sample at its surface is taken into account.

All methods of computing $\varepsilon_{RPA}(k\omega)$ are based on calculating the response of the electron gas to an external longitudinal field which varies in space and time, along the lines of the exact calculation leading from (3-108) to (3-110). In one method, the response, $<\rho(k\omega)>$, to an external field, $<\varphi_{ext}(k\omega)>$, is computed by taking into account *only that part of the Coulomb interaction which depends on the momentum transfer k*. This may be done by means of a canonical transformation,[28] by the BP collective description,[31] or by following the equations of motion of an electron-hole pair of momentum k.[32] In all cases, where averages over the state vectors of the system enter, one carries these out for the unperturbed free-electron gas.

A second way, which is in some ways more physical, is to write down the "quantum kinetic equation," which is the quantum mechanical analogue of the classical collisionless Boltzmann equation for the time rate of change of the electron distribution function in the presence of a time-dependent perturbing field, $\varphi_{ext}(r, t)$.[27,33-35] In the case of a long-wavelength, slowly varying disturbance, that equation reads

$$\frac{\partial}{\partial t}\,\delta n(prt) + \frac{p\cdot\nabla}{m}\,\delta n(prt) + \frac{e}{m}\,\nabla\varphi(rt)\cdot\nabla\,[n_o(p) + \delta n(prt)] = 0 \tag{3-153}$$

Here $n_o(p)$ is the unperturbed distribution function, while $\varphi(rt)$ is the net potential acting, i.e., the sum of the external potential and that associated with the polarization induced in the electron gas. If, now, one neglects the term involving $\nabla\varphi\cdot\nabla_p\,\delta n(prt)$ (an approximation which is valid in the case of a sufficiently weak total potential), and further determines $\varphi_{pd}(rt)$ in self-consistent fashion by means of Poisson's equation, one at once arrives at (3-147). We see this is, in a sense, a time-dependent self-consistent Hartree approximation, in that the field acting on the electrons is computed as a self-consistent average over all the electrons.[36-38]

A third method is based on the use of Feynman diagrams in time-dependent perturbation theory.[22,25,39] The appropriate pictures for the screening of the interaction between electrons are shown in Fig. 3-15. The dotted line is the bare Coulomb interaction, v_k. The

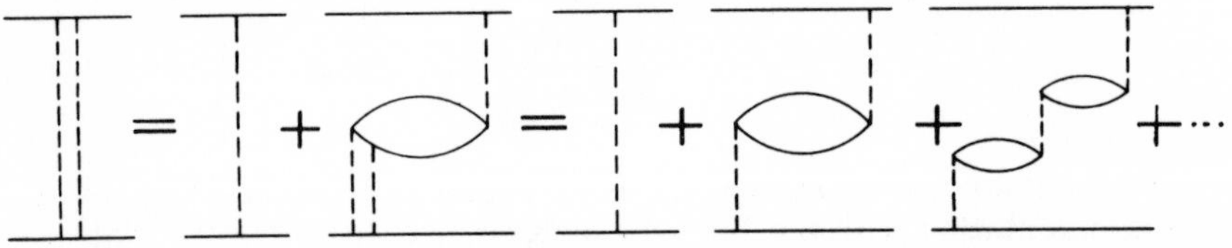

Fig. 3-15. Summation of polarization diagrams in the RPA.

double-dotted line is that interaction screened by the polarization of the medium, $v_k/\varepsilon(k\omega)$. The bubble represents the lowest-order polarization process, involving the excitation and subsequent deexcitation of a particle-hole pair. What is represented in Fig. 3-15 is the algebraic Dyson equation,

$$\frac{v_k}{\varepsilon(k\omega)} = v_k - \frac{v_k \cdot 4\pi\alpha_o(k\omega)}{\varepsilon(k\omega)} \tag{3-154}$$

which sums the series,

$$\frac{1}{\varepsilon(k\omega)} = 1 - 4\pi\alpha_o(k\omega) + [4\pi\alpha_o(k\omega)]^2 - [4\pi\alpha_o(k\omega)]^2 + \cdots \tag{3-155}$$

The result is, as before,

$$\varepsilon(k\omega) = 1 + 4\pi\alpha_o(k\omega)$$

for positive frequencies. [For negative frequencies, there is a slight difference between the value of $4\pi\alpha_o(k\omega)$ obtained by diagrammatic techniques and that given in (3-144), a difference which follows from the different boundary conditions employed. See Problem 3-5.] One sees clearly the relation between (3-155) and the Gell-Mann and Brueckner selected summation of terms in the perturbation series; in the present case, that summation is performed automatically by (3-154). Note, too, that the summation of a given set of polarization diagrams is equivalent to replacing the external potential, $\varphi_{ext}(k\omega)$, by $\varphi(k\omega)$, in passing from (3-150) to (3-151). This is the physical content of Dyson equations of the form (3-154).

We now carry out an explicit calculation of $\varepsilon_{RPA}(k\omega)$ by following the motion of an electron-hole pair of momentum $-\mathbf{k}$

$$\rho_\sigma(\mathbf{k}, \mathbf{p}) = c^+_{\mathbf{p}\sigma} c_{\mathbf{p}+\mathbf{k}\sigma} \tag{3-156}$$

in the presence of an external test charge specified by (3-109b). The method we present is essentially that of Ehrenreich and Cohen.[33] It is closely related to the equation-of-motion method introduced in Sec. 3-2. We seek to determine the mean value of

$$\rho(k) = \sum_{p\sigma} \rho_\sigma(\mathbf{k}, \mathbf{p})$$

in the presence of the test charge. Since we are interested only in the linear response, it suffices to keep only the single forcing term of frequency ω from (3-109b); hence the basic Hamiltonian we are led to consider is

$$H = \sum_{p\sigma} \frac{h^2 p^2}{2m} c^+_{p\sigma} c_{p\sigma} + \sum_{\substack{qq'k' \\ ss'}} \frac{V_{k'}}{2} c^+_{\mathbf{q}-\mathbf{k}'s} c^+_{\mathbf{q}'+\mathbf{k}s'} c_{\mathbf{q}'s'} c_{\mathbf{q}s}$$

$$- e\rho^+_k \varphi_{ext}(k\omega) e^{-i\omega t} e^{\delta t} + \text{c. c.} \tag{3-157}$$

where c.c. denotes the complex conjugate and we have introduced $\varphi_{ext}(k\omega)$ in place of $\rho_{ext}(k\omega)$. The equation of motion of $\rho_\sigma(k,p)$ is

$$i\hbar\dot{\rho}_\sigma(k, p) = [\rho_\sigma(k, p), H] \tag{3-158}$$

according to elementary quantum mechanics. Let us first neglect the electron-electron interaction term in (3-157), and see how the equation-of-motion method yields the Hartree-Fock approximation. We have

$$\begin{aligned} i\hbar\dot{\rho}_\sigma(k, p) &= \hbar\omega(p, k)\,\rho_\sigma(k, p) \\ &\quad - \left\{c^+_{p\sigma}c_{p\sigma} - c^+_{p+k\sigma}c_{p+k\sigma}\right\} e\varphi_{ext}(k\omega)\,e^{-i\omega t}e^{\delta t} \\ &\quad - \left\{c^+_{p}c_{p+2k} - c^+_{p-k}c_{p+k}\right\} e\varphi^+_{ext}(k\omega)\,e^{i\omega t}e^{\delta t} \end{aligned} \tag{3-159}$$

by direct evaluation of the commutator of $\rho_\sigma(kp)$ with the kinetic energy term and with the coupling to the external field. We solve this equation by taking the expectation value of both sides with respect to the appropriate states of the Hamiltonian (3-151). Since we keep only first-order terms in $\varphi_{ext}(k\omega)$, it suffices to replace the operators $c^+_{p\sigma}c_{p\sigma}$ and $c_{p+k\sigma}c_{p+k\sigma}$ by their expectation values in the absence of the interaction; we further note the term proportional to $e\varphi^+_{ext}(k\omega)$ drops out, as it should. Our result is

$$\begin{aligned} i\hbar\left\langle \dot{\rho}_\sigma(kp)\right\rangle &= \hbar\omega(k, p)\,\rho_\sigma(k, p) \\ &\quad - (n_{p\sigma} - n_{p+k\sigma})\,e\,\varphi_{ext}(k\omega)\,e^{-i\omega t}e^{\delta t} \end{aligned} \tag{3-160}$$

which possesses the solution

$$\left\langle \rho_\sigma(kp\omega)\right\rangle = \frac{-(n_{p\sigma} - n_{p+k\sigma})}{\hbar\{\omega - \omega(k, p) + i\delta\}}\,e\varphi_{ext}(k\omega) \tag{3-161}$$

and finally

$$<\rho(k\omega)> = \left\{\left(\frac{4\pi e^2}{\hbar k^2}\right)\sum_{p\sigma}\left(\frac{n_{p+k\sigma} - n_{p\sigma}}{\omega - \omega(p, k) + i\delta}\right)\right\}\left(\frac{k^2}{4\pi e}\right)\varphi_{ext}(k\omega) \tag{3-162}$$

on passing from $\rho_\sigma(kp\omega)$ to $\rho(k\omega)$. On making use of (3-150) we see that (3-162) yields the Hartree-Fock approximation, provided

$$4\pi\alpha_o(k\omega) = \frac{4\pi e^2}{\hbar k^2}\sum_{p\sigma}\frac{n_{p+k\sigma} - n_{p\sigma}}{\omega - \omega(p, k) + i\delta} \tag{3-163}$$

The polarizability in (3-163) looks somewhat different from that given by (3-144). To see that it is the same, we remark that in the first term on the right-hand side of (3-144) one can change the dummy index p to - p - k; on further putting $n_p = n_{-p'}$ and adding the second term, one arrives directly at (3-163).

We now take into account the effect of electron interaction on $\dot{\rho}_\sigma(\mathrm{kp})$. A straightforward calculation yields

$$i\hbar\dot{\rho}_\sigma(\mathrm{kp}) = \hbar\omega(\mathrm{p}, \mathrm{k})\,\rho_\sigma(\mathrm{kp})$$
$$- \left\{c^+_{p\sigma}c_{p\sigma} - c^+_{p+k\sigma}c_{p+k\sigma}\right\} e\varphi_{ext}(k\omega)\,e^{-i\omega t}e^{\delta t}$$
$$+ \sum_{k'\pm 0} (v_{k'}/2)\left\{\rho_{k'}\left[c^+_{p\sigma}c_{p+k-k'\sigma} - c^+_{p+k'\sigma}c_{p+k\sigma}\right]\right.$$
$$\left. + \left[c^+_{p\sigma}c^+_{p+k-k'\sigma} - c^+_{p+k'\sigma}c_{p+k\sigma}\right]\rho_{k'}\right\} \tag{3-164}$$

We now make the RPA in (3-164); that is, we keep only the term with k' = k in the third term on the right-hand side. We have then,

$$i\hbar\dot{\rho}_\sigma(\mathrm{kp}) = h\omega(\mathrm{p}, \mathrm{k})\,\rho_\sigma(\mathrm{kp})$$
$$+ \left\{c^+_{p\sigma}c_{p\sigma} - c^+_{p+k\sigma}c_{p+k\sigma}\right\}\left\{-e\varphi_{ext}(k\omega)e^{-i\omega t}e^{\delta t} + v_k\rho_k\right\} \tag{3-165}$$

If now we take the expectation values of this equation, and further its Fourier transform with respect to time, we have, in place of (3-162), the result

$$< \rho(k\omega) >_{RPA} = 4\pi\alpha_o(k\omega)\left(\frac{k^2}{4\pi e}\right)\left\{\varphi_{ext}(k\omega) - \frac{4\pi e}{k^2} < \rho(k\omega) >\right\}$$
$$= 4\pi\alpha_o(k\omega)\left(\frac{k^2}{4\pi e}\right)\varphi(k\omega) \tag{3-166}$$

on making use of (3-148) and (3-149). The result (3-166) is just the RPA result, (3-151), where the result (3-147) for $\varepsilon_{RPA}(k\omega)$ follows.

Explicit Expressions for $\epsilon_{RPA}(k\omega)$

Let us divide $\varepsilon_{RPA}(k\omega)$ into its real and imaginary parts, according to

$$\varepsilon_{RPA}(k\omega) = \varepsilon_1(k\omega) + i\varepsilon_2(k\omega) \tag{3-167}$$

where

$$\varepsilon_1(k\omega) = 1 - \frac{8\pi e^2}{\hbar k^2} \sum_{p\sigma} n_{p\sigma}(1 - n_{p+k\sigma}) \frac{\omega(p, k)}{\omega^2 - \omega^2(p, k)}$$

$$= 1 - \frac{4\pi e^2}{m} \sum_{\mu} \frac{f_{o\mu}}{\omega^2 - \omega_{\mu o}^2} \tag{3-168}$$

and

$$\varepsilon_2(k\omega) = \frac{4\pi^2 e^2}{\hbar k^2} \sum_{p\sigma} n_{p\sigma}(1 - n_{p+k\sigma})\, \delta[\omega - \omega(p, k)] \tag{3-169}$$

Here, in (3-168) we have introduced the *plane-wave* oscillator strengths,

$$f_{o\mu} = \frac{2m}{\hbar k^2} \omega_{\mu o} |(\rho_k)_{\mu o}|^2 = \frac{2m}{\hbar k^2} \omega(p, k)\, n_{p\sigma}(1 - n_{p+k\sigma}) \tag{3-170}$$

Explicit values of $\varepsilon_1(k\omega)$ and $\varepsilon_2(k\omega)$ were first obtained by Lindhard,[27] who found

$$\varepsilon_1(k\omega) = 1 + \frac{k_{FT}^2}{k^2}\left\{\frac{1}{2} + \frac{k_o}{4k}\left[\left\{1 - \frac{\left(\omega - \frac{\hbar k^2}{2m}\right)^2}{k^2 v_o^2}\right\}\right.\right.$$
$$\times \ell n \left| \frac{\omega - kv_o - \hbar k^2/2m}{\omega + kv_o - \hbar k^2/2m} \right|$$
$$\left.\left. + \left\{1 - \frac{\left(\omega + \frac{\hbar k^2}{2m}\right)^2}{k^2 v_o^2}\right\} \ell n \left| \frac{\omega + kv_o + \hbar k^2/2m}{\omega - kv_o + \hbar k^2/2m} \right| \right]\right\} \tag{3-171a}$$

$$\varepsilon_2(k\omega) = \frac{\pi}{2} \frac{\omega}{kv_o} \frac{k_{FT}^2}{k^2} \qquad \omega \le kv_o - \hbar k^2/2m$$

$$= \frac{\pi}{4} \frac{k_o}{k} \left[1 - \frac{(\omega - \hbar k^2/2m)^2}{k^2 v_o^2}\right] \frac{k_{FT}^2}{k^2} \qquad kv_o - \frac{\hbar k^2}{2m} \le \omega \le kv_o + \frac{\hbar k^2}{2m}$$

$$= 0 \qquad \omega \ge kv_o + \hbar k^2/2m \tag{3-171b}$$

where $\varepsilon_1(k\omega) = \varepsilon_1(k, -\omega)$ and k_{FT} is the Fermi-Thomas screening wave vector, defined by $k_{FT} = \sqrt{3\omega_p/v_o}$.

The most interesting region in which to consider $\varepsilon(k\omega)$ is that at long wavelengths, since it is in this wavelength region that the differences between the RPA and the Hartree-Fock approximation are most readily apparent. In Fig. 3-16 the general behavior of $\varepsilon_1(k\omega)$ and

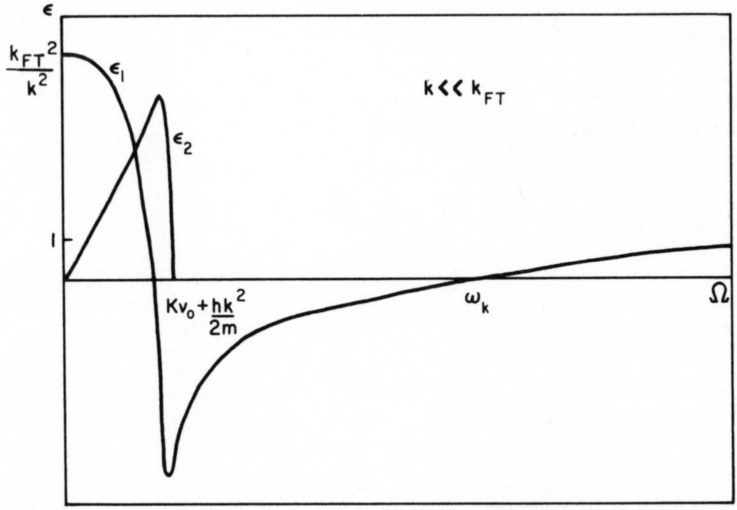

Fig. 3-16. The general behavior of ε_1 and ε_2 calculated in the RPA for the free-electron gas.

$\varepsilon_2(k\omega)$ is shown for a wave vector $k \ll k_{FT}$. One sees there three general features which characterize the long-wavelength behavior of $\varepsilon_{RPA}(k\omega)$.

1. $\varepsilon_1(k0) \gg 1$; this indicates that a low-frequency charge disturbance is strongly screened.

2. $\varepsilon_2 = 0$ for $\omega > kv_o + \hbar k^2/2m$; this is the expected cutoff in ε_2 at frequencies greater than the maximum energy for single particle excitation (i.e., the production of an electron-hole pair of momentum k in fashion consistent with the Pauli principle).

3. $\varepsilon_1(k\omega)$ possesses a zero at ω_k, in a region in which $\varepsilon_2(k\omega) = 0$. According to (3-128) this is the dispersion relation for the existence of polarization waves in the system; as we shall shortly see, it is the plasmon dispersion relation.

Let us now consider these features of the electron gas in more detail.

Screening

Let us consider the screening action of the electron gas in the RPA. Perhaps the simplest example to consider is the response of the electron gas to a static impurity of charge Z. If we suppose that impurity to be located at the origin, then we have seen that the potential which it produces as a point **r** is given by

$$\varphi(\mathbf{r}) = \sum_{\mathbf{k}} \frac{4\pi Z e^2}{k^2 \varepsilon_{RPA}(k,0)} e^{i\mathbf{k}\cdot\mathbf{r}}$$

In the RPA, we have from (3-171a),

$$\varepsilon_{RPA}(k,0) = 1 + \frac{k_{FT}^2}{k^2}\left[\frac{1}{2} + \frac{k_o}{2k}\left(1 - \frac{k^2}{4k_o^2}\right)\ell n\left|\frac{k+2k_o}{k-2k_o}\right|\right] \tag{3-172}$$

For small k, we see that

$$\varepsilon_{RPA}(k,0) \xrightarrow[k\to 0]{} 1 + \frac{k_{FT}^2}{k^2} \tag{3-172a}$$

so that the long-wavelength screening of a static charge in the RPA is identical to that calculated in the Fermi-Thomas approximation.

At first sight one would therefore expect that at large distances the amount of screening charge would be negligible, and that the potential due to the impurity would fall off as $(1/r)\,e^{-k_{FT}r}$. Such is not the case because $\varepsilon(k,0)$ possesses a logarithmic singularity; $\partial\varepsilon/\partial k$ is ∞ at $k = 2k_o$. As Kohn has emphasized, the origin of this singularity is the sharpness of the Fermi surface; one passes into a different physical regimes when going from $k < 2k_F$ to $k > 2k_F$ because one is passing into a region in which the momentum transfer can no longer take an electron from one part of the Fermi surface to another. Because of the logarithmic singularity in $\varepsilon(2k_o, 0)$, one finds that for large distances the induced charge density and the potential vary as $(\cos 2k_o r)/r^3$.[40] The disturbance is therefore effective at rather large distances, a result first proposed by Friedel,[41] which has been borne out by nuclear magnetic resonance experiments on the influence of impurities on the Knight shift.[42]

We remark that a long-wavelength charge fluctuation of finite frequency will likewise be screened, provided its frequency ω is such that $\varepsilon_1(k\omega)$ is appreciably greater than unity. Generally speaking this means for frequencies ω such that

$$\omega \lesssim kv_o$$

for the wavelength in question. One may note, too, that there will be an *enhancement* or antiscreening of a very high frequency distance ($\omega \gtrsim \omega_k$), since in this region $\varepsilon_1(k\omega)$ is less than unity.

Plasmons

As we have mentioned, the condition for undamped plasma oscillation of the electron gas is

$$\varepsilon_1(k_1 \omega_k) = 0 \tag{3-173a}$$

$$\varepsilon_2(k_2 \omega_k) = 0 \tag{3-173b}$$

To see that this condition is identical with that derived using the collective description we first remark that the condition (3-173b) is identical with the condition (3-91), that a plasmon cannot excite an electron-hole pair. The identity of (3-173a) and (3-90b) is less obvious. We note first that the Pauli principle restriction in the RPA expression (3-168a) for $\varepsilon_1(k\omega)$ can be neglected, as the interchange of indices $p \rightarrow -(p + k)$; $p + k \rightarrow -p$, readily shows. Hence

$$\begin{aligned}\varepsilon_1(k\omega) &= 1 - \frac{8\pi e^2}{\hbar k^2} \sum_{p\sigma} n_{p\sigma} \left\{ \frac{\omega(p, k)}{\omega^2 - \omega^2(p, k)} \right\} \\ &= 1 - \frac{4\pi e^2}{k^2} \sum_{p\sigma} n_{p\sigma} \left\{ \frac{1}{\omega - \dfrac{k \cdot p}{m} - \dfrac{k^2}{2m}} - \frac{1}{\omega + \dfrac{k \cdot p}{m} + \dfrac{k^2}{2m}} \right\}\end{aligned} \tag{3-174a}$$

If now in the second term on the right-hand side of (3-174a) we let $p \rightarrow -p$, we see at once that (3-173a) is indeed equivalent to (3-90b).

The plasmon dispersion relation, $\varepsilon_1(k\omega_k) = 0$, takes a simple form at long wavelengths, as we have already stressed in the discussion following (3-90). To see this in the present context we remark that at high frequencies ($\omega \gg \omega_{\mu o}$), $\varepsilon_1(k\omega)$, according to (3-168a), possesses the expansion

$$\begin{aligned}\varepsilon_1(k\omega) &= 1 - \frac{4\pi e^2}{m} \sum_{\mu} \frac{f_{o\mu}}{\omega^2} \\ &\quad - \frac{4\pi e^2}{m} \sum_{\mu} \frac{f_{o\mu}\, \omega_{\mu o}^2}{\omega^4} + \cdots \qquad \omega \gg \omega_{\mu o}\end{aligned} \tag{3-174b}$$

On using the f-sum rule, which the plane-wave oscillator strengths $f_{o\mu}$ must satisfy, one can write

$$\varepsilon_1(k\omega) = 1 - \frac{\omega_p^{\ 2}}{\omega^2} - \frac{4\pi e^2}{m} \sum_{\mu} \frac{f_{o\mu}\,\omega_{\mu o}^2}{\omega^4} + \cdots \tag{3-175}$$

From (3-175) we see that as long as $\omega \cong \omega_p >> \omega_{\mu o}$, one has

$$\omega_k \cong \omega_p \left\{1 + \frac{3}{10} k^2 v_o^{\ 2}/\omega_p^{\ 2} + \cdots\right\} \tag{3-176}$$

for the plasmon energy. Put another way, since $\omega_k \cong \omega_p$ the expansion (3-174b) is valid for long wavelengths. What now happens as one increases the wavelength? The plasmon energy, according to (3-171a) and (3-176) increases rather slowly with k; the maximum single-particle frequency,

$$kv_o + \frac{\hbar k^2}{2m}$$

increases rather more rapidly. As a result one arrives at a value of k, k_c, for which

$$\begin{aligned} \varepsilon\,[k, \omega_{k_c}] &= 0 \\ \omega_{k_c} &= k_c v_o + \frac{\hbar k_c^{\ 2}}{2m} \end{aligned} \tag{3-177}$$

This criterion for plasmon decay was first given by Sawada et al.[43] and by Ferrell.[38] It replaces our earlier estimate of k_c based on (3-68). For values of $k > k_c$, one no longer has according to (3-171b), $\varepsilon_2(k, \omega_k) = 0$; the plasmon spectrum has then merged with the single-particle (or pair-excitation) spectrum, and the plasmons readily decay into particle-hole pairs. The RPA predictions for the plasmon and pair-excitation spectrum for a metal of density, $r_s = 4$, are pictured in Fig. 3-17.

In practice, one can get a satisfactory estimate of k_c at metallic electron densities from our earlier criterion:

$$k_c = \omega_p/v_o$$

which is essentially equivalent to the long-wavelength limit of (3-177).

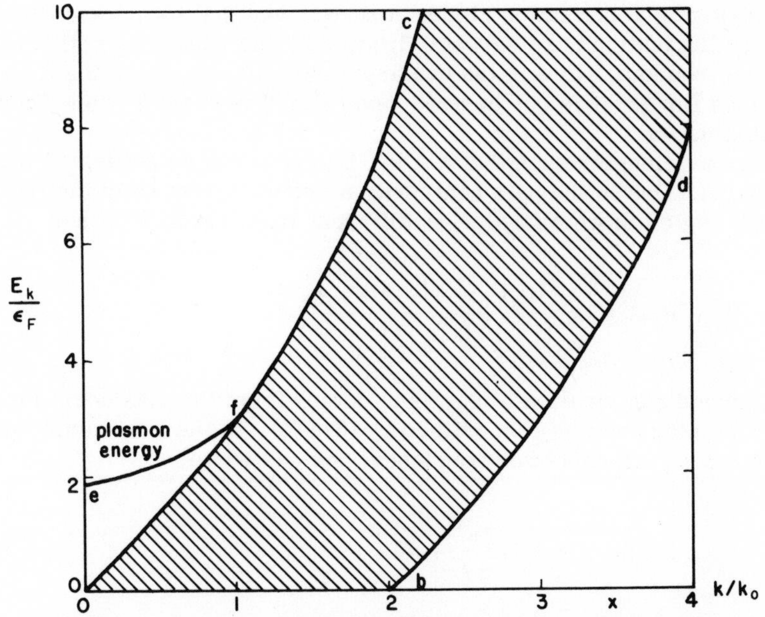

Fig. 3-17. Energy of RPA excitations shown as function of momentum for an electron gas of density $r_s = 4$. The pair excitations fall within the shaded area.

Properties of $S_{RPA}(k\omega)$

We may calculate the dynamic form factor in the RPA, $S_{RPA}(k\omega)$ by direct application of (3-116). We have

$$S_{RPA}(k\omega) = -\frac{\hbar k^2}{4\pi^2 e^2} \operatorname{Im} \frac{1}{\varepsilon_{RPA}(k\omega)} = \frac{\hbar k^2}{4\pi^2 e^2} \frac{\varepsilon_2(k\omega)}{|\varepsilon(k\omega)|^2}$$

$$= \sum_\mu \frac{|(\rho_k)_{\mu o}|^2 \, \delta(\omega - \omega_{\mu o})}{|\varepsilon(k\omega)|^2} = \sum_\mu \frac{|(\rho_k)_{\mu o}|^2 \, \delta(\omega - \omega_{\mu o})}{|\varepsilon(k, \omega_{\mu o})|^2} \tag{3-178}$$

where the matrix elements $(\rho_k)_{\mu o}$ and excitation frequencies $\omega_{\mu o}$ are those appropriate to the plane-wave states of the noninteracting electron gas. We see that in the RPA the Coulomb correlations are such as to reduce the matrix element calculated in the Hartree-Fock approximation, $(\rho_k)_{\mu o}$, by the appropriate *frequency-dependent* dielectric constant $\varepsilon(k, \omega_{\mu o})$. In other words, each electron moves surrounded by a dynamic polarization cloud, in such a way that long-wavelength density fluctuations are severely limited by the screening action of the electron gas. This is the quasi-particle picture which the RPA provides for us; it is our desired generalization of the Fermi-Thomas approximation.

For wavelengths such that $k < k_c$, $S_{RPA}(k\omega)$ can be separated into two parts. One is the pair contribution, which comes from the frequency region in which $\varepsilon_2(k\omega)$ is different from zero. It is just

$$S_{pair}(k\omega) = \sum_{\mu} \frac{|(\rho_k)_{\mu o}|^2 \, \delta(\omega - \omega_{\mu o})}{|\varepsilon(k\omega_{\mu o})|^2} \tag{3-179}$$

The second contribution to $S_{RPA}(k\omega)$ comes from the plasmons, i.e., from the frequency region defined by (3-173). In the immediate vicinity of $\omega = \omega_k$, the plasmon frequency, one can write

$$\varepsilon_{plasmon}(k\omega) = 1 - \frac{\omega_k^2}{\omega^2} + i\delta \tag{3-180}$$

Here we take a small imaginary part to take into account automatically the causal boundary condition. Then from (3-116),

$$S_{plasmon}(k\omega) = -\frac{\hbar k^2}{4\pi^2 e^2} \operatorname{Im} \frac{1}{\varepsilon_{plasmon}(k\omega)}$$

$$= -\frac{\hbar k^2}{4\pi^2 e} \operatorname{Im} \frac{1}{\left(\frac{\partial \varepsilon}{\partial \omega}\right)_{\omega=\omega_k} (\omega - \omega_k) + i\delta}$$

$$= \frac{\hbar \omega_k k^2}{8\pi e^2} \delta(\omega - \omega_k) = N \frac{\hbar k^2}{2m\omega_k} \delta(\omega - \omega_k) \tag{3-181}$$

where ω_k is defined by (3-173) and we have made use of the expansion (3-174).

The structure factor $S_{RPA}(k)$, and the pair-distribution function $g_{RPA}(r)$, may also be calculated with the aid of (3-178). Calculations of the pair-distribution function have been carried out by Glick and Ferrell[44] and by Ueda[45]; the integrals involved are sufficiently complicated that a machine calculation is required. There are two features of interest in these calculations. First for small r_s, the change in $g(r)$ is not very great; in this region the RPA does represent but a small correction to the Hartree-Fock approximation. On the other hand, as Glick and Ferrell[44] have shown, by the time one gets to $r_s \cong 2$, the value appropriate to Al, one finds $g_{RPA}(r) < 0$ for small r. This is a definite indication of the inadequacy of the RPA in this region, since in any correct theory g(r) will be positive.

Energy-Loss Spectrum

The two distinct contributions to the density-fluctuation excitation spectrum for $k \leq k_c$ can in principle be measured by the scattering of a fast electron. As we have seen, one thereby measures the energy-loss function

$$\text{Im}\ \frac{1}{\varepsilon(k\omega)} = -\ \frac{4\pi e^2}{\hbar k^2}\ S(k\omega)$$

In the RPA, as in the Hartree-Fock approximation, there is a continuous pair-excitation spectrum running from zero energy to $\hbar k v_0 + \hbar^2 k^2/2m$. The form of this part of the spectrum is, however, very much altered by the screening factor, $|\varepsilon(k, \omega_{\mu o})|^2$, which at long wavelengths reduces the pair contribution by a factor of k^4/k_{FT}^4, as one readily sees from the explicit expression for ε_1 and ε_2. The new feature of the RPA is, of course, the appearance of the plasmon mode. For wave vectors $k \leq k_c$ the plasmon mode will in fact dominate the energy-loss spectrum. This is perhaps most easily seen by considering the energy-loss sum rule (3-138). On making use of (3-116) and (3-181), one readily verifies that the plasmons exhaust the sum rule (3-138) through terms of order k^4/k_{FT}^4. Thus for momentum transfers $\leq \hbar k_c$, a fast electron transfers essentially all its energy to the plasmons. Such plasmon excitation is observed in the transmission or reflection of a beam of fast electrons by a thin solid film; we postpone our discussion of the phenomenon until after we have taken up the influence of the periodic lattice on plasmons in solids in Chapter 4.

In Fig. 3-18 we give a schematic sketch of the energy-loss function Im $1/\varepsilon(k\omega)$, for a momentum transfer small compared to k_c, as calculated in the Hartree-Fock approximation, and in the RPA.

For momentum transfers $k \gtrsim k_c$, the plasmon is damped, and so rapidly ceases to be the dominant excitation mode of the electron system. One finds then only particle-hole pair excitations present, whose strength is altered from the Hartree-Fock result by the screening factor $\varepsilon(k\omega)^{-2}$. A discussion of the energy-loss spectrum in this region has been given by Glick and Ferrell.[44]

Ground-State Energy

The calculation of the ground-state energy in the RPA proceeds directly from our basic expressions, (3-129) and (3-130). Perhaps the easiest way to arrive at the result is to exploit the analytic

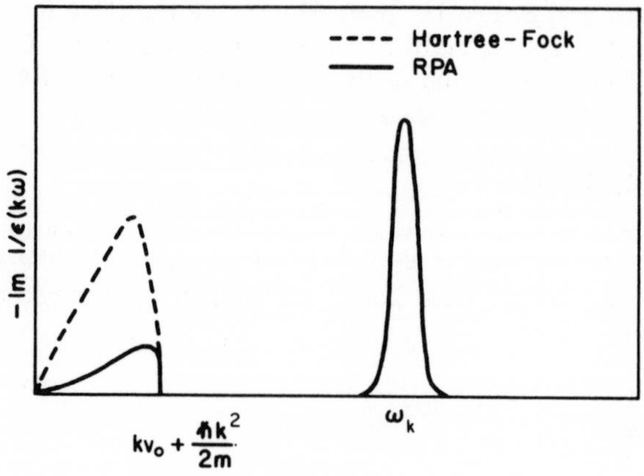

Fig. 3-18

behavior of $1/\varepsilon(k\omega)$; one can show by means of a suitable choice of contours in the complex ω plane that the expression (3-130) in the RPA reduces identically to that obtained by Gell-Mann and Brueckner by the summation of a selected set of diagrams in the perturbation-theoretic expansion for the ground-state energy.[43] The demonstration of this identity is given in Appendix C. Once the GB form for the ground-state energy is obtained, it is quite straightforward to pass to their result, (3-98a), for the correlation energy.

For momentum transfers $k \leq k_c$, one can regard the correlation energy as arising from two distinct contributions—one from the plasmons, one from the screened single-particle interactions. Such a separation corresponds to the separation of $S(k\omega)$ into a screened-pair part and a plasmon part, and is possible only so long as the plasmon represents a distinct excitation mode of the electron gas. The choice of a contour in the complex ω plane which leads to such a separation[43] is likewise given in Appendix C. When the separation is made, one can show without great difficulty that the long-range part of the correlation energy [as calculated in the RPA from (3-130)] is identical with that obtained by Bohm and the writer using the collective description.[17]

It should be emphasized that such a separation is not necessary; by a different choice of contour, the two contributions are lumped together, and one simply has the GB result for the correlation energy. Thus as far as the ground-state energy is concerned, it is a matter of taste whether or not one chooses (where possible) to make explicit the identification of plasmon zero-point energy and screened-particle contributions. That one can make such an identification is nontrivial, since one obtains thereby an explicit justification of the BP neglect of the subsidiary conditions in their calculation of the ground-state energy, a matter about which a certain amount of confusion once existed.

Quasi-Particle Properties

The quasi-particles in the RPA consist of electrons surrounded by comoving dynamic polarization clouds. As we have just seen, the screening cloud essentially acts to reduce the charge on the electron by a factor of $1/|\varepsilon(k\omega_e)|$, if ω_e is the frequency which characterizes the electron motion. Because of the screening cloud (which one might regard as a "correlation" hole surrounding the electron), the various quasi-particle properties (specific heat, spin susceptibility, etc.) are now well behaved. Moreover, in the high-density limit for which the RPA is valid, the corrections to quasi-particle properties in the RPA are rather small, as might be expected from the fact that in this region both exchange and correlation contributions to the ground-state energy are small.

One may calculate the specific heat directly from the derivative of the energy of a quasi-particle at the Fermi surface, according to (3-8) and (3-47). The electronic specific heat in the RPA has been calculated by Gell-Mann,[46] on the basis of an appropriate generalization of the GB calculation of the ground-state energy. He found

$$C_{RPA}/C_o = 1 + 0.083 r_s \ln r_s - 0.203 + \cdots \qquad (3\text{-}182)$$

for the ratio of the RPA specific heat C_{RPA} to the Sommerfeld value C_o [see (3-9b)]. We note the characteristic appearance of a logarithmic term in (3-182). For $r_s = 1$ (which is, as we shall see, roughly the maximum value of r_s for which the RPA is valid), the electron-electron interactions act to decrease the specific heat by some 2 per cent. Since at this density, the exchange and correlation-energy corrections to the ground-state energy are some 48 per cent, it is clear that electron interactions exert far less influence in the state density at the Fermi surface than they do on the ground-state energy.

The spin susceptibility may be calculated along the lines indicated in Sec. 3-1. One assumes a certain spin polarization, and then determines the dependence of the ground-state energy in the RPA on that polarization parameter, according to (3-10a). The calculation has been carried out by Brueckner and Sawada,[47] who obtain for the ratio of the RPA to the Pauli spin susceptibility,

$$\frac{\chi_{RPA}}{\chi_o} = \left\{1 - \frac{\alpha r_s}{\pi} + \frac{3}{4}(\alpha r_s)^2\,[0.225 - 0.676 \ln r_s]\right\}^{-1} \qquad (3\text{-}183)$$

where

$$\alpha = (4/9\pi)^{1/3}$$

Again, the correction to the spin susceptibility is small for $r_s \cong 1$.

Let us now look at the lifetime of a quasi-particle above the Fermi surface. Consider a quasi-particle lying above the Fermi surface; such a particle will not remain there indefinitely; it will scatter against the particles in the Fermi sphere, and so tend to lower its energy. Such an electron state therefore possesses a finite lifetime; the same argument applies equally well to a hole inside the Fermi surface. From a field-theoretic point of view, the lifetime appears as the imaginary part of the self-energy of a quasi-particle, and it was in this way that Quinn and Ferrell[48] first calculated the lifetime in the RPA. We may, however, derive their result from more elementary considerations in the following way.[39]

As we have seen, the physical content of the RPA is that a given electron is surrounded by an appropriate polarization cloud. Hence we may regard the process by which an electron is scattered from a state p ($p > k_o$) to some other state, p + k, as screened by the dynamic screening factor $\varepsilon[\mathbf{k}, -\omega(\mathbf{p}, \mathbf{k})]$, as shown in Fig. 3-19. We may proceed to calculate the lifetime by applying the usual golden rule of second-order perturbation theory. We have, then,

$$\frac{1}{\tau} = \frac{2\pi}{h^2} \sum_{kq\sigma} \frac{|v_k|^2}{|\varepsilon[\mathbf{k}, -\omega(\mathbf{p}, \mathbf{k})]|^2} n_{q\sigma}(1 - n_{q+k\sigma})(1 - n_{p+ks}) \times \delta[\omega(\mathbf{p}, \mathbf{k}) + \omega(\mathbf{q}, \mathbf{k})] \tag{3-184}$$

where $v_k = 4\pi e^2/k^2$. We remark that $\omega(\mathbf{q}, \mathbf{k})$ must be positive: $\omega(\mathbf{q}, \mathbf{k}) > 0$, or equivalently, $\omega(\mathbf{p}, \mathbf{k}) < 0$.

With the aid of (3-168b) the expression (3-184) is simplified as

$$\frac{1}{\tau} = \sum_k \frac{8\pi e^2 \operatorname{Im} \varepsilon[\mathbf{k}, -\omega(\mathbf{p}, \mathbf{k})]}{\hbar k^2 \, |\varepsilon[\mathbf{k}, -\omega(\mathbf{p}, \mathbf{k})]|^2} (1 - n_{p+ks})$$

$$= -\sum_k \frac{8\pi e^2}{\hbar k^2} \operatorname{Im} \frac{1}{\varepsilon[\mathbf{k}, -\omega(\mathbf{p}, \mathbf{k})]} (1 - n_{p+ks})$$

$$= -\sum_{k_o^2 < |p+k|^2 < p^2} \frac{8\pi e^2}{\hbar k^2} \operatorname{Im} \frac{1}{\varepsilon[\mathbf{k}, -\omega(\mathbf{p}, \mathbf{k})]} \tag{3-185}$$

By this expression we see that our calculation gives an identical result with that of Quinn and Ferrell, whose expression for the imaginary part of the self-energy reads

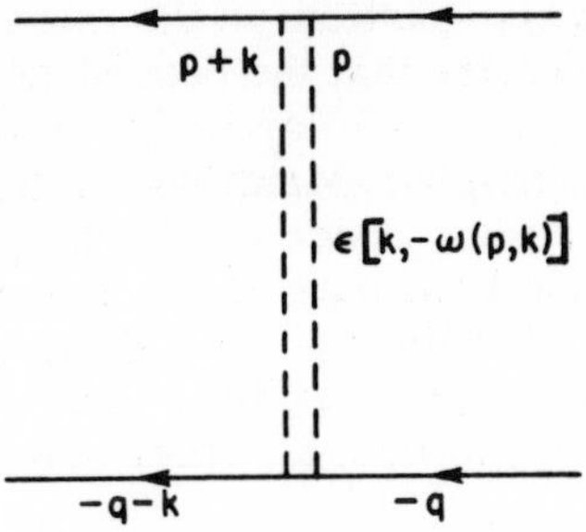

Fig. 3-19

$$E^{im}_{corr}(p) = \sum_{k_o^2<|p+k|^2<p^2} \frac{4\pi e^2}{k^2} \text{Im} \frac{1}{\varepsilon[k, -\omega(p, k)]} \tag{3-186}$$

Indeed the lifetime of the electron state is connected with the imaginary part of the self-energy as

$$\frac{1}{\tau} = -\frac{2}{\hbar} E^{im}_{corr}(p) \tag{3-187}$$

The factor of two stems from the fact that we are calculating the damping, not of the wave amplitude of the electron field, but of the actual density distribution of the electrons.

If we consider only low-lying excited states, the expression (3-185) is substantially simplified, since only low frequencies enter the expression. With the aid of (3-172a), we obtain

$$\frac{1}{\tau} = \sum_{k_o^2<|p+k|^2<p^2} \frac{4\pi e^2}{\hbar k^2} \frac{k_{FT}^2}{k^2} \frac{1}{|\varepsilon(k0)|^2} \frac{k\cdot p}{\hbar k_o}$$

$$= \frac{e^2 k_{FT}^2 k_o^2}{2\hbar}\left(\frac{p}{k_o} - 1\right)^2 \int_0^{2k_o} \frac{dk}{k^4 |\varepsilon(k, 0)|^2} \tag{3-188}$$

The last integral, as Quinn and Ferrell argue, would be severely divergent without the screening effect. Because of the screening, the integral converges, and one finds

$$\frac{1}{\tau} = \frac{\pi e^2 k_o^2}{4\hbar}\left(\frac{\hbar}{6m\omega_p}\right)^{1/2}\left(\frac{p}{k_o} - 1\right)^2 \tag{3-189}$$

for the lifetime of a quasi-particle in the immediate vicinity of the Fermi surface. We remark that the dependence of the lifetime on $(p - k_o)^2/k_o^2$ is just what we have argued would appear as a consequence of the Pauli principle restrictions on the number of scattering states available to particles inside the Fermi sea, and the final states available to the particle lying outside the Fermi sea.

We conclude that in the limit $p \to k_o$, the quasi-particle lifetime becomes infinite. Only a quasi-particle located *on* the Fermi surface will possess an infinite lifetime; all other states are subject to temporal decay.

3-6 PROPERTIES OF THE ELECTRON GAS AT METALLIC DENSITIES

The principal utility of the RPA in the treatment of the free-electron gas is that it furnishes us with a nontrivial *model* of an interacting electron system. Thus one can calculate the ground-state energy, specific heat, spin susceptibility, lifetime of quasi-particles near the Fermi surface, discontinuity in the distribution function at the Fermi surface, etc.; in general, one finds a series expansion for the various system properties which has the general structure as (3-98). The results show how electron interaction alters the system properties; they are also all quite accurate in the limit of very high electron densities ($r_s \ll 1$). It is a great step forward to have a soluble model for a many-body system; one which displays clearly the physical effects of importance. On the other hand, it is a far cry from the free-electron gas at high densities to a realistic account of electron interaction in solids. There are two hurdles which must be overcome: the extension of the free-electron theory into the region of actual metallic densities ($2 \lesssim r_s \lesssim 5.5$); and the extension of the theory to take into account the periodic lattice of ions present in a solid.

There has been a certain amount of progress made in both directions. It is possible to develop various approximate schemes which show promise of offering a reasonable account of electron interaction in the "free-electron" gas at metallic densities, and we shall discuss these briefly in this section. It is also possible to extend the RPA to take into account the effects of the ionic potential on the long-wavelength behavior of the electron gas, and that extension will form the topic of the following chapter.

The breakdown of the RPA at densities of the order of $r_s = 1$ may be seen in a number of ways. For example, as we have mentioned, Gell-Mann and Brueckner calculated the second-order "exchange" correction to the ground-state energy, and found it to be 0.046 rydberg. At a density of $r_s = 1$, such a correction amounts to some 30 per cent of the RPA calculation of the correlation energy (- 0.142 rydberg).

One might hope, however, to improve the RPA calculating the next terms in the perturbation series expansion for the polarizability, the ground-state energy, etc. Such calculations have, for example, been carried by DuBois[22] for the specific heat, and, in principle, for the ground-state energy. They are interesting as a study of the structure of the series expansion; however, it seems very doubtful that one can in this way arrive at an accurate account of an electron gas at metallic densities.

The essential reason for this is that a series expansion like (3-98) for the ground-state energy (and the comparable expansions for the specific heat, spin susceptibility, etc.) possesses validity only when one is in a weak-coupling region, one in which the influence of the potential energy on the electronic motion is small compared to that of the kinetic energy. On the other hand, as we have already remarked, at metallic electron densities, the kinetic and potential energies are comparable; this fact renders it equally doubtful that any extension of the strong-coupling calculations can likewise offer a reliable guide to metallic behavior.

In attempting to understand the behavior of the electron gas at metallic densities, it is illuminating to consider the contributions to the correlation energy from different momentum transfers. We have seen in, for example, (3-129) and (3-130), how it is always possible to isolate the contribution from a given momentum transfer by calculating, say, $E_{int}(k)$, and then carrying out the integration over the coupling constant. We have considered the RPA long-range part of the correlation energy (the contributions from $k \leq k_c$, say) in Sec. 3-3, and discussed there the RPA result, (3-94). We have also discussed there two terms which represent corrections to the RPA calculation of the long-range part of the correlation energy: the corrections to the plasmon energy arising from U and from H_{sr}. To these should be added the correction to the single-particle contribution arising from H_{sr}, one that is due to an admixture of H_{sr} and H_{rp}. Such a correction has been estimated to be $\approx 0.014\beta^4/r_s$ rydberg.[17] All three corrections possess in common the feature that they become increasingly important as one increases either β or r_s. For metallic densities and $\beta = 0.47\, r_s^{1/4}$, they are small, and may be neglected. On the other hand, as one goes to larger values of momentum transfer, they will clearly *not* be small for the metallic electron-density region of interest.

It is, in fact, clear that at large momentum transfers the RPA runs into real difficulties, as Hubbard[25] and Nozières and the writer[17] have argued. As we have seen, there is no distinction in the RPA between the contribution to correlation effects from electrons of parallel spin and antiparallel spin. On the other hand, physically, one would expect that electrons of parallel spin simply don't feel the short-range part of the interaction, inasmuch as they are kept apart by the Pauli principle. Mathematically, such an effect appears because for large momentum transfers the "exchange" parts of the perturbation-theoretic expansion (which occur only for electrons of parallel spin and which are neglected in the RPA) cancel that one-half of the "direct" interaction which may be attributed to electrons of parallel spin. The result: only electrons of antiparallel spin interact via the large momentum transfer part of the Coulomb interaction. The origin of such a cancellation is simple: to a given direct process for electrons of parallel spin going by a matrix element V_k, there exists an exchange "conjugate" process, going by a matrix element $-V_{k+p+q}$. (For electrons of antiparallel spin, no such exchange processes are possible.) For small momentum transfers, as we have seen, the exchange terms are not important; on the other hand, for large momentum transfers the exchange process will cancel that part of the direct process which is attributed to interactions between particles of parallel spin.

We may obtain an estimate of the size of this effect in second order. The total contribution made by electrons of parallel spin to the short-range part of the correlation energy is[17]

$$E_{\parallel}^{(2)}(k \geq k_c) = \frac{E_2^{(a)}}{2} + E_2^{(b)}$$

$$\cong (0.021 + 0.062 \ \ln \beta - 0.021\beta^2) \quad \text{rydberg} \tag{3-190}$$

The result, (3-190), is valid for $\beta \lesssim 3/4$, and something of an underestimate for larger values of β. It illustrates clearly the cancellation which occurs at large momentum transfers.

At this point one may ask: Why then does the RPA work at any metallic density? The answer is that at high densities the important contributions to the correlation energy (which come from $\beta \lesssim 0.81 r_s^{1/2}$) come from *low* momentum transfers, for which the RPA result is valid. It is only as one goes toward metallic densities that the high momentum transfer contributions become appreciable; one must then go beyond the RPA to calculate the system properties.

Hubbard's proposal for overcoming the large momentum transfer difficulty is based on the following approximation for $\varepsilon(k\omega)$:

$$\varepsilon_H(k\omega) = 1 + \frac{4\pi\alpha_0(k\omega)}{1 + f(k)\,4\pi\alpha_0(k\omega)} \tag{3-191}$$

where

$$f(k) = \frac{1}{2}\,\frac{k^2}{k^2 + k_F^2}$$

One sees that for small k, $\varepsilon_H(k\omega) \cong \varepsilon_{RPA}(k\omega)$. On the other hand, for large k, the use of $\varepsilon_H(k\omega)$ in the expression for the ground-state energy has the effect of reducing by a factor of two the contribution to the correlation energy of a given momentum transfer. This reduction is equivalent to the "exchange" cancellation of one-half the direct term at this momentum transfer. The results which Hubbard obtained for the correlation energy are given in Table 3-8.

Table 3-8
Correlation Energies (rydbergs per electron)

r_s	2	3	4	5
E_{corr} calculated by Wigner	-0.090	-0.082	-0.075	-0.069
E_{corr} calculated by Hubbard[25]	-0.099	-0.086	-0.074	-0.067
E_{corr} calculated from (3-194)[17]	-0.094	-0.081	-0.072	-0.065
E_{corr} calculated by Gaskell[49]	-0.105	-0.088	-0.076	-0.069

Nozieres and the writer proposed that one treat the large momentum transfers by making a virtue out of necessity—by assuming that for large momentum transfers one consider only the interaction between electrons of antiparallel spin. Furthermore, we argued that these could be treated reasonably well by second-order perturbation theory. This procedure should work well for, say, $\beta \gtrsim 1.5$. As we have seen, the RPA works for $\beta \lesssim 0.47\, r_s^{1/2}$. To obtain the contribution from intermediate momentum transfers, one then interpolates smoothly between the low k region and the high k region. The procedure thus assumes that the RPA furnishes a reasonable account of matters at low k, and that the effect of the Coulomb interaction on the system property in question is a smoothly varying function of the momentum transfers involved.

In Fig. 3-20 the contributions to the correlation energy from different momentum transfers are plotted for Na. The Nozières-Pines curve is based on using the RPA expression (3-94) for $k/k_0 \le 0.47 r_s^{1/2}$, and for $k/k_0 \ge 0.47 r_s^{1/2}$, the second-order perturbation-theory result (for antiparallel spins only),

$$E_2^{a\text{-}||} = -\{0.025 - 0.063 \ln \beta + 0.0064 \beta^2\} \text{ rydbergs} \qquad (3\text{-}192)$$

obtained by taking one-half of the direct contribution, (3-96). The Hubbard curve is based on his numerical calculations for the ground-state energy, using the approximate dielectric constant, (3-191). One sees the two methods yield very nearly the same result. In fact, since

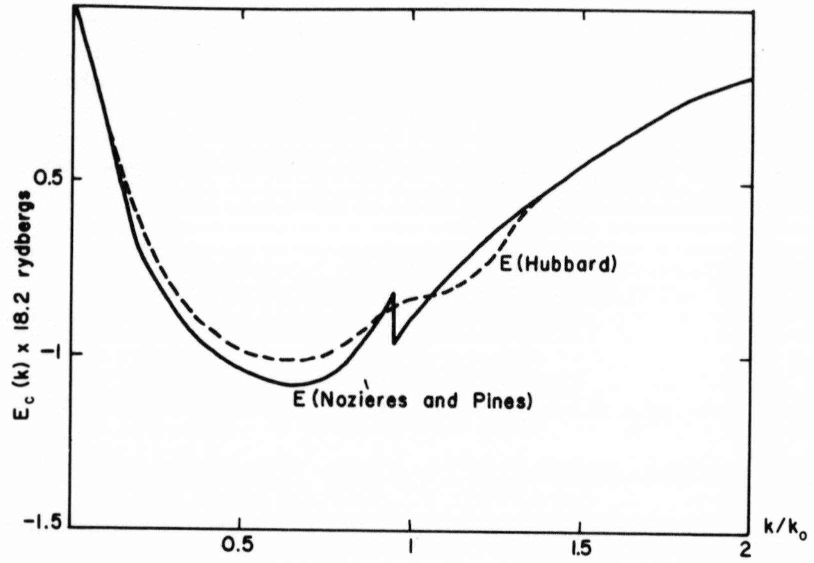

Fig. 3-20. Contributions to the correlation energy from different momentum transfers, $E_c(k)$, shown as a function of k.

the discontinuity in $E_c(k)$ at $k/k_o = 0.47\, r_s^{1/2}$ is rather symmetrically located, one can obtain an explicit expression for E_{corr} by simply substituting $\beta = 0.47\, r_s^{1/2}$ into the expressions (3-94) and (3-192) for the long-range and short-range correlation energy, respectively. One then finds

$$\begin{aligned} E^{\ell.r.}_{corr}\ (\beta) &= -\ 0.043 \quad \text{rydberg} \quad \beta = 0.47\, r_s^{1/2} \\ E^{s.r.}_{corr}\ (\beta) &= -\ 0.072 + 0.031\ \ell n\ r_s \quad \text{rydberg} \end{aligned} \tag{3-193}$$

and

$$E_{corr} \cong -\ 0.115 + 0.031\ \ell n\ r_s \quad \text{rydberg} \tag{3-194}$$

The resulting numerical values for the correlation energy are shown in Table 3-8.

Yet another method for calculating the correlation energy at metallic densities has been put forth by Gaskell.[49] Gaskell has carried out a variational calculation of the ground-state energy using a wave function of the following form:

$$\Psi = D \prod_{i<j} f(r_{ij}) \tag{3-195}$$

where D is a determinant of plane waves. It may be seen, on comparing (3-195) with (3-83) that this form is in accord with the predictions of the collective description. Gaskell then carried out the rather difficult variational calculation with the aid of certain approximations due to Edwards,[50] which permit one to express a Slater determinant as a function which depends on ρ_k. The results that Gaskell has obtained are likewise given in Table 3-8.

We see from this table that there is general accord between all the different methods for estimating the correlation energy at intermediate densities. Moreover, as may be seen from Table 3-7 the different methods will lead to, on the whole, good agreement between theory and experiment for the cohesive energies of the alkali metals. Gaskell has also carried out a calculation of g(r) using the wave function (3-195). He finds a well-behaved g(r) for $r_s \leq 2.66$, but for $r_s \geq 2.66$, g(r) for small r becomes negative. Again, such behavior should be taken as indication of the breakdown of the particular approximations involved in the calculation. As yet, no calculations of g(r) based on either the Hubbard or the Nozières-Pines interpolation procedures have been carried out.

Recently Silverstein[51] has used the interpolation procedure of Nozières and the writer to calculate the influence of electron interaction on the specific heat and spin susceptibility of an electron gas at metallic densities. Thus he has calculated the explicit contribution to each property from low-momentum transfers (using the RPA), and from high-momentum transfers (using second-order perturbation theory and neglecting the interaction between electrons of parallel spin). The contributions from intermediate momentum transfers are then obtained by a smooth interpolation between the regions of low and high momentum transfer. His results for the specific heat are compared with those of DuBois in Fig. 3-21. One sees that the "improved" high-density calculation of DuBois differs markedly from that of Silverstein once $r_s \gtrsim 1$. Silverstein's results show that the specific heat of a free-electron gas is not markedly influenced by electron interaction, with corrections at most of some 20 per cent.

These results may be applied directly to the alkali metals, once one knows the average effective mass, m*, of the electrons at the Fermi surface. The results which Silverstein has obtained for the specific heat and spin susceptibility of the alkali metals are shown in Table 3-9. The agreement between theory and experiment for the spin susceptibility of Li and Na may be regarded as quite satisfactory. The theoretical values for the specific heat will be further altered by consideration of the electron-phonon interactions. (As Simkin[52] has shown, electron-phonon interactions do not affect χ_s.) If the theoretical values of the specific heat are regarded as accurate (~ 10 per cent, say), one can but conclude that electron-phonon interactions act to enhance the specific heat for Li and Na, while reducing it for K, Rb, and

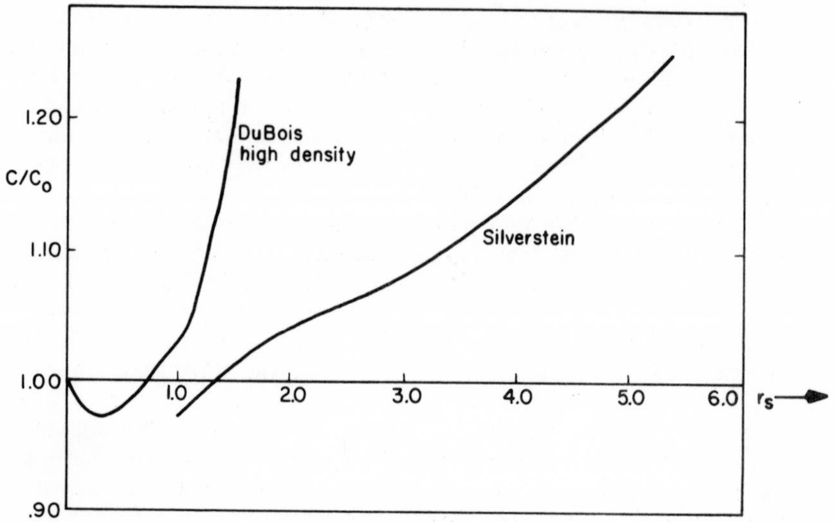

Fig. 3-21

Table 3-9
Specific Heat and Spin Susceptibility for the Alkali Metals

	Li	Na	K	Rb	Cs
r_s	3.22	3.96	4.87	5.18	5.57
$\left(\frac{m^*}{m}\right)$ [a]	1.66	1.00	1.09	1.21	1.76
$\left(\frac{C^*}{C_0}\right)_{theo}$	1.96	1.15	1.35	1.56	2.86
$\left(\frac{C}{C_0}\right)_{exp}$	2.19[b]	1.27[b]	1.25[c]	1.25[c]	1.47[c]
$\chi^*_{corr} \times 10^{+6}$	2.21	0.86	0.73	0.78	1.15
$\chi_{expt} \times 10^{+6}$	2.08 ± 0.1	0.89 ± 0.04			

[a]From F. S. Ham, *Phys. Rev.* **128**, 2524 (1962).
[b]D. L. Martin, *Phys. Rev.* **124**, 238 (1961); *Proc. Roy. Soc. (London)*, A236, 378 (1961).
[c]W. H. Lien and N. E. Phillips, as quoted in Ref. a.

Cs. The calculations of Simkin[52] show an enhancement for Na which is of the right order of magnitude to explain the discrepancy between theory and experiment in Table 3-9.

To sum up, this procedure for treating the influence of electron interaction on various metallic properties is scarcely ideal, but it seems to be the best we can do at present. Not only has it been assumed that the above interpolation procedure is valid, but also that the effects of periodicity are not large. This latter assumption may be supportable, because one is, in fact, averaging over all momentum transfers in calculating gross metallic properties; indeed, the agreement with experiment of the calculations thus far carried out gives one hope in this direction. On the other hand, it is essential to take into account the effects of periodicity when computing the long-wavelength response of the electrons in a solid to external disturbances, as we shall see in Chapter 4.

References

1. A. Sommerfeld, *Z. Physik*, **47**, 1 (1928).
2. See, for example, F. Seitz, "The Modern Theory of Solids," McGraw-Hill, New York, 1940.
3. W. Pauli, *Z. Physik*, **41**, 81 (1927).
4. R. T. Schumacher and C. P. Slichter, *Phys. Rev.*, **101**, 58 (1956); R. T. Schumacher and W. E. Vehse, *Bull. Am. Phys. Soc.*, **4**, 296 (1960).

4a. Calculations of the influence of the periodic lattice on one-electron properties of alkali-metals have recently been carried out by F. S. Ham, *Phys. Rev.*, **128**, 82 (1962); **128**, 2524 (1962).

5. F. Seitz, "The Modern Theory of Solids," McGraw-Hill, New York, 1940.
6. For an introductory survey of the application of field-theoretical techniques to the many-body problem, see D. Pines, "The Many-Body Problem," Benjamin, New York, 1961.
7. The details of such a calculation are given in D. Pines, *Phys. Rev.*, **92**, 636 (1953).
8. E. P. Wigner and F. Seitz, *Phys. Rev.*, **43**, 804 (1933).

8a. D. Bohm and D. Pines, *Phys. Rev.*, **92**, 609 (1952); K. Sawada, *Phys. Rev.*, **106**, 372 (1957); K. Sawada, K. Brueckner, N. Fukuda, and R. Brout, *Phys. Rev.*, **108**, 507 (1957); P. W. Anderson, *Phys. Rev.*, **112**, 1900 (1958); H. Suhl and N. R. Werthamer, *Phys. Rev.*, **122**, 359 (1961). The derivation presented here follows closely that of Ref. 6, where further references to and applications of the method are discussed.

9. For a review of cohesive energy calculations in simple metals, see H. Brooks, *Nuovo Cimento Suppl.*, **7**, 165 (1958).
10. J. C. Slater, *Phys. Rev.*, **81**, 385 (1951).

11. J. Bardeen, *Phys. Rev.*, 50, 1098 (1936); see also E. P. Wohlfarth, *Phil. Mag.*, 41, 534 (1950).
11a. P. T. Landsberg, *Proc. Phys. Soc. (London)*, A62 (1948).
12. E. P. Wigner, *Phys. Rev.*, 46, 1002 (1934); *Trans. Faraday Soc.*, 34, 678 (1938).
13. D. Pines and D. Bohm, *Phys. Rev.*, 85, 338 (1952).
14. D. Bohm and D. Pines, *Phys. Rev.*, 92, 609 (1953).
15. For a summary of the developments carried out with this theory up to 1955, see D. Pines, "Advances in Solid State Physics," ed. by F. Seitz and D. Turnbull, Academic Press, New York, 1955, Vol. I, p. 373.
15a. The early published values of Wigner's interpolation formula give it as $-0.58/(r_s + 5.1)$ rydberg. This expression was based on an incorrect low-density limit for the correlation energy of $-0.58/r_s$ rydberg, as Wigner points out in a footnote to the second paper cited in Ref. 12.
16. W. J. Carr, *Phys. Rev.*, 122, 1437 (1961); W. J. Carr, R. A. Caldwell-Horsefall, and E. A. Fein, *Phys. Rev.*, 124, 747 (1961).
17. P. Nozières and D. Pines, *Phys. Rev.*, 111, 442 (1958).
18. N. F. Mott and H. Jones, "The Theory of Metals and Alloys," Oxford University Press, New York, 1936, p. 87.
19. J. G. Fletcher and D. C. Larson, *Phys. Rev.*, 111, 455 (1958).
20. A general discussion of the collective coordinate approach may be found in the lectures by D. Bohm, in "The Many-Body Problem," Dunod-Wiley, 1959, p. 401.
21. D. Bohm, K. Huang, and D. Pines, *Phys. Rev.*, 107, 71 (1957). (See also Problem 3-4.)
22. D. F. DuBois, *Ann. Phys.*, 7, 174 (1959); *Ann. Phys.*, 8, 24 (1959).
23. M. Gell-Mann and K. A. Brueckner, *Phys. Rev.*, 106, 364 (1957); often referred to as GB.
24. W. Macke, *Z. Naturforsch.*, 5a, 192 (1950).
25. J. Hubbard, *Proc. Roy. Soc. (London)*, A243, 336 (1957).
26. The writer would like to thank Dr. John Hubbard for an illuminating discussion on this subject.
27. J. Lindhard, *Kgl. Danske Videnskab. Selskab, Mat-fys. Medd.*, 28, 8 (1954).
28. P. Nozières and D. Pines, *Nuovo Cimento*, [X] 9, 470 (1958).
28a. For a system with a ground state which is invariant under time inversion ($t \to -t$), to a given matrix element, $(\rho_q^n)_{no}$ there corresponds a complex-conjugate matrix element, $(\rho_q)_{mo}$, which differs at most by a phase factor, $e^{i\delta}$, from $(\rho_q^+)_{no}$. Moreover the energy of the time-reversed excited state E_m is equal to the energy of the excited state E_n. Hence it follows directly that

$$\frac{\sum_n |(\rho_q^+)_{no}|^2}{\omega + \omega_{no} + i\delta} = \frac{\sum_m |(\rho_q)_{mo}|^2}{\omega + \omega_{mo} + i\delta}$$

whence (3-110a) follows. The writer would like to thank Dr. P. Nozières for a helpful discussion in this connection.
29. Such an approach was first developed by E. Fermi, *Phys. Rev.*, 57, 485 (1940). Applications to the electron gas may be found in the papers of H. A. Kramers, *Physica*, 13, 401 (1947), A. Bohr, *Kgl. Danske Videnskab. Selskab, Mat-fys. Medd.*, 24, 19 (1948); J. Hubbard, *Proc. Phys. Soc. (London)*, A68, 441 (1955), 916 (1955); H. Fröhlich and H. Pelzer, *Proc. Phys. Soc. (London)*, A68, 525 (1955), and R. H. Ritchie, *Phys. Rev.*, 106, 874 (1957).
29a. The relation between $\varepsilon(k\omega)$ and $S(k\omega)$ was perhaps first recognized by U. Fano, *Phys. Rev.*, 103, 1202 (1956).
30. L. van Hove, *Phys. Rev.*, 95, 249 (1954).
31. P. Nozières and D. Pines, *Phys. Rev.*, 109, 741 (1958).
32. G. Rickayzen, *Phys. Rev.*, 115, 795 (1959).
33. H. Ehrenreich and M. Cohen, *Phys. Rev.*, 115, 786 (1959).
34. J. Goldstone and K. Gottfried, *Nuovo Cimento*, [X] 13, 849 (1959).
35. Y. Klimontovitch and V. Silin, *Uspekhi Fiz. Nauk*, 70, 247 (translation: *Soviet Physics-Uspekhi*, 3, 84 (1960)), where many other relevant references to the Russian literature in this field may be found.
36. D. Pines, Ph.D. thesis, Princeton University, 1950, unpublished.
37. P. Wolff, *Phys. Rev.*, 92, 18 (1953).
38. R. A. Ferrell, *Phys. Rev.*, 107, 450 (1957).
39. R. N. Ritchie, *Phys. Rev.*, 114, 644 (1959).
40. J. Langer and S. J. Vosko, *J. Phys. Chem. Solids*, 12, 196 (1960).
41. J. Friedel, *Nuovo Cimento Suppl.*, 7, 287 (1958).
42. T. Rowland, *Phys. Rev.*, 119, 900 (1960); W. Kohn and S. H. Vosko, *Phys. Rev.*, 119, 912 (1960).
43. K. Sawada, K. A. Brueckner, N. Fukuda, and R. Brout, *Phys. Rev.*, 108, 507 (1957).
44. A. Glick and R. Ferrell, *Ann. Phys.*, 11, 359 (1960).
45. S. Ueda, *Progr. Theoret. Phys.*, 26, 45 (1961).
46. M. Gell-Mann, *Phys. Rev.*, 106, 369 (1957).
47. K. A. Brueckner and K. Sawada, *Phys. Rev.*, 112, 328 (1958).
48. J. Quinn and R. Ferrell, *Phys. Rev.*, 112, 812 (1958).
49. T. Gaskell, *Proc. Phys. Soc. (London)*, 77, 1182 (1961); 80, 1091 (1962).
50. S. F. Edwards, *Proc. Phys. Soc. (London)*, 72, 685 (1958).
51. S. P. Silverstein, *Phys. Rev.*, 128, 631 (1962); *Phys. Rev.* (to be published).
52. D. Simkin, Ph.D. thesis, University of Illinois, 1963, unpublished.

Problems

3-1 Derive the result (3-44) for the static form factor in the Hartree-Fock approximation, by carrying out the summation specified in (3-43); calculate the pair-distribution function (3-45).

3-2 Determine the coefficient of

$$\lim_{k \to 0} E_2^{(a)} \qquad \text{[Eq. (3-53)]}$$

[*Hint*: Make use of (3-52) in carrying out the Pauli principle summations.] Use this result to obtain the coefficient of the $\ln r_s$ term in the correlation energy result of Gell-Mann and Brueckner.

3-3 A canonical transformation which eliminates H_{int}, (3-78), in the BP collective description, to lowest order in g_k^2, is generated by

$$S = \sum_{ki} \left(\frac{4\pi e^2}{k^2}\right)^{1/2} \frac{\mathbf{k} \cdot \mathbf{p}_i}{m\omega_p^2} \pi_k^+ e^{-i\mathbf{k}\cdot\mathbf{r}_i}$$

Verify that this is the case, and use this transformation to calculate the following quantities to order g_k^2: (a) the RPA shift in plasmon energy, (b) $H_{r.p.}$, and (c) the "exchange" shift in the plasmon energy, (3-93).

3-4 Further insight is obtained into the reason the collective coordinate method proves successful for calculating the ground-state energy if one regards the additional terms in the extended Hamiltonian, (3-70), as being weakly coupled to the basic electron Hamiltonian, (3-15). Show, by means of a second-order perturbation-theoretic calculation (based on *exact* states for the electron Hamiltonian) that the net effect of the added terms is to increase the ground-state energy by

$$\sum_{k<k_c} \pi_k^+ \pi_k / \varepsilon(k, o)$$

Hence, if $\varepsilon(k, o) \geq 0$ (see Appendix B), it follows that the ground-state energy of the extended Hamiltonian is greater than or equal to that of the original Hamiltonian, (3-15).

3-5 The linear response function defined in Appendix B is the *retarded* linear response function, $K(k\omega)$. Show that it is the Fourier transform in time of the *retarded* commutator:

$$-i \left\langle \Psi_o | [\rho_k(\tau), \rho_{-k}(0)] | \Psi_o \right\rangle \theta(\tau)$$

where the operators and state functions are given in the Heisenberg representation, and

$$\theta(\tau) = 1 \quad \tau > 0$$

$$= 0 \quad \tau < 0$$

Show that the propagating response function

$$K_p(k, \omega) = \sum_n \left(\rho_k^+\right)_{no}^2 \left\{ \frac{1}{\omega - \omega_{no} + i\delta} - \frac{1}{\omega + \omega_{no} - i\delta} \right\}$$

is the Fourier transform of the density-fluctuation propagator,

$$K_p(k, \tau) = -i\left\{ \left\langle \Psi_o \right| \rho_k(\tau)\, \rho_k^+(0) \left| \Psi_o \right\rangle \theta(\tau) + \left\langle \Psi_o \right| \rho_k^+(0)\, \rho_k(\tau) \left| \Psi_o \right\rangle \theta(-\tau) \right\}$$

In field-theoretic calculations it is the propagators which always enter. Discuss the difference in the analytic behavior of $1/\varepsilon(k\omega)$ and $1/\varepsilon_p(k\omega)$, the latter being related to $K_p(k, \omega)$ by an equation like (A-34).

3-6 Calculate the k^2 term in the plasmon dispersion relation, (3-176).

Chapter 4

ELECTRONS, PLASMONS, AND PHOTONS IN SOLIDS

4-1 INTRODUCTORY CONSIDERATIONS

We now consider electron interaction in actual solids, as distinct from the interacting electron gas in a uniform background of positive charge we have discussed in the preceding chapter. The general plan of the present chapter is to consider in some detail the response of electrons in solids to both longitudinal and transverse external probes. We shall discuss characteristic energy-loss experiments (in which a fast electron is used as a high-frequency longitudinal probe) and optical experiments (in which high-frequency electromagnetic radiation is used as a transverse probe). We begin with a brief review of some of the properties of Bloch wave-matrix elements and excitation energies which are relevant for our purposes. (Our treatment parallels closely that of Ref. 1.)

We shall restrict our attention to those solids for which there exist well-defined groups of valence electrons (electrons outside the last closed shell of the atoms which make up the solid) which are acted upon by a position-dependent periodic potential due to the ion cores. The Hamiltonian of the system is then

$$H = \sum_i \frac{p_i^2}{2m} + V(\mathbf{r}_i) + \sum_k (2\pi e^2/k^2)(\rho_k^+ \rho_k - N) \tag{4-1}$$

where $V(\mathbf{r}_i)$ is the periodic ion-core potential plus the Hartree potential of the valence electrons.

We shall find it convenient to specify the electron states in terms of the eigenstates, Φ_μ, of the operator

$$H_B = \sum_i \left\{ \frac{p_i^2}{2m} + V(\mathbf{r}_i) \right\} \tag{4-2}$$

H_B is a sum of one-electron operators. Each term has a complete spectrum of eigenstates, φ_μ, which are the usual Bloch functions. Thus the Bloch function for an electron of momentum p in the band m (we are using the reduced zone scheme) satisfies an equation:

$$\left\{\frac{p^2}{2m} + V(r)\right\} \psi_{pm}(r) = \varepsilon_{pm}\,\varphi_{pm}(r) \tag{4-3}$$

where ε_{pm} is the appropriate one-electron energy. The states Φ_μ may be regarded as Slater determinants built up of the various φ_μ, in the same way that one may characterize states of the free-electron gas in terms of determinants of plane waves. Alternatively, we may use the representation of second quantization, in which case we specify the state function Φ_μ by the occupation of the one-electron states, pm. In that case we introduce the creation and annihilation operators, c^+_{pm} and c_{pm}, which satisfy the anti-commutation relations (see Appendix A)

$$\begin{aligned} \left[c^+_{pm}, c^+_{p'n}\right]_+ &= \left[c_{pm}, c_{p'n}\right]_+ = 0 \\ \left[c^+_{pm}, c_{p'n}\right]_+ &= \delta_{pp'}\,\delta_{mn} \end{aligned} \tag{4-4}$$

In terms of the second-quantized operators, H_B may be written.

$$H_B = \sum_{pm} \varepsilon_{pm} c^+_{pm} c_{pm} \tag{4-5}$$

We shall, as in the preceding chapter, be interested particularly in the transitions introduced between the ground state Φ_o and certain excited states Φ_μ by the density fluctuations ρ^+_k. Since ρ^+_k is a sum of one-electron operators, and belongs to the representation of the translation group with wave vector **k**, it will induce transitions in which a single electron is excited from a level described by some φ_{pm} to another level described by $\varphi_{p+k,m'}$. Moreover, to be consistent with the Pauli principle, the state p, m must be occupied, while the state p + k, m' must be empty. We should therefore label the excited states, Φ_μ, which couple to Φ_o, by the indices p, k, m, m' (and, as well, take into account the Pauli principle in so doing); in order to simplify our notation, we shall speak simply of the transition

$$(\rho^+_k)_{\mu o}$$

and make explicit the definite sums involved only where necessary.

We shall also have occasion to consider the oscillator strengths for the Bloch wave states. We first remark that the f-sum rule, (3-133), applies equally well to the case of electrons moving in a periodic potential, since it must hold for the exact states of a many-particle system for which there are no velocity-dependent forces. In particular, we can introduce the Bloch-wave oscillator strengths, defined by

$$f_{o\nu} = \frac{2m}{hk^2} |(\rho_k^+)_{\nu o}|^2 \omega_{\nu o} \tag{4-6}$$

which obey the f-sum rule

$$\sum_{\nu} f_{o\nu} = N_v \tag{4-7}$$

where N_v is the number of valence electrons in the band (or bands) under consideration.

The single-particle excitations which contribute to $(\rho_k^+)_{\nu o}$ are now of two kinds: intraband excitations, in which an electron makes a transition within a given band, and interband excitations, corresponding to a transition between different bands. Intraband transitions occur only for electrons in the conduction bands of a metal or a semiconductor (they are forbidden by the Pauli principle for the valence band of an insulator or an intrinsic semiconductor at low temperatures); such transitions are essentially the same as the single-particle-like excitations of a free-electron gas. The interband excitations are the essentially new feature arising from the periodic structure of the solid.

The Bloch-wave matrix elements, excitation frequencies, and oscillator strengths take a simple form in the long-wavelength limit ($k << k_o$). For intraband transitions, one finds readily

$$|(\rho_k^+)_{\nu o}|^2 = 1 + 0(k^2) \tag{4-8}$$

as for the free-electron gas. The excitation energy is

$$h\omega_{\nu o} = \varepsilon_{p+k\mu} - \varepsilon_{p\mu} \cong k \cdot \nabla_p \varepsilon_{p\mu} + \frac{1}{2} (k \cdot \nabla_p) k \cdot \nabla_p \varepsilon_{p\mu} + \cdots \tag{4-9}$$

If we now average over directions of **k** and, further, assume we deal with an isotropic solid (an assumption we shall make throughout this chapter), we have then

$$\hbar < \omega_{\nu o} > \cong \frac{k^2}{2} \left\langle \frac{\partial^2 \varepsilon_{p\mu}}{\partial_p{}^2} \right\rangle = \frac{\hbar^2 k^2}{2m^*} \tag{4-10}$$

where m^* is the average inverse effective mass for the conduction electron in question. The intraband oscillator strength therefore becomes, in the long-wavelength limit,

$$\lim_{k\to 0} f_{o\nu}^{\text{intra}} = \lim_{k\to 0} \frac{2m}{\hbar k^2} \omega_{\nu o}^{\text{intra}} \left| \left(\rho_k^+\right)_{\nu o}^{\text{intra}} \right|^2 = \frac{m}{m^*} \tag{4-11}$$

The interband matrix element may be obtained most simply by taking the Bloch-wave matrix elements of the relation (3-134), which expresses longitudinal current conservation,

$$\omega_{\nu o}\left(\rho_k^+\right)_{\nu o} = \left[\sum_i \left[\left(k\cdot p_i/m\right) + \hbar k^2/2m\right] e^{ik\cdot r_i}\right]_{\nu o} \tag{4-12}$$

One has, in the limit $k \to 0$, a transition from a state pv, say, to a state $p\ell$ in another band; the excitation frequency is

$$\hbar\omega_{\ell v}(p) = \varepsilon_{\ell p} - \varepsilon_{vp} \tag{4-13}$$

The matrix element for the transition is, from (4-12),

$$\lim_{k\to 0} \left(\rho_k^+\right)_{\nu o} = \frac{(k\cdot p)_{\ell v}}{\omega_{\ell v}(p) m} \tag{4-14}$$

The oscillator strength averaged over directions of k is

$$f_{\ell v}(p) = \left\langle \frac{2m}{\hbar k^2} \frac{(k\cdot p)_{\ell v}^2}{\omega_{\ell v}^2 m^2} \omega_{\ell v} \right\rangle = \frac{2}{m} \frac{|(p)_{\ell v}|^2}{\hbar\omega_{\ell v}(p)} \tag{4-15}$$

One novel feature of the f-sum rule, (4-7), is worthy of especial mention. Since one is considering all one-electron states appropriate to the periodic potential, the summation in (4-7) is to be carried out over all transitions possible for the electrons in the band under consideration. It is therefore necessary to consider not only transitions to higher bands but also transitions to lower bands. The latter contribute a negative oscillator strength, since the excitation frequency is negative. Consider, for example, the sum rule for the conduction electrons in a metal, which may be written, according to (4-7) and (4-11),

$$\frac{m}{m^*} = 1 - \frac{1}{N_v}\left\{ \sum_{\substack{\ell > v \\ p}} f_{\ell v}(p) + \sum_{\substack{\ell < v \\ p}} f_{\ell v}(p) \right\} \tag{4-16}$$

where the index v refers to the conduction band. If the oscillator strengths which connect the conduction band to those bands lying above it are larger than those to the bands lying below it, then $(m/m^*) < 1$

and $m^* > m$. On the other hand, when the reverse is true, $m^* < m$. This switch in the role of the interband transitions is seen clearly for the alkali metals (cf. Table 3-5), in which one passes from $m^* \cong 1.45$ m for Li to $m^* \cong 0.83$ m for Cs, as the core electrons play an increasingly important role.

We note, too, that for the valence electrons in a semiconductor or insulator, we may write the "f"-sum rule as

$$\sum_{\ell > v} f_{\ell v} + \sum_{\ell < v} f_{\ell v} = N_v$$

so that

$$\sum_{\ell > v} f_{\ell v} = N_v - \sum_{\ell < v} f_{\ell v} = N_v + \sum_{\ell < v} f_{v\ell} \tag{4-17}$$

In other words the "core" bands act to enhance the oscillator strengths appropriate to transitions from the valence band to higher lying bands.

4-2 MODIFICATION OF $\epsilon(k\omega)$

At long wavelengths it is again very fruitful to describe the effects of electron interaction in terms of the wave-vector and frequency-dependent dielectric constant $\varepsilon(k\omega)$. At shorter wavelengths such a procedure is less useful; because one deals with a *periodic* system, which is *not* translationally invariant, the complete specification of the response to a perturbation wave vector **k** and frequency ω involves not only excitations of momentum **k** but also excitations of momentum $\mathbf{k} + \mathbf{K}_n$, where $\mathbf{K}_n$ is any reciprocal lattice vector. These give rise to *local field* corrections, as Adler[1a] has recently shown in an elegant calculation of the static dielectric constant of an insulator which possesses cubic symmetry. Such corrections are comparatively weak at long wavelengths for metals, semiconductors, and many insulators. We shall neglect them in what follows.

We may calculate $\varepsilon(k\omega)$ in the Hartree-Fock approximation by simply inserting the relevant Bloch wave matrix elements and excitation frequencies in the exact result (3-110). One thus finds

$$\frac{1}{\varepsilon_{HF}(k\omega)} = 1 - 4\pi\alpha_B(k\omega) \tag{4-18}$$

where $4\pi\alpha_B(k\omega)$ is the Bloch-wave free-electron polarizability, defined by

$$4\pi\alpha_B(k\omega) = -\frac{4\pi e^2}{\hbar k^2}\sum_{\mu} \left|\left(\rho_k^+\right)_{\mu o}\right|^2 \left\{\frac{1}{\omega - \omega_{\mu o} + i\delta} - \frac{1}{\omega + \omega_{\mu o} + i\delta}\right\} \tag{4-19}$$

and the matrix elements, $(\rho_k^+)_{\mu o}$, and excitation frequencies, $\omega_{\mu o}$, are those for the Bloch-wave states we have been discussing. Thus in the Hartree-Fock approximation, the energy-loss spectrum is determined by the dynamic form factor:

$$S_{HF}(k\omega) = \sum_{\mu} \left|\left(\rho_k^+\right)_{\mu o}\right|^2 \delta\left(\omega - \omega_{\mu o}\right) \tag{4-20}$$

An incident fast electron will excite intraband and interband single-particle excitations.

One may calculate $\varepsilon(k\omega)$ in the random phase approximation, $\varepsilon_{RPA}(k\omega)$, by a straightforward generalization of any of the techniques discussed previously; we leave the calculation as an exercise for the reader. One finds

$$\varepsilon_{RPA}^{B}(k\omega) = 1 + 4\pi\alpha^{B}(k\omega) \tag{4-21}$$

where $4\pi\alpha^B(k\omega)$ is the Bloch-wave polarizability defined by (4-19). We may write

$$\varepsilon_{RPA}^{B}(k\omega) = \varepsilon_1^B(k\omega) + i\varepsilon_2^B(k\omega) \tag{4-22}$$

where

$$\varepsilon_1^B(k\omega) = 1 - \frac{8\pi e^2}{\hbar k^2} \sum_{\nu} \frac{|(\rho_k^+)_{\nu o}|^2 \omega_{\nu o}}{\omega^2 - \omega_{\nu o}^2} = 1 - \frac{4\pi e^2}{m} \sum_{\nu} \frac{f_{o\nu}}{\omega^2 - \omega_{\nu o}^2} \tag{4-23}$$

and

$$\varepsilon_2^B(k\omega) = \frac{4\pi^2 e^2}{\hbar k^2} \sum_{\nu} (\rho_k^+)_{\nu o}^2 \delta(\omega - \omega_{\nu o}) \tag{4-24}$$

The $f_{o\nu}$ are the Bloch-wave oscillator strengths, defined by (4-6).

In the RPA one finds again the physical phenomena of screening and collective oscillation. Let us consider the screening behavior first. Suppose we deal with an insulator or with the polarizability of the valence electrons in an intrinsic semiconductor near T = 0. Then at long wavelengths and low frequencies, we have

$$\varepsilon_1(k, 0) = 1 + \frac{4\pi e^2}{m} \sum_{\nu} \frac{f_{o\nu}^{\text{inter}}}{\omega_{\nu o}^2} = 1 + 4\pi\alpha_o^v \tag{4-25}$$

since there are no intraband excitations which contribute. Here $4\pi\alpha_o^v$ is the static valence electron polarizability; we can write (4-25) as

$$\varepsilon_1(k0) = \varepsilon_o \cong 1 + \omega_{pv}^2/\bar{\omega}_{\nu o}^2 \tag{4-26}$$

where ω_{pv}^2 is given by

$$\omega_{pv}^2 = \frac{4\pi N_v e^2}{m} \tag{4-27}$$

and where $\left(\omega_{\nu o}^{\bar{2}}\right)^{-1}$ is the mean of the squared inverse interband excitation frequencies. A rough measure of $\left(\omega_{\nu o}^{\bar{2}}\right)$ is $\omega_g{}^2$, where ω_g is the frequency of the dominant electron transition between the valence band and the conduction band. Thus we may write

$$\varepsilon_o \cong 1 + \omega_{pv}^2/\omega_g{}^2 \tag{4-26a}$$

For example, in Si and Ge, $\omega_g \sim 4$ ev, while $\omega_{pv} \sim 16$ ev, whence $\varepsilon_o \sim 17$ for those semiconductors in fair agreement with the experimental values of ~ 12 for Si and ~ 16 for Ge. More detailed calculations, based on a simple model for the interband transitions of these elements, have recently been carried out by Penn.[1b] In the long-wavelength limit he finds only small corrections to the approximate formula, (4-26a). In general, one may expect $\varepsilon_o \gg 1$ for all insulators and semiconductors for which the band gap is small compared to the valence electron plasma frequency, the latter quantity generally being of the order of 15 ev.

For a semiconductor, we must add to (4-25) the contribution from the conduction electrons. Because the number of these is small compared to N_v, the resulting modification in $\varepsilon(k\omega)$ will only be of importance at low frequencies. In the case of a degenerate semiconductor at absolute zero, one may easily show (see Problem 4-2) that

$$\varepsilon_1(k0) = \varepsilon_o + \frac{k_s{}^2}{k^2} \tag{4-28}$$

where

$$k_s{}^2 = \frac{12\pi N_c e^2}{m^* v_o{}^2} \tag{4-29}$$

k_s is the Fermi-Thomas screening wave vector appropriate to the effective mass m^* and density N_c of the conduction electrons, while v_o is the Fermi velocity, k_o/m. At finite temperatures, for a nondegenerate semiconductor, one can likewise show (see Problem 4-3) that

$$\varepsilon_1(k,0) \cong \varepsilon_o\left[1 + \left(k_D^2/k^2\right)\right] \tag{4-30}$$

where

$$k_D^2 = \frac{4\pi N_c e^2}{\varepsilon_o kT} \tag{4-31}$$

Here k_D represents the Debye-Hückel screening wave vector appropriate to a classical plasma (immersed in a medium of dielectric constant ε_o). We note that for semiconductors, $\omega_g^2 << \omega_p^2$, so that $\varepsilon_o >> 1$. We note, too, that in semiconductors the highly mobile free carriers will screen very effectively any static charge distribution.

For a metal in which the conduction band is well separated from the core bands, the static dielectric constant takes the form

$$\varepsilon(k,0) = 1 + \frac{k_s^2}{k^2} + \frac{4\pi e^2}{m} \sum_{\ell > v} \frac{f_{\ell v}^{\text{inter}}}{\omega_{\ell v}^2} \tag{4-32}$$

where k_s^2 is given by an expression of the form (4-29). The screening is altered slightly from that appropriate to the free-electron gas, by the appearance of the effective mass appropriate to the conduction electrons in (4-29) and of a static polarizability associated with the interband transitions. In case core bands are of some importance, one simply adds to (4-32) a contribution

$$4\pi\alpha_o^c = \frac{4\pi e^2}{m} \sum_{\ell > c} \frac{f_{\ell c}}{\omega_{\ell c}^2} \tag{4-33}$$

representing the static polarizability associated with the core electrons.

As the excitation frequency increases, the form which $\varepsilon_1(k\omega)$ and $\varepsilon_2(k\omega)$ take depends very much on the solid in question; it is determined by the interband transitions which are of importance, and the contribution these make is in turn very sensitive to the character of the bands between which transitions take place. We return to this question in more detail presently; here we wish only to point out that if $\omega \lesssim \bar{\omega}$, the average excitation frequency of importance for the solid, one expects a certain amount of screening, while if $\omega \gtrsim \bar{\omega}$, the effect of electron interaction may well be such as to enhance the disturbance in question.

We consider now the high-frequency behavior of $\varepsilon_1(k\omega)$ and $\varepsilon_2(k\omega)$ and the possibility of plasmons existing as a well-defined excitation for electrons in solids.

Suppose we deal with a solid in which there is only one band of importance, the valence electron band. [Examples are metals for which the conduction band is very well separated from the core electron bands, or semiconductors and insulators for which the filled valence band is again far removed in energy from the core electron states.] Suppose further that we deal with a frequency which is large compared to the intraband and interband transitions for which the oscillator strength is appreciable. This condition may easily be achieved at long wavelengths for the intraband transitions (which possess a maximum frequency kv_o); whether it works for the interband transitions depends on the solid in question. Under these circumstances we may expand the second term of (4-23) in powers of $\omega_{\nu o}^2/\omega^2$; we find, on making use of the f-sum rule, (4-7), that

$$\varepsilon_1^B(k\omega) = 1 - \frac{\omega_{pv}^2}{\omega^2} - \frac{4\pi e^2}{m}\sum_\nu \frac{f_{o\nu}^B \omega_{\nu o}^2}{\omega^4} \tag{4-34}$$

$$\varepsilon_2^B(k\omega) = \frac{2\pi^2 e^2}{m} \sum_{\ell > v} \frac{f_{\ell v}^{inter}}{\omega_{\ell v}(k)} \delta[\omega - \omega_{\ell v}(k)] \tag{4-35}$$

Under the assumptions we have made the third term in (4-34) is small compared to the second; further $\varepsilon_2 \ll 1$, since we have argued that we deal with a frequency for which the interband transitions possess a comparatively weak oscillator strength.

Let us assume that the plasmon energy is such that the expressions (4-34) and (4-35) apply. We can then write for the plasmon dispersion relation

$$\varepsilon_1(k, \omega_k) + i\varepsilon_2(k, \omega_k) = 0 \tag{4-36}$$

where ω_k is the complex plasmon energy

$$\omega_k = \omega_1 + i\omega_2 \tag{4-37}$$

Since $\varepsilon_2(k, \omega_1) \ll 1$, we can, on making use of (4-34), (4-35), (4-36) and (4-37), obtain the two equations

$$\varepsilon_1(k, \omega) = 1 - \frac{\omega_{pv}^2}{\omega_1^2} - \frac{4\pi e^2}{m}\sum_\nu \frac{f_{o\nu}\omega_{\nu o}^2}{\omega_1^4} = 0 \tag{4-38}$$

and

$$\left(\frac{\partial \varepsilon_1}{\partial \omega}\right)_{\omega=\omega_1} \omega_2 = -\varepsilon_2(k, \omega_1) \tag{4-39}$$

The solution of these equations is then given by

$$\omega_1{}^2 = \omega_{pv}^2 + \frac{4\pi e^2}{m} \sum_{\nu} \frac{f_{o\nu}\omega_{o\nu}^2}{\omega_p{}^2} \tag{4-40}$$

and

$$\omega_2/\omega_1 = -\varepsilon_2(k, \omega_1)/2 \tag{4-41}$$

As Mott[2] first pointed out, the expansions, (4-38) and (4-39), are justified for many solids because plasmon energies (10 to 20 ev) are really quite large compared to energies characteristic of interband transitions ($\lesssim$ 5 ev, say). To put it another way, the electrons oscillating at the plasma frequency move so quickly that the periodic field of the ion cores plays essentially no role. Thus it is the free-electron mass (and not m^*) which enters into the plasma frequencies of (4-38) and (4-40). Still, the plasmon dispersion relations, (4-40) and (4-41), differ in three important ways from their free-electron counterparts:

1. Because of the interband transitions, ω_1 does not in general go to ω_p in the limit of $k \to 0$.

2. There is no reason to expect the k^2 term in the dispersion relation to be the same as that observed for a free-electron gas.

3. Again, because of the interband transitions, even in the RPA the plasmons will decay; thus we expect in general a nonvanishing value of ω_2, according to (4-41).

A sketch of the general features of the expected density-fluctuation excitation spectrum for a simple valence electron solid (as calculated in the RPA) is given in Fig. 4-1. We see there the screening of the intraband and low-frequency interband transitions, the appearance of the plasmon mode, and the "antiscreening" of a high-frequency interband transition.

A case of interest [and for which $\varepsilon(k\omega)$ may take a simple form] is that in which there are only two bands of importance, a valence band and a simple filled core electron band, let us say. Let us further suppose that the frequency of interest is such that

$$\omega_{\ell v}^2 << \omega^2 << \omega_{\ell c}^2 \tag{4-42}$$

for the oscillator strengths of importance. This means that we are working with frequencies which are large compared to the valence electron transitions of interest (either intraband, where they exist, or interband), yet less than the frequency required to excite a core electron interband transition which possesses an appreciable oscillator strength. This is, as we shall see, a well-defined region for a number of metals, semiconductors, and insulators. We can then write

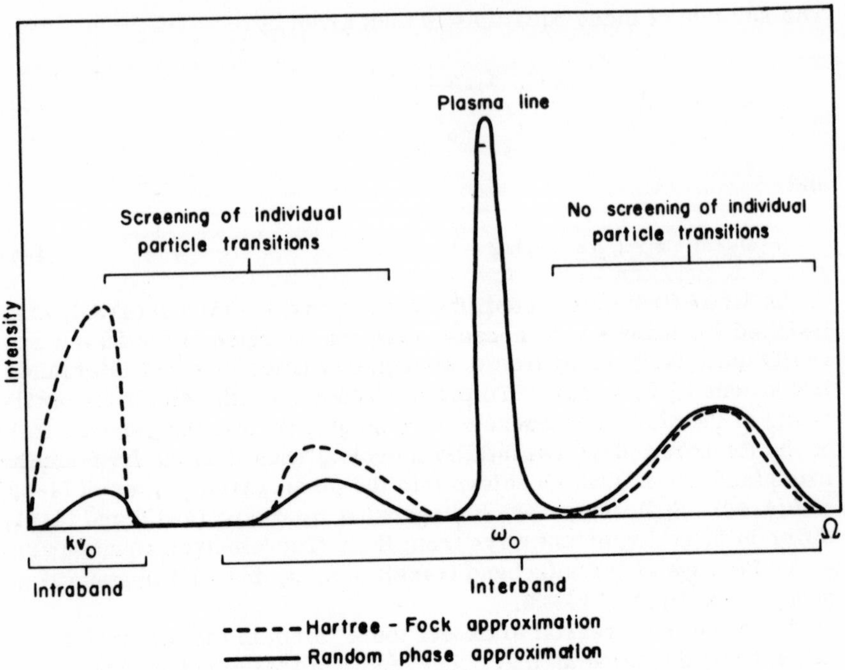

Fig. 4-1. A schematic representation of the expected density-fluctuation excitation spectrum for a nontransition metal, as calculated in the Hartree-Fock approximation and in the RPA. (From Nozières and Pines.[9])

$$\lim_{k \to 0} \varepsilon_1(k, \omega) = 1 - \frac{4\pi N_v e^2}{m^* \omega^2} - \frac{4\pi e^2}{m} \sum_{\ell > v} \frac{f_{\ell v}}{\omega^2} - \frac{4\pi e^2}{m} \times \sum_{\ell > v} f_{\ell \nu} \frac{\omega_{\ell \nu}^2}{\omega^4} + 4\pi\alpha_o^c \tag{4-43a}$$

$$\lim_{k \to 0} \varepsilon_2(k, \omega) = \frac{4\pi^2 e^2}{\hbar k^2} \sum_{\ell > v} \frac{f_{\ell v}}{\omega_{\ell v}} \delta(\omega - \omega_{\ell v}) + \sum_{\ell > c} \frac{f_{\ell c}}{\omega_{\ell c}} \delta(\omega - \omega_{\ell c}) \tag{4-43b}$$

where again we have chosen ω such that $\varepsilon_2(k\omega) << 1$.

In (4-43a) the first term in the polarizability comes from the valence electron intraband transitions, the next two from their interband transitions, while the last represents the static polarizability due to the core electrons.

We now make use of the sum rule (4-17), which takes the form

$$N_v \frac{m}{m^*} + \sum_{\substack{\ell > v \\ p}} f_{\ell v}(p) = \left(1 + \sum_p f_{vc}(p)\right) N_v = \tilde{N}_v$$

and which accounts for the enhancement of the valence-band oscillator strengths by the core electrons. We therefore write

$$\lim_{k \to 0} \varepsilon_1(k, \omega) = 1 - \frac{\tilde{\omega}_{pv}^2}{\omega^2} + 4\pi\alpha_o^c - \frac{4\pi e^2}{m} \sum_{\ell > v} \frac{f_{\ell v}\,\omega_{\ell v}^2}{\omega^4} \tag{4-44}$$

In this approximation, then, the core band acts to increase the plasmon energy via $\tilde{N}_v$, and decrease it through $4\pi\alpha_o^c$, in such a way that the plasmon energy is shifted to

$$\omega_k^2 \cong \frac{\tilde{\omega}_{pv}^2 + \dfrac{4\pi e^2}{m} \displaystyle\sum_{\ell > v} \dfrac{f_{\ell v}\,\omega_{\ell v}^2}{\omega^4}}{1 + 4\pi\alpha_o^c} \tag{4-45}$$

Where the condition (4-42) is not satisfied, the plasmon dispersion relation depends quite sensitively on the position and strength of the interband transitions of importance. A rather general discussion, in which it is assumed that there is only *one* interband transition of importance, has been given by Wilson.[2a] The possibilities found for plasmon behavior are many and varied, so that rather detailed experiments are required to disentangle the situation. We shall consider an example of such disentanglement in Sec. 4-5. Here we content ourselves with the remark that a class of solids for which interband effects are surely important in determining plasmon behavior are the transition metals and those lying just beyond them.

As a final example we consider the plasma oscillations appropriate to the conduction electrons in a semiconductor. Consider first a degenerate semiconductor at absolute zero; in the limit in which $kv_o \ll \omega \ll \omega_{\ell v}$, where v_o is the velocity of a conduction electron at the top of the Fermi distribution and $\omega_{\ell v}$ is an interband frequency of importance, one has

$$\lim_{k \to 0} \varepsilon_1(k, \omega) \cong 1 - \frac{4\pi N^* e^2}{m^* \omega^2} + 4\pi\alpha_o^v \tag{4-46}$$

Here N^* is the number of conduction electrons, and m^* their effective mass (we have assumed isotropy once more). The second term on the right-hand side of (4-46) represents the polarizability of the conduction electrons. The effective mass, m^*, appears because we have assumed that *only* intraband excitations contribute. The third term on the right-hand side of (4-46) represents the static polarizability of the valence electrons. The long-wavelength plasma oscillations are therefore found at a frequency

$$\omega_k = \left(\frac{4\pi N^* e^2}{m^* \varepsilon_o}\right)^{1/2} \tag{4-47}$$

a result one might have easily anticipated for electrons of mass m^* interacting in a dielectric medium of dielectric constant

$$\varepsilon_o = 1 + 4\pi\alpha_o^v$$

The plasma dispersion relation at finite temperatures is obtained by a simple generalization of the expression (3-163); one replaces the occupation numbers $n_{p\sigma}$ appropriate to the zero-temperature plasma by the occupation numbers, $f_{p\sigma}$, appropriate to an electron gas at finite temperatures;

$$f_{p\sigma} = \frac{1}{e^{\beta(\varepsilon(p)-\mu)} + 1} \tag{4-48}$$

where $\beta = 1/kT$, and $\varepsilon(p)$ and μ are the single-particle energy and chemical potential for a free-electron gas. The generalization is straightforward because the RPA is essentially an *operator* approximation; as is clear from the derivation of (3-163) and (3-166), one inserts the single-particle occupation numbers only at the end of the calculation. If one now passes to the classical limit, with the aid of the relations,

$$\begin{gathered} \frac{\hbar k}{m} \to v \qquad f_p \to f(v) \\ f_{p+k} \to f(v + \hbar k/m) = f(v) + \frac{\hbar}{m} k \cdot \nabla_v f(v) \end{gathered} \tag{4-49}$$

one finds in place of (3-153), the result

$$\varepsilon(k, \omega) = 1 + \frac{4\pi e^2}{mk^2} \int d^3v \, \frac{k \cdot \nabla_v f(v)}{\omega - k \cdot v + i\delta} \tag{4-50}$$

where f(v) is the Maxwellian velocity distribution appropriate to the temperature T. For the conduction electrons in a semiconductor, (4-50) is replaced by

$$\varepsilon(k, \omega) = \varepsilon_o + \frac{4\pi e^2}{m^* k^2} \int d^3v \, \frac{k \cdot \nabla_v f(v)}{\omega - k \cdot v + i\delta} \tag{4-51}$$

In the long-wavelength limit, $\varepsilon_1(k\omega)$ as determined from (4-51) is identical to (4-46); effects of finite temperature show up only in the k^2 term in the conduction electron polarizability. However, in contrast to the T = 0 case, there is now a nonvanishing value of ε_2, viz.,

$$\varepsilon_2(k, \omega) = \frac{4\pi^2 e^2}{mk^2} \int d^3v \; k \cdot \nabla_v f(v) \delta(\omega - k \cdot v) \tag{4-52}$$

From this one finds the plasma waves are damped; their frequency is $\omega_1 - i\omega_2$, where ω_1 is given by (4-47) and ω_2 is given by

$$\frac{\omega_2}{\omega_1} = + \frac{2\pi^2 e^2}{m^* k^2} \int d^3v \; k \cdot \nabla_v f(v) \delta(\omega - k \cdot v) \tag{4-53}$$

This damping, the famous Landau damping of classical plasma physics, is directly traceable to the (very slight) overlap of the single-particle excitation spectrum and the plasma spectrum because there always exist electrons in the tail of the Boltzmann distribution which are capable of absorping a plasmon with conservation of energy and momentum. In classical language, one attributes the damping to electrons which move at the phase velocity of the wave, and therefore can absorb energy from it. For a long-wavelength plasma wave the number of such electrons is exponentially small, so that the corresponding Landau damping is unimportant (see Problem 4-3).

There are many indications that solid-state "classical" plasmas (for which the electrons obey classical statistics) may play an important role as a convenient laboratory for studying oscillations and instabilities in classical plasmas. Plasmas which appear particularly promising for this purpose are the electron-hole plasma of InSb, and the other III-V compounds. We refer the reader interested in the various collective phenomena observed or observable in classical solid-state plasmas to some of the papers listed under Ref. 3.

4-3 EXPERIMENTAL OBSERVATION OF PLASMONS IN SOLIDS: CHARACTERISTIC ENERGY-LOSS EXPERIMENTS

The principal experimental evidence for the existence of plasmons as a well-defined excitation mode of the valence electrons in solids comes from characteristic energy-loss experiments.[4] In such experiments, one observes the energy spectrum of kilovolt electrons either as they emerge from a thin solid film,[5] or after they are reflected from a solid surface.[6] Usually one measures the energy transfer to the electrons in the solid, with no attempt at resolving the angular distribution of the inelastically scattered electrons. The results of some typical transmission experiments are shown in Fig. 4-2; one sees that some solids show a series of narrow loss lines, while others show only a single broad loss. The magnitude of the losses ranges from about 5 to 30 ev. If one measures, as well, the angular distribution of the inelastically scattered electrons, one effectively measures both the energy and momentum transfer to the electrons in the solid. A plot of the results of such an experiment[7] for Al is given in Fig. 4-3; it corresponds to a measurement not only of the position of the loss line, but also its variation with angle, and the angle (or momentum transfer) beyond which the mechanism ceases to be effective.

In the first theoretical work on plasmon excitation, the equation-of-motion technique described in the last chapter was used.[6a] However, in our present discussion we shall make use of the general theoretical framework for the interpretation of such experiments, which we have developed in this and the preceding chapters. In Refs. 7, 8, and 9, and in the references cited therein, further theoretical details may be found. We have seen that, under circumstances that the Born approximation applies, when one measures the angular distribution of the inelastically scattered electrons, one measures directly the dynamic form factor, $S(k\omega)$, or what is equivalent, Im $\{1/\varepsilon(k\omega)\}$, for the electrons in the solid. A sketch of the expected behavior of $S_{RPA}(k\omega)$ for a simple valence electron solid was given in Fig. 4-1. For such a solid we should therefore expect to see plasmon excitation (or plural plasmon excitation for a sufficiently thick film), and, perhaps, some interband transitions, depending on their oscillator strengths. The continuum of intraband transitions is too broad, and too strongly screened, to be visible at the low momentum transfers at which the experiments are generally carried out.

In the present section we shall concentrate on the mechanism of plasmon excitation, and the information one can obtain concerning it from characteristic energy-loss experiments. Our reason for doing so is that, for the reasons we have already given, plasmons with an energy near $\hbar\omega_{pv}$ represent a quite general elementary excitation of solid-state systems; indeed plasmon excitation dominates the low-momentum transfer characteristic energy-loss spectrum of most

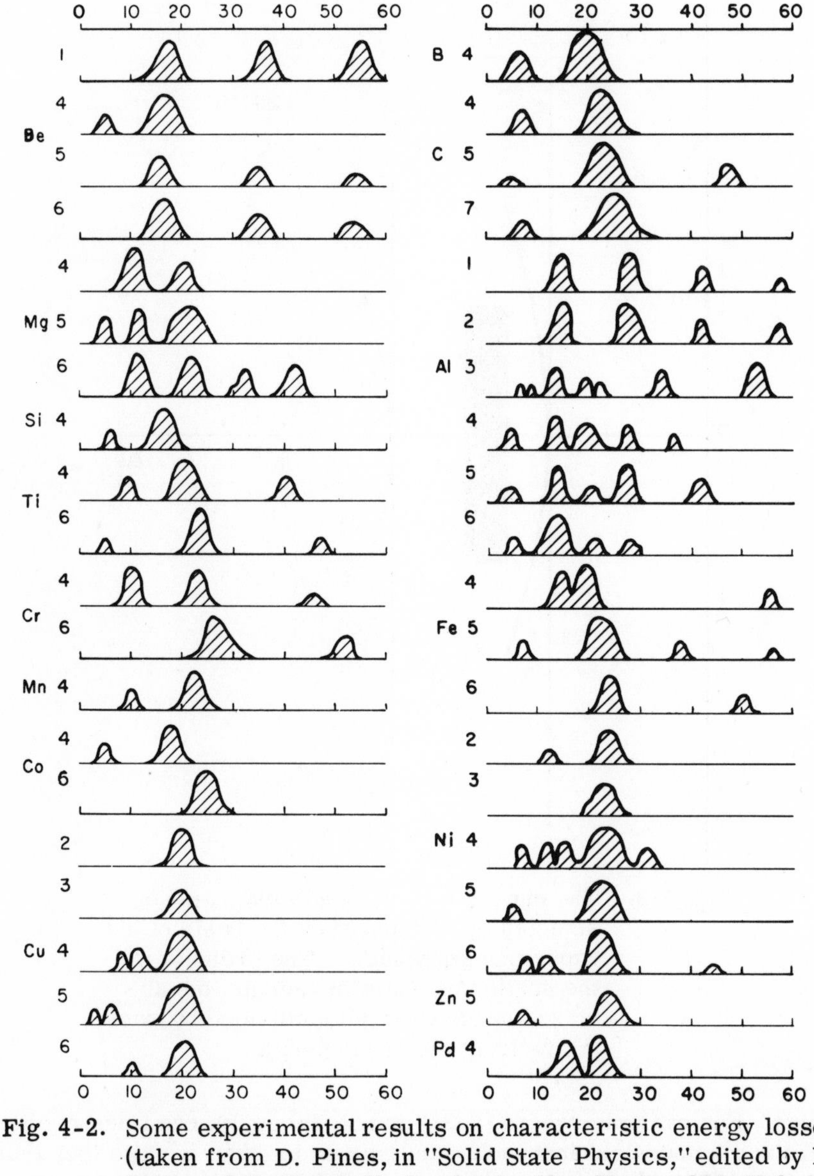

Fig. 4-2. Some experimental results on characteristic energy losses (taken from D. Pines, in "Solid State Physics," edited by F. Seitz and D. Turnbull, Academic, New York, 1955, Vol. 1, p. 432). The code numbers refer to the work of the following investigators: (1) Ruthemann[5]; (2) W. Lang[5]; (3) G. Mollenstedt, *Optik,* 5, 499 (1949); (4) L. Marton and L. B. Leder, *Phys. Rev.,* 94, 203 (1954); (5) W. Kleinn, *Optik,* 11, 226 (1954); (6) H. Watanabe, *J. Phys. Soc. Japan,* 8, 1035 (1954); (7) D. Gabor and W. Jull, *Nature,* 175, 718 (1955).

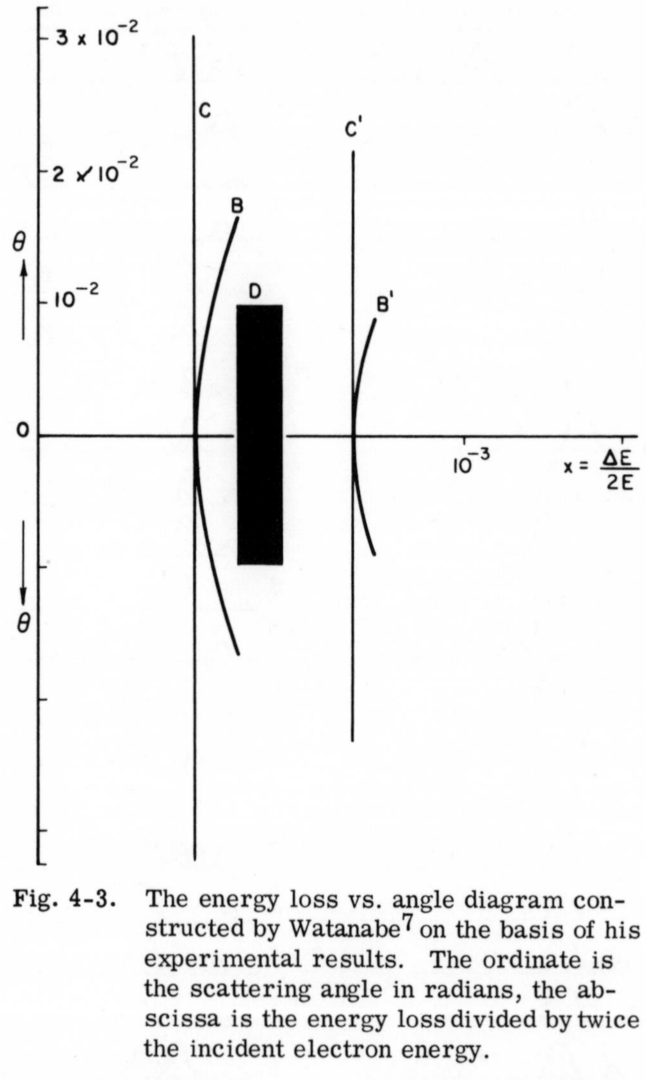

Fig. 4-3. The energy loss vs. angle diagram constructed by Watanabe[7] on the basis of his experimental results. The ordinate is the scattering angle in radians, the abscissa is the energy loss divided by twice the incident electron energy.

solids. For example, where (4-38) and (4-39) apply, one finds readily that the plasmons exhaust the f-sum rule up to order k^4/k_F^4; they thus represent the only long-wavelength longitudinal excitation of importance. Interband excitations, on the other hand, may or may not be resolvable; they represent, as well, a particular property of the solid in question. It should be remembered, however, that in general if one measures only rather low energy losses ($\lesssim$ 3 ev, say), one would see only interband excitations. Moreover there will always be interband excitations from the bands lying below the valence electron band to the unoccupied higher-band states. Such transitions (~ 30 to ~ 50 ev, say) are not much affected when free atoms are brought together to make a solid, since changes in atomic-energy levels upon forming a solid are small compared to 30 ev. These high-energy "interband" transitions are often referred to as ionization losses.

In a transmission experiment, one can in principle obtain the following information about plasmons and their excitation mechanism:

1. Plasmon energy.
2. Plasmon lifetime.
3. Plasmon dispersion: the explicit dependence of ω_1 on k.
4. The maximum wave vector, k_c, for which the plasmon continues to be a well-defined excitation.
5. Mean free path (or what is equivalent, cross section) for plasmon production.

We consider first the measurements of the plasmon energy and lifetime since these offer a check on whether the general theoretical considerations we have put forth are consistent with experiment. We might summarize the theoretical considerations as follows:

1. The RPA offers a good qualitative account of the density-fluctuation excitation spectrum.
2. A large group of metals, semiconductors, and insulators are simple valence solids, in the sense that the oscillator strength for transitions in the vicinity of ω_{pv} are weak; for such solids one expects to see narrow loss lines, at energy quite close to ω_{pv}.
3. For the transition metals, and those immediately beyond them, the interband transitions from the d band to higher bands act to shift and broaden the plasmons composed of s and p electrons; for such metals one therefore expects to see broad loss lines, shifted appreciably from ω_{pv} (where N_v is the density of valence electrons outside the d band).

In the interpretation of the experimental results on characteristic energy losses, the first problem is to decide which of the observed losses is to be interpreted as the plasmon loss. In a survey of a few years ago, the following criteria were used[8]:

1. Where a solid has been investigated in several different experiments, we consider only those loss lines that have been found by all observers.
2. Either the loss appears through a series of equally spaced lines, or only one broad line is found under circumstances that would have precluded observing the multiple losses.
3. In cases where the relative intensity of the different loss lines is given, the plasmon lines are identified with the most prominent lines in the spectrum. Such criteria were necessary because there was a fair amount of variation in the losses reported by different observers; the criteria proved, on the whole, quite successful in identifying the plasma losses. Today, moreover, thanks to the work of Swan

and his collaborators at the University of Western Australia, an unambiguous identification of plasmon losses is possible for a large number of solids. Before going on to a consideration of plasmon energies and lifetimes, let us consider the work of Swan et al.[11-17]

In this work, primary electrons of 1500 and 800 ev are reflected from clean target surfaces deposited *in situ* immediately prior to, or during, analysis. The entire apparatus is located in a vacuum chamber, with pressures ranging from 10^{-5} to 10^{-6} mm Hg. Using it, Swan and Powell[11] were able to show, first, the existence of "surface" plasmons as well as "volume" plasmons in solids, and second, to identify unambiguously the loss spectrum characteristic of the solid in question—as distinct from the losses resulting from sample oxidation and contamination.

Surface plasmons were first proposed by Ritchie,[18] who showed, with the aid of a dielectric theory of the energy-loss act, that for a thin film of a free-electron gas there is a plasmon loss at $\omega_p/\sqrt{2}$ as well as at ω_p. The modification in plasmon energy arises from depolarizing effects associated with certain of the plasmon modes. A simple physical explanation of the new loss as one due to a "surface" wave of charge bound at a vacuum-plasma interface has been given by Stern and Ferrell.[19] Ferrell and Stern show that the surface-plasmon dispersion relation, for a plasma with dielectric constant ε_A, bounded by a dielectric medium, of dielectric constant ε_B, is

$$\varepsilon_A + \varepsilon_B = 0 \tag{4-54}$$

Hence, if

$$\varepsilon_A \cong 1 - \omega_p{}^2/\omega^2$$

and $\varepsilon_B \cong$ const for the frequencies in question, one has

$$\omega_s \cong \omega_p/(1 + \varepsilon_B)^{1/2} \tag{4-55}$$

Powell and Swan[11] studied the reflection of electrons from newly evaporated films of Al and Mg during the quite short time (of the order of minutes for a vacuum of 10^{-5} mm Hg) required for the formation of an oxide layer. Some of their results are summarized in Table 4-1 and Fig. (4-4).

The measurements show that initially one observes both a volume loss at ω_p and a surface loss at $\omega_p/\sqrt{2}$, characteristic of a vacuum-plasma interface. Then, as the surface oxidizes, the intensity of the loss at $\omega_p/\sqrt{2}$ decreases and a new "modified" loss, characteristic of the oxide-plasma interface, appears. Eventually one sees only the energy loss characteristic of the oxide.

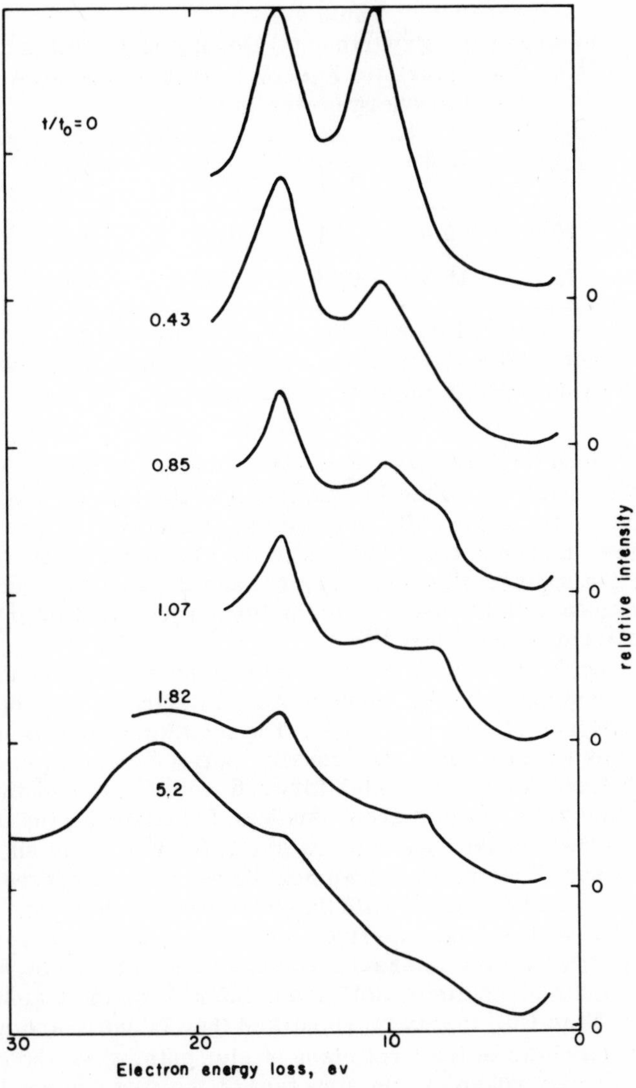

Fig. 4-4. Portions of the characteristic energy-loss spectra of aluminum in progressive stages of oxidation, from the work of Powell and Swan.[11] The number opposite each curve is the average value of t/t_0, where t is the elapsed time after evaporation of aluminum and t_0 is the time in which the measured intensity of the volume plasmon loss decreases to half its initial value.

Table 4-1
A Summary of the Experimental Results of Powell and Swan[11] on Characteristic Energy Losses in Mg and Al (all energies are in ev)

Element	$\hbar\omega_{pv}$	E_V[a]	E_s[a]	$E_V/\Delta E_s$	E_{mod}[a]	ε
Mg	10.9	10.6	7.1	1.49	4.9	1.91
Al	15.9	15.3	10.3	1.48	7.1	1.91

[a]E_V is the loss identified with the volume plasmon; E_s, with the surface plasmon; and E_{mod}, with the modified surface plasmon appropriate to an oxide layer of dielectric constant ε.

Thus by doing reflection experiments with clean surfaces, it is possible to be confident of the identification of the loss as a volume loss characteristic of the solid in question. Moreover, where there are important interband contributions to the plasmon energy, a measurement of the surface plasmon energies, and those of the modified surface plasmons, yields useful information on just what interband transitions are of importance.[10]

In analyzing the reflection experiments on some 33 elements which have been investigated by the Western Australia group, one finds essentially two kinds of loss spectra.[16] The first kind exhibits narrow lines associated with volume and, usually, surface plasmon excitations. Such spectra permit straightforward identification of the volume plasmon losses. In this group one has, for example, the determination by Robins[16] of the loss spectra of Ga, In, and Tl, as shown in Fig. 4-5. In such spectra the agreement between the observed volume-plasmon energy and $\hbar\omega_{pv}$, the calculated free-electron value, is excellent. In the second kind, one finds broad lines, which possess not infrequently considerable internal structure. As an example, we present in Fig. 4-6 the results of Robins and Swan[13] for the transition metals from Ti to Cu. It may be remarked that Ti and V are more nearly characteristic of the first class of elements, while the elements from Cr on display considerable structure of the sort one would expect to be characteristic of interband excitations associated with the d-band electrons in these metals. In this second group of elements, identification of the volume-plasmon lines is less obvious. If, with Robins and Swan, we identify the most prominent loss line as the volume-plasmon loss, we find no direct correlation between the plasmon energy and $\hbar\omega_{pv}$, whether the latter is calculated for s (and p) valence electrons, or these together with the d-shell electrons.

In Table 4-2 we present, for elements of the first group (with narrow loss lines), a comparison of the observed volume-plasmon energy

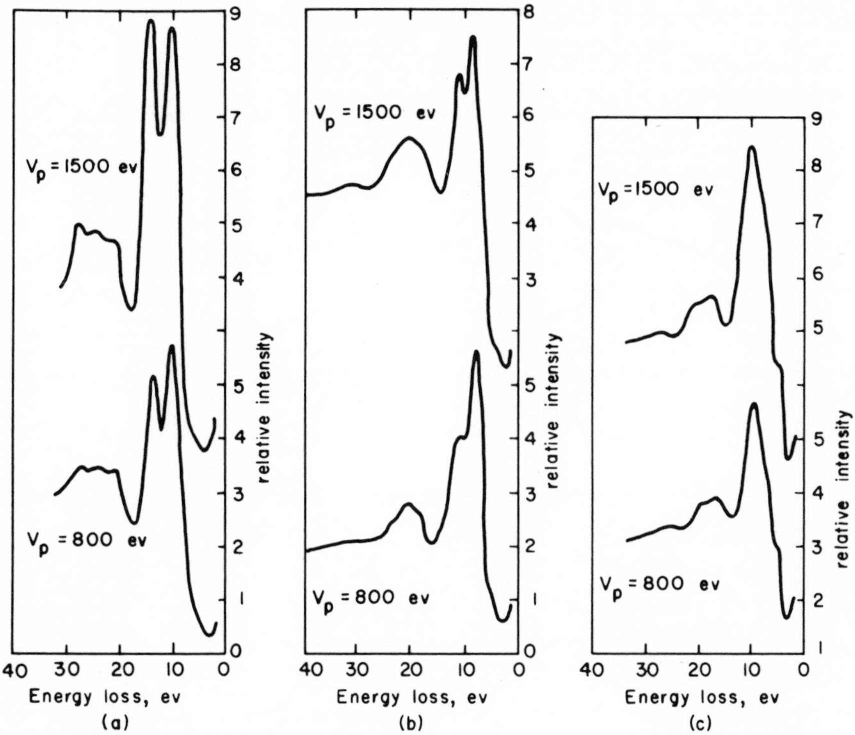

Fig. 4-5. Characteristic energy-loss spectra for primary electron energies of 1500 and 800 ev (from J. L. Robins[14]): (a) gallium; (b) indium; (c) thallium.

and $\hbar\omega_{pv}$. The latter quantity is calculated on the basis of the indicated number of valence electrons per atom. We have used only two significant figures, since the observed losses represent, in fact, the energy loss averaged over the momenta for which it exists as a well-defined excitation. For in such experiments, the incident electron may suffer a Bragg reflection (with no energy loss) either before or after the energy loss, so that a knowledge of the angle at which the electron emerges provides no information about the momentum of the plasmon involved. Hence such experiments resemble the transmission experiments in which one measures only the energy of the emerging electron; they yield a plasmon energy somewhat greater than the long-wavelength limit. The agreement between ΔE and $\hbar\omega_{pv}$ is seen to be remarkably good.

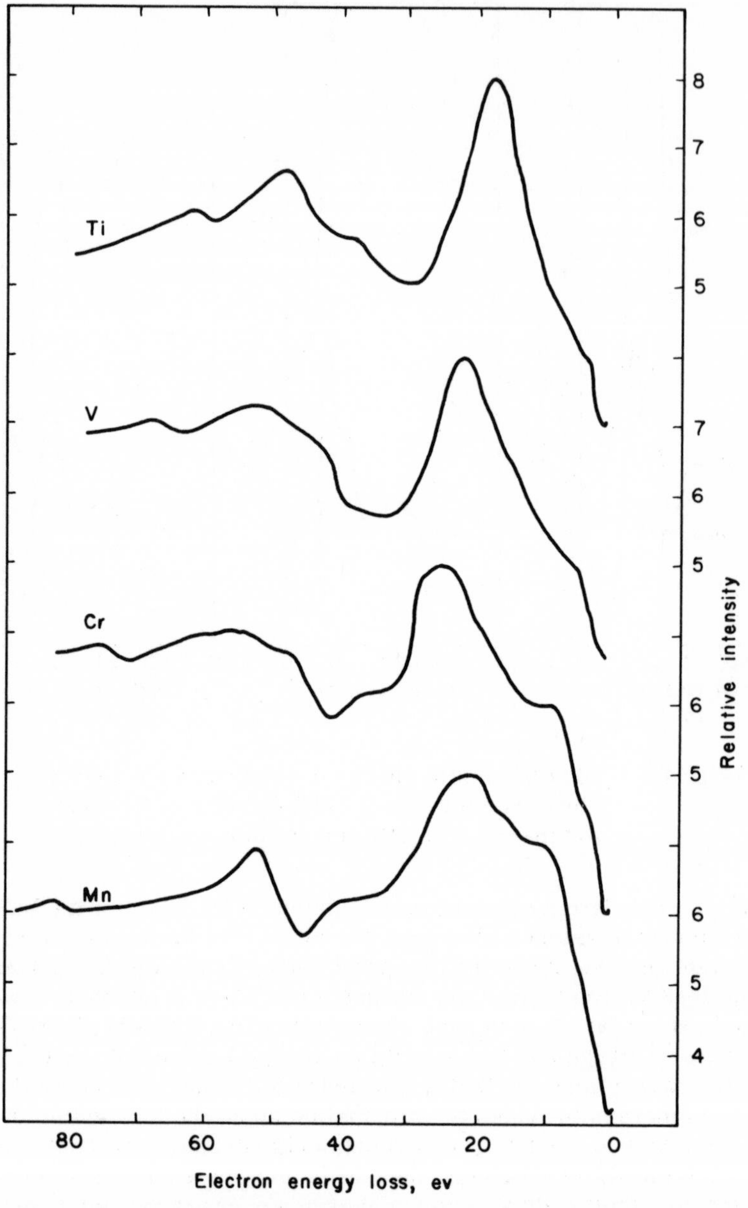

Fig. 4-6. Characteristic energy-loss spectra for the transition metals, from J. L. Robins and J. B. Swan.[13]

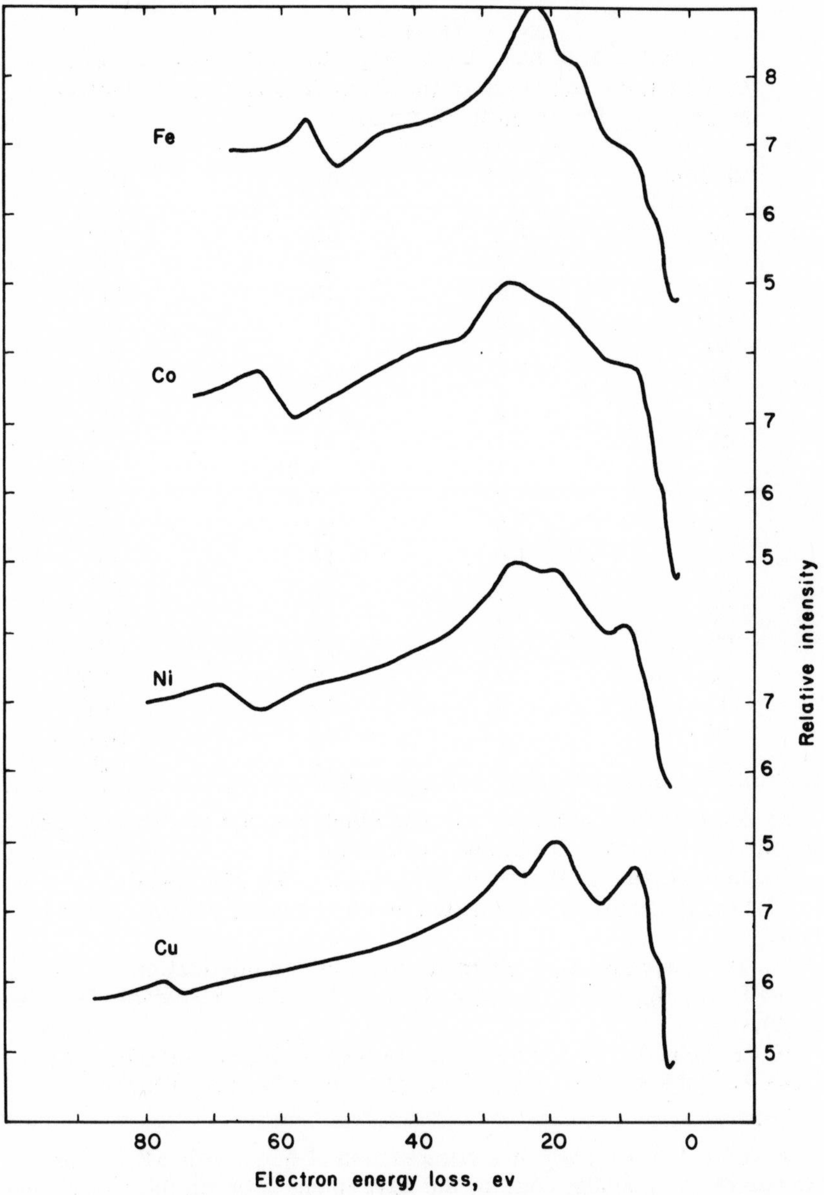

Fig. 4-6. Characteristic energy-loss spectra for the transition metals, from J. L. Robins and J. B. Swan[13]—Continued.

Table 4-2
A Comparison of $\hbar\omega_{pv}$ with ΔE_{obs} for a Number of Solids for Which the Influence of the Periodic Ion-Core Potential on ΔE_{obs} Is Expected to Be Small

Element	Z[a]	$\hbar\omega_{pv}$	ΔE_{obs}
Be	2	19	19[b]
B	3	24	19[b]
C_1[c]	4	19	20[d]
C_2[c]	4	25	25[d]
Na	1	5	5.9[e]
Mg	2	11	11[f]
Al	3	16	15[c]
Si	4	17	17[c]
K	1	3.9	3.9[e]
Ca	2	8.0	8.8[e]
Ga	3	14	14[g]
Ge	4	16	16[g]
In	3	13	11[g]
Sn	4	14	14[g]
Sb	5	15	16[g]
Ba	2	6.5	6.5[e]
Tl	3	12	9.6[e]
Pb	4	14	14[g]
Bi	5	14	15[g]

[a]Z denotes the number of valence electrons per atom which are assumed to take part in plasma oscillation.

[b]L. Marton and L. B. Leder, *Phys. Rev.*, 94, 203 (1954).

[c]C_1 and C_2 refer to evaporated and amorphous carbon, respectively.

[d]L. B. Leder and J. C. Suddeth, private communication.

[e]J. L. Robins and P. E. Best, *Proc. Phys. Soc. (London)*, 79, 110 (1962).

[f]C. J. Powell, *Proc. Phys. Soc. (London)*, 76, 593 (1960).

[g]J. L. Robins, *Proc. Phys. Soc. (London)*, 79, 119 (1962).

In Table 4-3 we present a comparison of $\hbar\omega_{pv}$ with ΔE_{obs} for a number of compounds. Again, the agreement between the two values is remarkably good. Indeed, as has been remarked already some time ago,[8] what puzzles exist have to do with why the agreement is so good, rather than with explaining existing disagreements.

On the other hand, for those metals in which one expects interband transitions to play an important role, the observed structure shows that such transitions are present; moreover, while detailed analysis is required to decide what may or may not be a plasmon loss, it is clear that the loss lines in question are all broad, and that no simple correlation exists, in general, between ΔE_{obs} and $\hbar\omega_{pv}$ for such solids. The solids in question include Cr, Mn, Fe, Co, Ni, Cu, Zn, Zr, Pd, Ag, Cd, Pt, and Au.

Table 4-3
A Comparison of $h\omega_{pv}$ with ΔE_{obs} for a Number of Compounds[a]

Compound	Z^a	$\hbar\omega_{pv}$	ΔE_{obs}
ZnS	4	17	17[b]
PbS	5	16	15[b]
SbS_3	5.6	18	19[b]
MoS_2	6	23	21[c]
PbTe	5	14	15[b]
PbSe	5	15	15[b]
Mica	4.7	24	25[d]
BeO	4	29	29[c]
MgO	4	25	25[c]
Li_2CO_3	4	24	24[c]
$Ca(OH)_2$	3.2	21	22[c]
MoO_3	6	24	25[c]
SiO_2	5.3	25	25[c]
Al_2O_3	4.8	27	25[c]
TeO_2	6	23	23[c]
SnO_2	4	26	18[b]
KBr	4	13	20[c]
KlC	4	14	13[b]
NaCl	4	16	16[b]

[a]Z denotes the average number of valence electrons per atom we assume to take part in plasma oscillation.

[b]L. Marton and L. B. Leder, *Phys. Rev.*, 94, 203 (1954).

[c]H. Watanabe, *J. Phys. Soc. Japan*, 9, 1035 (1954).

[d]G. Möllenstedt, *Optik*, 5, 499 (1949).

Detailed information on the plasma frequency in the alkali metals, some noble metals, and a number of semiconducting intermetallic compounds, has been obtained from optical experiments, and we consider that in Sec. 4-5.

We now consider the experiments of Watanabe[7] on the angular variation of the characteristic energy losses. The angular distribution of particles which have excited a plasmon is determined by applying conservation of momentum and energy to the plasmon excitation act. The transfer of energy ΔE and momentum $\hbar k$ are such that

$$\Delta E(k) \cong \hbar\omega_p \left(1 + \frac{3}{5}\,\frac{\hbar^2 k^2 k_o^2}{m^2 \omega_p^2} + \cdots\right) \qquad (4\text{-}56)$$

For a fast incident particle of momentum P_o

$$\hbar k \cong P_o \theta \qquad (4\text{-}57)$$

where θ is the angle by which the particle is scattered in exciting a plasmon of energy ΔE (compare Fig. 3-14). Hence the relation between energy transfer and scattering angle is parabolic,

$$\Delta E(\theta) \cong \hbar\omega_p + \frac{P_o^2}{m}\left(\frac{3}{5}\,\frac{\hbar k_o^2}{m\omega_p}\right)\theta^2 + \cdots \qquad (4\text{-}58)$$

In Table 4-4[10] we give a summary of the experimental results[7] for the coefficient of the θ^2 term (in terms of α such that $\omega = \omega_p + \alpha\hbar k^2/m$), together with the theoretical free-electron results [including the exchange correction of (3-93)]. The agreement is good but cannot be regarded as significant in the absence of knowledge of the influence of the periodic ion cores on the angular distribution.

Table 4-4

Element	α_{exp}	α_{free}
Be	0.42 ± 0.04	0.41
Mg	0.62 ± 0.04	0.37
Al	0.50 ± 0.05	0.40

From the maximum energy loss observed in a pattern like B in Fig. 4-3, one can infer a maximum wave vector k_c beyond which the plasmon does not exist as a well-defined elementary excitation. Here, in addition to a similar problem related to the influence of the periodic ion core, there is the further difficulty that it is for these wave vectors that the RPA and the corrections to it previously discussed are likely to be least accurate. In view of these facts, the agreement between the experimental result of 15 to 18 milliradians observed with 25-kev electrons on Al, and the theoretical estimates of 16 milliradians[20] based on (3-85), appears satisfactory.

Finally we mention that it is quite straightforward to calculate the cross section for plasmon production by a fast electron moving through a simple valence solid. One finds[21,8] that the mean free path λ, for production of a plasmon of energy $\hbar\omega_{pv}$, is given by

$$\lambda = 2a_o \frac{E_o}{\hbar\omega_{pv}} \frac{1}{\ln k_c P_o/m\omega_{pv}}$$

where P_o and E_o are the momentum and energy of the incident fast electron. For the excitation of a 15-ev plasmon in Al by a 10-kev electron one finds a mean free path of ~ 250 A. The probability of two plasmon production is negligible; what one expects for a thick foil is plural production, that is, repetition of a single plasmon production act. Blackstock, Ritchie, and Birkhoff[22] have carried out a careful investigation of plasmon excitation as a function of foil thickness and bombardment energy and find satisfactory agreement between theory and experiment for Al.

4-4 OPTICAL PROPERTIES OF SOLIDS

General Considerations

Let us turn now to the case of a transverse probe of the excitation spectrum of electrons in solids, namely the coupling of the electrons to the electromagnetic field. Just as $\varepsilon(k\omega)$ describes the response of the electron gas to a time-varying longitudinal field, so also can we introduce a transverse dielectric constant, $\varepsilon_\perp(k\omega)$, to describe the system response to an external electromagnetic field. Maxwell's equations in the presence of matter read

$$\nabla \times H = \frac{1}{c}\frac{\partial D}{\partial t} = \frac{1}{c}\frac{\partial E}{\partial t} + \frac{4\pi J}{c} \tag{4-59}$$

$$\nabla \times E = -\frac{1}{c}\frac{\partial H}{\partial t} \tag{4-60}$$

where J is the current density. We define $\varepsilon_\perp(k\omega)$ through the relation

$$D(k\omega) = \varepsilon_\perp(k\omega)\, E(k\omega) \tag{4-61}$$

In general the dielectric constant is a tensorial quantity. To simplify the discussion we restrict our attention to the case of an isotropic or cubic system; for reasons of symmetry the dielectric constant is then a scalar quantity. We find from (4-59), (4-60), and (4-61) that the dispersion relation for optical waves in the electron gas is

$$\omega^2 = c^2k^2/\varepsilon_\perp(k\omega) \tag{4-62}$$

It is customary to introduce the complex index of refraction,

$$N = n + iK \tag{4-63}$$

through the phase velocity of the electromagnetic wave,

$$v_{ph} = \frac{\omega}{k} = \frac{c}{N} \tag{4-64}$$

Here n is the (real) index of refraction, measuring a real velocity change from the vacuum value c, and K is the absorption coefficient. If we write

$$\varepsilon_{\perp}(k\omega) = \varepsilon_{1\perp}(k\omega) + i\varepsilon_{2\perp}(k\omega) \tag{4-65}$$

then the real and imaginary parts of $\varepsilon_{\perp}(k\omega)$ are related to the optical constants in the long-wavelength limit through the equations

$$\varepsilon_{1\perp}(0, \omega) = n^2 - K^2 \tag{4-66a}$$

$$\varepsilon_{2\perp}(0, \omega) = 2nK \tag{4-66b}$$

There is a simple relation between $\varepsilon_{\perp}(k\omega)$ and the complex conductivity $\sigma_{\perp}(k\omega)$ which is defined by

$$J_{\perp}(k\omega) = \sigma_{\perp}(k\omega)\, E_{\perp}(k\omega) \tag{4-67}$$

On comparing (4-59) and (4-61), one finds

$$\varepsilon_{\perp}(k\omega) = 1 + \frac{4\pi i \sigma_{\perp}(k\omega)}{\omega} \tag{4-68}$$

On introducing the real and imaginary parts of $\sigma_{\perp}(0, \omega)$, one has, for example,

$$2\sigma_{1\perp}(0, \omega)/\omega = nK \tag{4-69}$$

In the same way, one has [writing $\varepsilon_{1\perp}(0, \omega)$ and $\sigma_{1\perp}(0, \omega)$ simply as ε_1 and σ_1]

$$n = \sqrt{\frac{1}{2}\left[\varepsilon_1 + \sqrt{\varepsilon_1^2 + \left(\frac{4\pi\sigma_1}{\omega}\right)^2}\,\right]} \tag{4-70a}$$

$$K = \sqrt{\frac{1}{2}\left[-\varepsilon_1 + \sqrt{\varepsilon_1^2 + \left(\frac{4\pi\sigma_1}{\omega}\right)^2}\,\right]} \tag{4-70b}$$

The reflectance of the medium for a normally incident electromagnetic wave is calculated as

$$R = \frac{(n-1)^2 + K^2}{(n+1)^2 + K^2} \tag{4-71}$$

When σ_1 is small, which means weak light absorption, then if $\varepsilon > 0$, K is very small and the medium is transparent; if $\varepsilon < 0$, n is negligible and thus the medium is strongly reflecting. Hence $\varepsilon = 0$ roughly marks the transition from a reflecting to a transmitting region for electromagnetic waves.

In the case of weak electromagnetic fields (which is the case for all but laser beams), we use an approach closely related to that of the preceding chapter to obtain an expression for $\varepsilon_\perp(k\omega)$ in terms of certain exact eigenstates and excitation frequencies of the many-electron system.[9] Let us begin by writing down the Hamiltonian for a system of electrons interacting with a transverse electromagnetic field. It may be written as

$$H = \sum_i [p_i + e\,A(r_i)/c]^2/2m + \sum_i V(r_i) + H_{field} + H_{Coul} \tag{4-72}$$

where V(r) is the periodic potential of the ions, H_{Coul} is the electron-electron interaction, H_{field} is the Hamiltonian for the free electromagnetic wave field, and A(r) represents the vector potential. We are working in the transverse gauge,

$$\nabla \cdot \mathbf{A} = 0 \tag{4-73}$$

We expand A(r) in a Fourier series in a cube of unit volume with periodic boundary conditions,

$$A(r) = \sum_{k\mu} (4\pi c^2)^{1/2}\, Q_{k\mu}\eta_{k\mu} e^{ik\cdot r} \tag{4-74}$$

Here $\eta_{k\mu}$ is a unit polarization vector and, for the transverse field, μ takes on values 1 and 2, representing the two possible values of polarization perpendicular to the direction of propagation k. The reality conditions for A(r) are

$$\begin{aligned} \eta_{k\mu} &= \eta_{-k\mu} \\ Q^*_{k\mu} &= Q_{-k\mu} \end{aligned} \tag{4-75}$$

We shall also write $P_{k\mu}$ for the conjugate momentum for $Q_{k\mu}$.

In this subsection we shall not be concerned with the quantization of the electromagnetic field but shall instead regard A(r) as representing an external source, a transverse probe of the electron system. This approximation is often called a semiclassical approximation, since one treats the field classically, but the electrons quantum mechanically. It is well justified for electromagnetic fields of the strength commonly used to probe solids. We shall also, for the time being, consider only the linear term

$$H_1 = \frac{e}{mc} \sum_i \mathbf{p}_i \cdot \mathbf{A}(\mathbf{r}_i) \tag{4-76}$$

in the coupling of the electromagnetic waves to the electrons. For small A's, this term which gives rise to light absorption by the electrons, will be the most important one. We shall consider the A^2 term, which gives rise to light scattering, later on in this section.

Let us rewrite H_1, (4-76), in the following form:

$$H_1 = \frac{e}{2c} \int d^3r \; \mathbf{A}(\mathbf{r} \cdot t) \cdot \mathbf{j}(\mathbf{r}) \tag{4-77}$$

where j(r), the electron current density, is defined by

$$\mathbf{j}(\mathbf{r}) = \sum_i \frac{1}{2m} [\mathbf{p}_i \delta(\mathbf{r} - \mathbf{r}_i) + \delta(\mathbf{r} - \mathbf{r}_i)\mathbf{p}_i] \tag{4-78}$$

We can Fourier-analyze (4-77), as

$$H_1 = \lim_{\delta \to 0} \frac{e}{c} \sum_{k\omega} \mathbf{j}_k^+ \cdot \mathbf{A}_{k\omega} e^{-i\omega t} e^{\delta t} \tag{4-79}$$

with

$$\mathbf{j}_k = \sum_i (\mathbf{p}_i /m + \hbar \mathbf{k}/2m) e^{-i\mathbf{k} \cdot \mathbf{r}_i} \tag{4-80}$$

In (4-79) we have introduced the exponential factor, $e^{\delta t}$, to turn on the interaction adiabatically, so that the response of the system to the electromagnetic wave will necessarily be causal.

Note the close resemblance between (4-79) and (3-109b); viewed as a weak transverse probe, the electromagnetic wave is seen to couple directly to the current density fluctuation, $\mathbf{j}_k^+$ in a fashion similar to the coupling of an external test charge to ρ_k^+. The treatment of the system response can now be carried through in exactly the same way as was developed for the response of the electrons to a longitudinal probe. What we wish to calculate is the electric current J(r t) induced by A; in the presence of A, J is given by

$$\mathbf{J}(\mathbf{r}) = -\frac{e}{2} \sum_i \{\mathbf{v}_i \,\delta(\mathbf{r} - \mathbf{r}_i) + \delta(\mathbf{r} - \mathbf{r}_i)\mathbf{v}_i\}$$

$$= -e\mathbf{j}(\mathbf{r}) - \frac{e^2}{mc} \mathbf{A}(\mathbf{r}_i t)\, \delta(\mathbf{r} - \mathbf{r}_i) \tag{4-81}$$

and possesses the Fourier component

$$J_k = -ej_k - \frac{e^2}{mc}\sum_{k'} A_{k'}(t)\rho_{k-k'} \tag{4-82}$$

We are, as before, only going to be interested in the linear response of the electrons to A; therefore we can neglect the term with $k' \neq \mathbf{k}$ in (4-82), and write

$$J_k = -ej_k - \frac{e^2 n}{mc} A_k(t) \tag{4-83}$$

In the absence of A, the expectation value of J_k, $\langle J_k \rangle$, averaged over the exact states of the many-body system, vanishes because of translational invariance. In the presence of A, this will no longer be the case. Again, perturbation-theoretic methods can be used to determine $\langle j(k\omega) \rangle$ in the presence of A; the response will be proportional to $A_{k\omega}$, so that we can write

$$\langle J_{k\omega} \rangle = K(k\omega)A(k\omega) \tag{4-84}$$

where K is, in general, a second-rank tensor. Straightforward application of first-order time-dependent perturbation theory to the interaction (4-79) yields

$$K_{\mu\nu}(k\omega) = \frac{e^2}{\hbar c}\sum_n \frac{\left[j_\nu^+(k)\right]_{on}\left[j_\mu(k)\right]_{no}}{\omega - \omega_{no} + i\delta} - \frac{\left[j_\mu(k)\right]_{on}\left[j_\nu^+(k)\right]_{no}}{\omega + \omega_{no} + i\delta} - \frac{ne^2}{mc}\delta_{\mu\nu} \tag{4-85}$$

where the ω_{no} are the exact excitation frequencies going with the exact current-density-fluctuation matrix elements, $[j_\mu(k)]_{no}$, for the many-electron system.

We pause to comment on several interesting features of (4-85). The last term in (4-85) is the so-called diamagnetic part of the kernel, $K_{\mu\nu}$; we see that at sufficiently high frequencies ($\omega \gg$ all ω_{no} of importance) it is the leading term. In the limit of $\omega \to 0$, and then $k \to 0$, one obtains from (4-85) the response of the electrons to a static magnetic field. For a normal metal, if one substitutes plane-wave states for the exact states of (4-85), one finds that to lowest order in k the first, paramagnetic term, cancels the second, diamagnetic term; there remains a weak diamagnetic term, of order k^2, which represents the usual Landau diamagnetic susceptibility. For a superconductor, the first term vanishes, while the second yields the Meissner effect (in the London limit). (To see this, remark that in the limit of $k \to 0$, the numerator of the first term is of order **k**; on the other hand, for a superconductor, the finite energy gap in the single-particle excitation spectrum means that ω_{no} goes to a constant in this limit.)

We return now to the optical properties of solids. For an isotropic solid, $K_{\mu\nu}(k\omega)$ reduces to a scalar, $K(k\omega)$. Moreover, from (4-59) and (4-84), we see that

$$\varepsilon_\perp(k\omega) = 1 + \frac{4\pi c}{\omega^2} K(k\omega) \tag{4-86}$$

so that we can write

$$\varepsilon_\perp(k\omega) = 1 - \frac{\omega_p^2}{\omega^2} + \frac{4\pi e^2}{\hbar\omega^2} \sum_n \left| \left[\eta_k \cdot j^+(k)\right]_{no} \right|^2 \times \left\{ 2P \frac{\omega_{no}}{\omega_{no}^2 - \omega^2} + i\pi\delta(\omega_{no} - \omega) \right\} \tag{4-87}$$

where η_k is a polarization vector in the direction of A_k, and P, as before, indicates that principal parts are to be taken.

Before going on to a discussion of calculations of $\varepsilon_\perp(k\omega)$, we comment on some general properties that it must satisfy. Because we have considered a causal response of the electrons to the transverse probe, there exist appropriate Kramers-Kronig relations between the real and imaginary parts of $\varepsilon_\perp(k\omega)$, or between the real and imaginary parts of $\sigma_\perp(k\omega)$. Moreover, there exists a sum rule for Im $\varepsilon_\perp(k\omega)$:

$$\int_0^\infty d\omega \; \omega \; \mathrm{Im} \; \varepsilon_\perp(k\omega) = \frac{\pi}{2} \omega_p^2 \tag{4-88}$$

This may be derived by remarking that at high frequencies, one finds

$$\varepsilon_\perp(k\omega) \underset{\omega \to \infty}{\rightarrow} 1 - \frac{\omega_p^2}{\omega^2}$$

We leave it as an exercise to the reader to show that a suitable contour integration then yields the result (4-88).

In the limit of long wavelengths, one has the quite general result

$$\varepsilon_\perp(0, \omega) = \varepsilon_{\parallel}(0, \omega) \tag{4-89}$$

for an istropic solid.[23] This result is not especially obvious from inspection of the defining equations, (3-110a) and (4-87); that it must be true follows from a macroscopic argument based on the defining equation

$$< \mathbf{j}(k\omega) > = \sigma(k\omega)\,\mathbf{E}(k\omega) \qquad (4\text{-}90)$$

which holds for both longitudinal and transverse perturbing fields [recall that $\mathbf{E}(k\omega)$ is the *local* electric field], and the result, (3-107),

$$\varepsilon(k\omega) = 1 + \frac{4\pi i}{\omega}\,\sigma(k\omega)$$

which is likewise true for a transverse external disturbance. We now pass to the limit $k = 0$ in (4-89); in this limit one cannot distinguish between an electric field perpendicular or parallel to k; both $\varepsilon_{\parallel}(0, \omega)$ and $\varepsilon_{\perp}(0, \omega)$ are scalars, and obviously $\varepsilon_{\parallel}(0, \omega) = \varepsilon_{\perp}(0, \omega)$. On the other hand, if one considers the limit, $\varepsilon(\mathbf{k}, 0)$, the direction of k plays an important role; the longitudinal and transverse dielectric constants are different. For example, in the RPA one has for a free-electron gas,

$$\varepsilon_{\parallel}(k, 0) = 1 + \frac{k_{FT}^2}{k^2} \qquad \sigma_{\parallel}(k, 0) = 0$$

while (see Problem 4-4),

$$\sigma_{\perp}(k, 0) = \frac{3\pi N e^2}{4 q k_o}$$

Calculations of $\epsilon_{\perp}(k\omega)$

The first approximation for $\varepsilon_{\perp}(k\omega)$ in a solid consists in replacing the exact states which appear in (4-87) by Bloch wave states. This approximation is, in fact, simply the transverse analogue of the RPA, and we may refer to the value of $\varepsilon_{\perp}(k\omega)$ so obtained as the RPA value. That this should be the case is at first sight surprising, because we have clearly not taken the Coulomb interactions into account in making the transverse RPA. On second thought, one at once sees why. Within the RPA, which says to keep the kth component of the Coulomb interaction in calculating $\varepsilon_{\perp}(k\omega)$, there is no effect of the Coulomb interaction. For in this order there is no influence of the longitudinal field (to which that k^{th} component corresponds) on the transverse response of the electrons; the two effects (longitudinal and transverse) are independent of each other. From a diagrammatic point of view, this result is also obvious; consider Fig. 4-7, in which we see an electromagnetic wave exciting an electron-hole pair, which then decays with photon emission. An RPA correction to this process would look as shown in Fig. 4-8. But such a contribution vanishes because the particle-hole pair excited by the light wave are transverse in character, and cannot therefore decay into another electron-hole pair by the "longitudinal" Coulomb interaction. In other words, there is no screening of the transverse probe within the RPA.

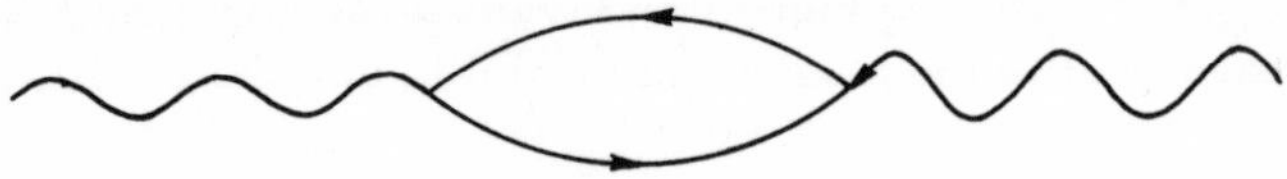

Fig. 4-7

We have, therefore,

$$\varepsilon_{\perp}^{RPA}(k\omega) = 1 - \frac{\omega_p^2}{\omega^2} + \frac{4\pi e^2}{\hbar\omega^2}\sum_{\nu}\left|\left[\eta_k \cdot j^+(k)\right]_{\nu o}\right|^2 \times\left\{2P\frac{\omega_{\nu o}}{\omega_{\nu o}^2 - \omega^2} + i\pi\delta(\omega_{\nu o} - \omega)\right\} \tag{4-91}$$

The result, (4-90), looks rather different from the longitudinal result for $\varepsilon(k\omega)$, (4-23) and (4-24). There is, however, a close resemblance. To see this, let us rewrite (4-23) and (4-24) by making use of longitudinal current conservation, (4-12):

$$(k \cdot j_k^+)_{\mu o} = \omega_{\mu o}(\rho_k^+)_{\mu o}$$

and the Bloch wave f-sum rule, (4-7). We find

$$\varepsilon_{||}^{RPA}(k\omega) = 1 - \frac{\omega_p^2}{\omega^2} + \frac{4\pi e^2}{\hbar\omega^2}\sum_{\nu}\left|\left[\eta_k \cdot j^+(k)\right]_{\nu o}\right|^2 \times\left\{2P\frac{\omega_{\nu o}}{\omega_{\nu o}^2 - \omega^2} + i\pi\delta(\omega_{\nu o} - \omega)\right\} \tag{4-92}$$

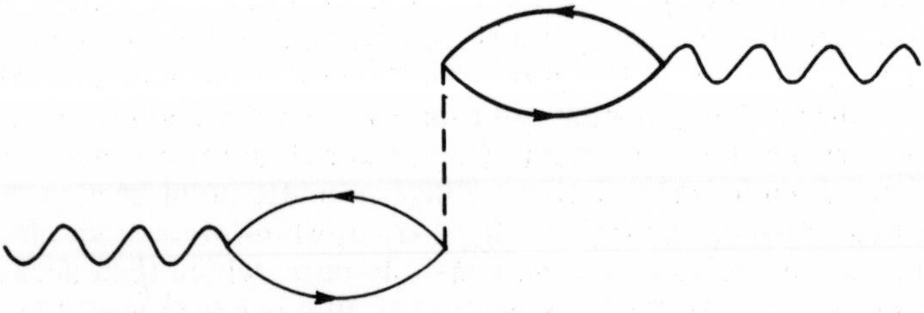

Fig. 4-8

We see that $\varepsilon_{\perp}^{RPA}$ and $\varepsilon_{\parallel}^{RPA}$ differ only in that the transverse polarization vector $\eta_{k\perp}$ is replaced by its longitudinal counterpart $\eta_{k\parallel}$. Hence the two are identical for an isotropic solid—or for a polycrystalline sample of an anisotropic solid, in which $\varepsilon_{\parallel}$ and $\varepsilon_{\perp}$ will be averaged over all directions.

In fact, the long-wavelength limit is the only one of interest to us for optical experiments. Within the frequency range of interest (for phonons, say, of up to 30 ev), the wavelength of the incident light waves are long compared to interelectron or interatomic spacing, so that one could simply pass to the limit $k \to 0$ in the expression (4-92). In this limit ($k = 0$, ω finite) the equality of $\varepsilon_{\parallel}^{RPA}(0, \omega)$ and $\varepsilon_{\perp}^{RPA}(0,\omega)$ is a special case of the more general identity, (4-89). Thus for optical properties we can happily forget about the developments of this section, and rely upon our discussion of the longitudinal $\varepsilon_{RPA}(k\omega)$. As we shall shortly see, the RPA provides us with a rather good account of optical properties, with one notable exception which we must now consider.

Suppose we consider separately the intraband and interband contributions to $\varepsilon(k\omega)$ in the limit $k \to 0$, with, of course, $\omega = ck$. We see then that since ω is large compared to all intraband excitation frequencies,

$$\varepsilon_1(0, \omega) = 1 - \frac{4\pi N_v e^2}{m^2 \omega^2} - \frac{4\pi e^2}{m} \sum_{\ell} \frac{f_{\ell v}}{\omega^2 - \omega_{\ell v}^2} \tag{4-93}$$

$$\varepsilon_2(0, \omega) = \frac{2\pi^2 e^2}{m} \sum_{\ell} \frac{f_{\ell v}}{\omega_{\ell v}} \delta(\omega - \omega_{\ell v}) \tag{4-94}$$

Therefore as long as one considers ω less than the minimum interband excitation frequency, $\varepsilon_2(0, \omega) = 0$ in the RPA. The reason is simple; one cannot have a photon of energy $\hbar ck$ decay directly into an electron-hole pair of energy $\hbar k v_F$, so that in the RPA there are no intraband contributions to the high-frequency conductivity. Such a result is not found experimentally; what is missing in the RPA, and must be included in order to bring about agreement with experiment, is that electrons in the conduction band possess a finite lifetime as a result of collisions with phonons, impurities or possibly one another. Such collisions give rise to a spread in the one-electron energies, so that it then becomes possible for an electron-hole pair which is coupled to impurities (or phonons) to absorb a phonon. A simple derivation, which assumes that a relaxation time τ describes the external scattering mechanism, may be obtained by a slight generalization of the approach introduced by Lindhard.[24] Lindhard uses a quantum version of the Boltzmann equation, and computes the response of the electrons to a transverse field, $E(k\omega)$. The result one obtains, assuming that the collision mechanism is important for intraband transitions only, is the following generalization of (4-93) and (4-94):

$$\varepsilon_1(0,\omega) = 1 - \frac{4\pi N_v e^2}{m^*} \frac{1}{\omega^2 + \tau^{-2}} - \frac{4\pi e^2}{m} \sum_{\ell} \frac{f_{\ell v}}{\omega^2 - \omega_{\ell v}^2} \quad (4\text{-}95)$$

$$\varepsilon_2(0,\omega) = \frac{4\pi N_v e^2}{m^* \omega\tau} \frac{1}{\omega^2 + \tau^{-2}} + \frac{2\pi^2 e^2}{m} \sum_{\ell} \frac{f_{\ell v}}{\omega_{\ell v}} \delta(\omega - \omega_{\ell v}) \quad (4\text{-}96)$$

It should be added that it is not altogether trivial to derive (4-95) and (4-96) for the response of the electron system to a longitudinal field. If one uses a Boltzmann-like approach, one must take care to ensure that the distribution function relaxes toward its local value, rather than the uniform, average value.[25] In this way one avoids the pile up of space charge and the lack of particle conservation characteristic of the more offhand approach. Finally we mention that it is also nontrivial to calculate (4-95) and (4-96) directly from the exact expressions, (4-85) and (4-87).[26]

General Quantum-Mechanical Treatment[9]

Before going on to a comparison of theory and experiment, we comment briefly on the quantum treatment of the basic Hamiltonian (4-72). On making use of the Fourier expansion (4-74), one can rewrite (4-72) as

$$H = H_0 + H_{field} + H_1 + H_2 \quad (4\text{-}97)$$

where

$$H_0 = \sum_i \left[p_i^2/2m + V(\mathbf{r}_i) \right] + H_{Coul} \quad (4\text{-}98)$$

$$H_{field} = \frac{1}{2} \sum_{k\mu} \left[P_{k\mu}^+ P_{k\mu} + \left(\omega_p^2 + c^2 k^2\right) Q_{k\mu}^+ Q_{k\mu} \right] \quad (4\text{-}99)$$

$$H_1 = \sum_{k\mu} (4\pi e^2)^{1/2} (\eta_{k\mu} \cdot j_k) Q_{k\mu} \quad (4\text{-}100)$$

$$H_2 = \sum_{\substack{k,k' \\ \mu,\mu'}}{}' \frac{2\pi e^2}{m} (\eta_{k\mu} \cdot \eta_{k'\mu'}) \rho_{k-k'}^+ Q_{k\mu}^+ Q_{k'\mu'} \quad (4\text{-}101)$$

where j_k is given by (4-80). In the photon field Hamiltonian, H_{field}, we observe the first effect of the electron-photon interaction to shift the photon frequency from ck to $\left(c^2k^2 + \omega_p^2\right)^{1/2}$.

The first interaction term, H_1, gives rise to single photon absorption or emission processes. It is the transverse analogue of the interaction term, H_{int}, of the BP theory [compare (3-78)]; in fact, the plasmon may be formally regarded as a longitudinal photon. H_1 also gives rise to a shift in the photon energies, an effect we consider shortly. H_2, on the other hand, describes two-photon processes, processes in which two photons are absorbed, or created, or processes in which one photon is annihilated, and another created. These latter scattering processes are the only ones of physical importance; they correspond to Compton scattering by the electrons in the solid, and offer a way to measure by optical means the dynamic form factor, $S(k, \omega)$, as we shall see presently.

The shift in photon frequencies brought about by H_1 may be easily evaluated by perturbation-theoretic techniques. For example, one may use a canonical transformation which eliminates H_1 to the lowest order[1,27] (compare the BP theory). If one neglects the Coulomb interaction between the electrons in treating the photon-transverse electron coupling, one thereby obtains

$$\omega_{k\mu}^2 = c^2k^2 + \omega_p^2 - \frac{4\pi e^2}{\hbar} \times \sum_{\nu} |(\eta_{k\mu} \cdot j_k)_{\nu o}|^2 \left\{ P \frac{2\omega_{\nu o}}{\omega_{\nu o}^2 - \omega_{k\mu}^2} + i\pi\delta(\omega_{\nu o} - \omega_{k\mu}) \right\} \tag{4-102}$$

where P denotes taking the principal part, and the causal boundary conditions have determined the imaginary part uniquely. The determination of the frequency to this order is equivalent to making the transverse analogue of the RPA, as may be seen on comparing (4-102) with (4-87), and making use of (4-62). The quantum mechanical treatment thus yields results identical to those of the semiclassical treatment of the previous section.

Let us now turn to the consideration of the Compton effect in the nonrelativistic limit. In the usual experimental situation, one uses photons in the x-ray region (~ 10 kev), and measures the number of photons scattered as a function of angle θ, summing over all possible energy transfers and polarizations. For the moment, however, we distinguish the energy transfers and polarizations as well.

We find it convenient to introduce the creation and annihilation operators, $A_{k\mu}^+$ and $A_{k\mu}$, in the Hamiltonian (4-101):

$$H_2 = \frac{4\pi e^2}{m} \sum_{\substack{k,k' \\ \mu,\mu'}}{}' \left(\frac{\hbar^2}{4\omega_k \omega_{k'}}\right)^{1/2}$$
$$\times \left(\eta_{k\mu} \cdot \eta_{k'\mu'}\right) \left(A^{+}_{k'\mu'} + A_{-k'\mu'}\right) \left(A^{+}_{-k\mu} + A_{k\mu}\right) \rho^{+}_{k-k'} \tag{4-103}$$

We wish to calculate the probability per unit time for those processes in which a photon of the incident wave is absorbed, while a new photon is created in a different state; the state of the electron system undergoes a quantum shift from the ground state. To avoid unwieldy notations we use the subscripts 0 and 1 to indicate the quantities associated with the incident and scattered radiations, respectively. The differential cross section $d^2\sigma/d\Omega\ d\omega$, for the transfer of momentum $\hbar k$ (corresponding to scattering into a solid angle $d\Omega$) and energy $\hbar\omega$ from an electromagnetic wave to the electrons is defined as

$$\frac{d^2\sigma}{d\Omega\ d\omega} = \frac{\hbar\omega_1 \times \begin{bmatrix}\text{number of photons per second scattered into} \\ d\Omega\ d\omega \text{ in the direction of } k_1 \text{ with polarization} \\ \eta_1 \text{ and frequency } \omega_1\end{bmatrix}}{\hbar\omega_0 \times \begin{bmatrix}\text{number of the incident photons per unit area} \\ \text{per second}\end{bmatrix}} \tag{4-104}$$

where

$$k = k_0 - k_1 \tag{4-105}$$

$$\omega = \omega_0 - \omega_1 \tag{4-106}$$

The denominator in (4-104) is the energy flux of the incident electromagnetic radiation, while the numerator means the scattered power of the electromagnetic radiation with polarization η_1 into the solid angle $d\Omega$ (in the direction of k_1) and into the frequency interval $d\omega$. Such a cross section is obtainable directly from the interaction Hamiltonian (4-103) by means of usual time-dependent perturbation theory; the result is

$$\frac{d^2\sigma}{d\Omega\ d\omega} = \left(\frac{e^2}{mc^2}\right)^2 (\eta_0 \cdot \eta_1)^2\ S(k\omega) \tag{4-107}$$

where we have assumed that $\omega_0 \cong \omega_1$, and the dynamic form factor $S(k\omega)$ has been defined by (3-112). The $(e^2/mc^2)^2\ (\eta_0 \cdot \eta_1)$ is the usual Rayleigh-Thomson scattering cross section for the scattering of a photon by a single electron. If the experiment pays no attention to the polarizations, we have to average (4-107) over the polarizations of the incident wave and sum over the polarizations of the scattered wave; the result then is

$$\frac{d^2\sigma}{d\Omega\, d\omega} = \left(\frac{e^2}{mc^2}\right)^2 \left(1 - \frac{1}{2}\sin^2\theta\right) S(k\omega) \tag{4-108}$$

where θ is the angle between the propagations of the incident and scattered waves. Finally if we measure only the number of photons scattered into certain directions with no attempt at all to distinguish their frequencies, we must integrate (4-108) over all frequencies ω to obtain

$$\frac{d\sigma}{d\Omega} = N \left(\frac{e^2}{mc^2}\right)^2 \left(1 - \frac{1}{2}\sin^2\theta\right) S(k) \tag{4-109}$$

Here we have made use of the relation (3-121).

We conclude, on the basis of (4-108) and (4-109), that it is possible to measure the density-fluctuation excitation spectrum $S(k\omega)$ and the form factor, $S(k)$ by means of a transverse probe, the electromagnetic wave. We note, in passing, that the expressions (4-108) and (4-109) apply equally well to coherent X-ray scattering by lattice vibrations, provided one makes the obvious modifications (the charge density is that of the electrons bound to the nucleus, and, in general, the temperature dependence must be taken into account via the Debye-Waller factor).

4-5 OPTICAL STUDIES OF SOLIDS

Let us now apply the theoretical considerations of the preceding section to interpret some experiments on the optical properties of solids. In this section, we shall consider three kinds of experiments:

1. The determination of plasmon energies from the condition

$$\varepsilon_1(\omega) = 0$$

which marks the transition from the reflecting to a transmission region, provided $\varepsilon_2(\omega) \ll 1$.

2. The investigations by Ehrenreich and Philipp[28] of $\varepsilon(\omega)$ for Ag and Cu in the energy range 1 to ~ 25 ev.

3. The investigations by Philipp and Ehrenreich[29] of $\varepsilon(\omega)$ for a group of semiconductors (Si, Ge, GaP, GaAs, InAs, and InSb) in the range of photon energies between 1.5 and 25 ev. [Throughout this section we use $\varepsilon(\omega)$ in place of $\varepsilon(0, \omega)$.] The first group of experiments serves to supplement our knowledge of plasmon energies in

solids. The second shows, in dramatic fashion, the way in which interband transitions serve to modify $\varepsilon(\omega)$ from its free-electron-like value, and provide, as well, an accurate measurement of m* for the metals in question. The third group provides valuable information on specific interband transitions, discloses a large region of nearly free-electron-like behavior, and indicates the onset of d-band contributions to the polarizability in those semiconductors possessing same.

We first remark that, when plasmons are damped, the frequency at which $\varepsilon_1(\omega) = 0$ does not quite provide us with the plasmon energy.[30] To see this, consider a simple example; the dielectric constant for a free-electron gas in the presence of a damping mechanism characterized by a relaxation time τ. One has then, in the high-frequency limit,

$$\varepsilon(\omega) = 1 - \frac{\omega_p^2}{\omega(\omega + i/\tau)} \tag{4-110}$$

The plasmon energy, $\tilde{\omega} = \omega_1 + i\omega_2$ is determined by the condition

$$\varepsilon(\omega) = 0 \tag{4-111}$$

One finds

$$\begin{aligned} \omega_1^2 &= \omega_p^2 - 1/4\,\tau^2 \\ \omega_2 &= 1/2\,\tau \end{aligned} \tag{4-112}$$

The frequency at which $\varepsilon_1(\omega) = 0$ is given by

$$\omega_{refl}^2 = \omega_p^2 - 1/\tau^2 \tag{4-113}$$

Finally, the plasmon energy, as measured in a characteristic energy-loss experiment, would be determined from the maximum in Im $1/\varepsilon(\omega)$. In that way one would find

$$\omega_{\Delta E}^2 \cong \omega_p^2 - 1/4\,\tau^2 \tag{4-114}$$

For this simple model, then, the plasmon energies from (4-111) and from the maximum in Im $1/\varepsilon(\omega)$ are the same; in general they need not be. Both are higher than ω_{refl}, a result which Mendlowitz has argued should occur quite generally.[30]

In Table 4-5 we present a comparison of the optical determination of plasmon energies, based on reflection experiments, for the alkali metals; the recently determined characteristic energy values for Na and K are also included. We remark that the agreement between the two methods is quite good for these metals. Another interesting feature of the results is the evidence for a not inappreciable core polarizability, in that the agreement between theory and experiment is improved if one includes the core polarizability in the calculation of $\hbar\omega$ according to (4-45). The remaining discrepancy between theory and experiment is presumably due either to the low-energy interband transitions or to the enhancement of the effective oscillator strength of the conduction electrons [compare (4-45)]; either effect would increase the theoretical value of $\hbar\omega$.

Table 4-5
A Comparison between Theoretical and Experimental Results for Plasmon Energies (in ev) in the Alkali Metals

Element	$\hbar\omega_p$ [a]	$\hbar\omega$ [b]	$\hbar\omega_{opt}$ [c]	$\hbar\omega_{el}$ [d]
Li	8.1	8.0	8.02	
Na	6.0	5.7	5.91	5.87
K	4.4	3.9	3.94	3.87
Rb	4.0	3.4	3.65	
Cs	3.6	2.9	3.27	

[a] ω_p = plasmon frequency for free electrons.
[b] ω = same, corrected for core polarizability (the core polarizabilities are taken from J. H. Van Vleck, "The Theory of Electric and Magnetic Susceptibilities," Oxford, New York, 1932, p. 225.
[c] ω_{opt} = frequency at which optical transmission begins.
[d] ω_{el} = value measured in energy-loss experiments (see Ref. 15).

Table 4-6, which is taken from a paper by Robins,[16] compares the free-electron plasmon energy with the threshold energy for transmission, the region of a sharp increase in the transmissivity, and the characteristic energy-loss measurement. Finally, in Table 4-7, due to Philipp and Ehrenreich,[29] comparable data for a series of semiconductors is presented. The plasmon energy, $\hbar\omega^*_{pv}$, is based on (4-45), and includes the effects of the d-band electrons in Ge, GaP, GaAs, and InSb. The optical determination of the maximum in Im ε^{-1} is seen to be in good agreement with the characteristic energy-loss measurement. Note that the latter is larger, as it should be, since it represents an average of plasmon energies over all momentum transfers $\lesssim k_c$, while the optical determination is for $k \ll k_c$. The agreement between $\hbar\omega^*_{pv}$ and the values of Max ε^{-1} is also good.

The experiments on the optical properties of Ag and Cu described by Ehrenreich and Philipp[28] consist in measurements of the reflectance of electrolytically polished bulk surfaces of these materials in the region between 1 and ~ 25 ev. With the aid of a Kramers-Kronig analysis of the reflectance data, one may obtain the values of $\varepsilon_1(\omega)$

and $\varepsilon_2(\omega)$ in this energy range. Earlier experiments on silver in the range between 1 and 10 ev were carried out by Taft and Philipp[32]; measurements below 1 ev have been carried out by Schulz[33] for Ag and Cu, and by Roberts[34] for Cu.

Table 4-6

Comparison between the Observed (ΔE_p) and Theoretical ($\hbar\omega_p$) Plasma Energies and the Optical Data of Weissler et al.,[a] which includes the Threshold Energy (E_T) and the Region of Sharp Increase (E_{inc}) in the Optical Transmissivity (in ev)[b]

Element	E_T	E_{inc}	E_p	p
Al	14.6		15.3	15.8
Sn	13.6		14.1	14.3
In	11.1		11.3	12.6
Bi	14.5		14.7	13.9
Sb	15.0	~ 17	15.9	15.0
Te	15.0	~ 18	17.0	15.6
Ti	18.0	~ 22	17.6	17.7

[a]W. C. Walker, O. P. Rustgi, and G. L. Weissler, *J. Opt. Sci. Am.*, 49, 471 (1959); and as quoted in Ref. 30.

[b]From Robins.[16]

Table 4-7

Comparison of Various Determinations of the Plasmon Energy (in ev) in a Series of Semiconductors[a]

Element	$\hbar\omega_{pv}$	$\hbar\omega_{pv}^{*}$ [b]	$\varepsilon_1(\omega) = 0$	-Max Im ε^{-1} (optical)	-Max Im ε^{-1} (energy loss)
Si	16.6	16.6	15.0	16.4	16.9[c]
Ge	15.5	16.2	13.8	16.0	16.4[d]
GaP	16.6	16.3	13.3	16.9	
GaAs	15.5	12.3	9.7	14.7	
InSb	12.7	11.5	10.9	12.0	13.0[e]

[a]From Philipp and Ehrenreich.[29]

[b]The effective plasmon energy, $\hbar\omega_{pv}^{*}$, is that determined after appropriate corrections for the influence of the d-band electrons on the valence-electron plasmon energies.

[c]H. Dimigen.[36]

[d]C. J. Powell.[12]

[e]B. Gauthe, *Phys. Rev.*, 114, 1265 (1959).

The spectral dependence of ε_1, ε_2, and Im ε^{-1} for Ag and Cu is shown in Figs. 4-9 and 4-10. For the theoretical analysis of these curves[35] it is convenient to refer to (4-95) and (4-96), which may be written

$$\varepsilon_1(\omega) = 1 - \frac{4\pi N_v e^2}{m^*(\omega^2 + \tau^{-2})} + \delta\varepsilon_1^{(b)}(\omega) \tag{4-115a}$$

$$\varepsilon_2(\omega) = \frac{4\pi N_v e^2}{m^*\omega\tau} \frac{1}{\omega^2 + \tau^{-2}} + \delta\varepsilon_2^{(b)}(\omega) \tag{4-115b}$$

What we have done is to separate out, in ε_1 and ε_2, a contribution due to intraband transitions, which we characterize by an effective mass m^* and a constant lifetime τ,

$$\varepsilon^f(\omega) = 1 - \frac{4\pi N_v e^2}{m^* \omega(\omega + i/\tau)} \tag{4-116}$$

and a remaining part, $\delta\varepsilon^{(b)}(\omega)$, associated with the interband transitions.

At the lowest frequencies depicted, we note that $\varepsilon_2(\omega)$ is decreasing rapidly. This is what one expects if one had *only* intraband contributions, with ε_2 determined by (4-116). Then, at a frequency ω_i, (3.9 ev for Ag, 2.1 ev for Cu), there is a sudden increase in ε_2, which may be attributed to the onset of interband transitions.

Let us look in more detail at the low-frequency behavior of $\varepsilon_1(\omega)$, i.e., that for $\omega \lesssim \omega_i$. Because $\varepsilon_2(\omega)$ is small at $\omega \lesssim \omega_i$, one can, to a rather good degree of approximation, distinguish between the contributions to ε_1 and ε_2 arising from intraband and interband excitations, respectively. Thus EP assume that $\varepsilon_2(\omega) = \delta\varepsilon_2^b(\omega)$ for $\omega \geq \omega_i$; they then use the Kramers-Kronig relation,

$$\delta\varepsilon_1^b(\omega) = \frac{2}{\pi} \int_{\omega_i}^{\infty} d\omega' \frac{\delta\varepsilon_2^b(\omega')\omega'}{\omega'^2 - \omega^2} \qquad \omega < \omega_i \tag{4-117}$$

to determine the contribution to $\varepsilon_1(\omega)$ (for frequencies $\omega < \omega_i$) arising from the interband transitions contained in $\delta\varepsilon_2^b(\omega)$. Given this effect of the interband contributions, one can then choose τ = const (as determined, for example, from the d-c conductivity), and choose m^* in (4-114) so as to obtain agreement between theory and experiment in the region in which $\omega\tau >> 1$. The resulting comparison of theory and experiment is shown in Fig. 4-11. The theoretical values of $m^* = m_a$, $m_a = 0.96$ and 1.09, were obtained by matching, respectively, at

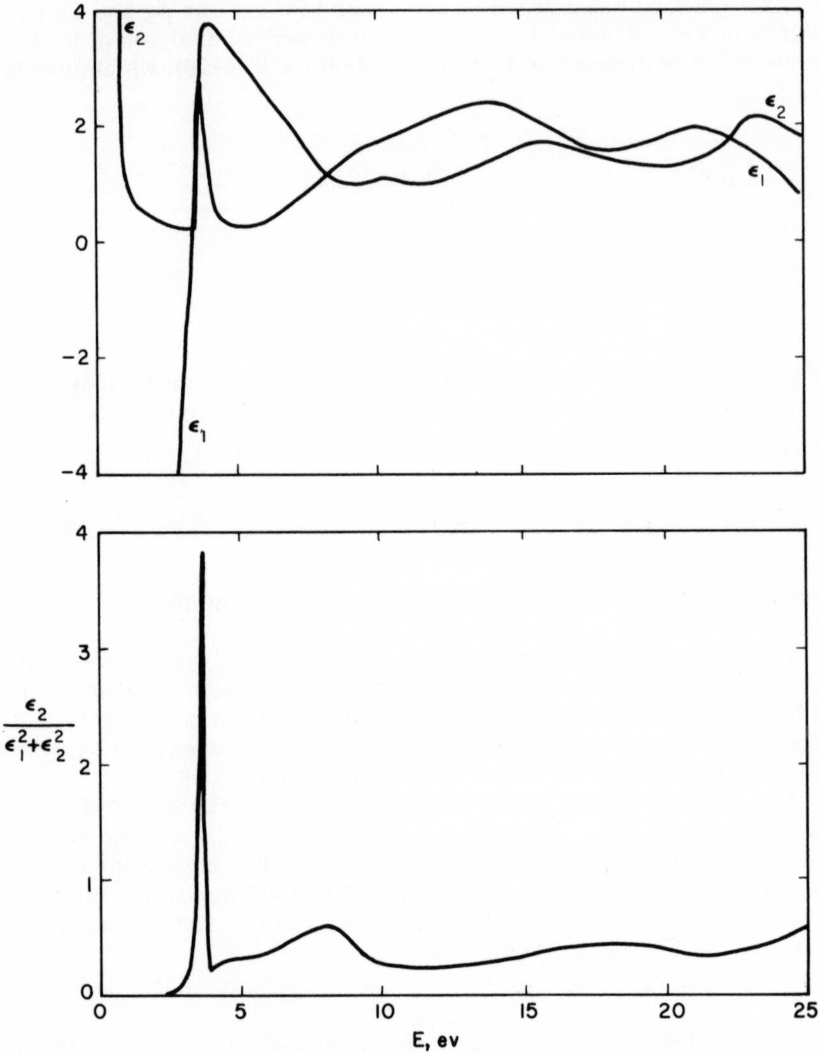

Fig. 4-9. Spectral dependence of the real and imaginary parts of the dielectric constant and the loss function $\varepsilon_2/(\varepsilon_1^2 + \varepsilon_2^2)$ for Ag. (From H. Ehrenreich and H. R. Phillip.[28])

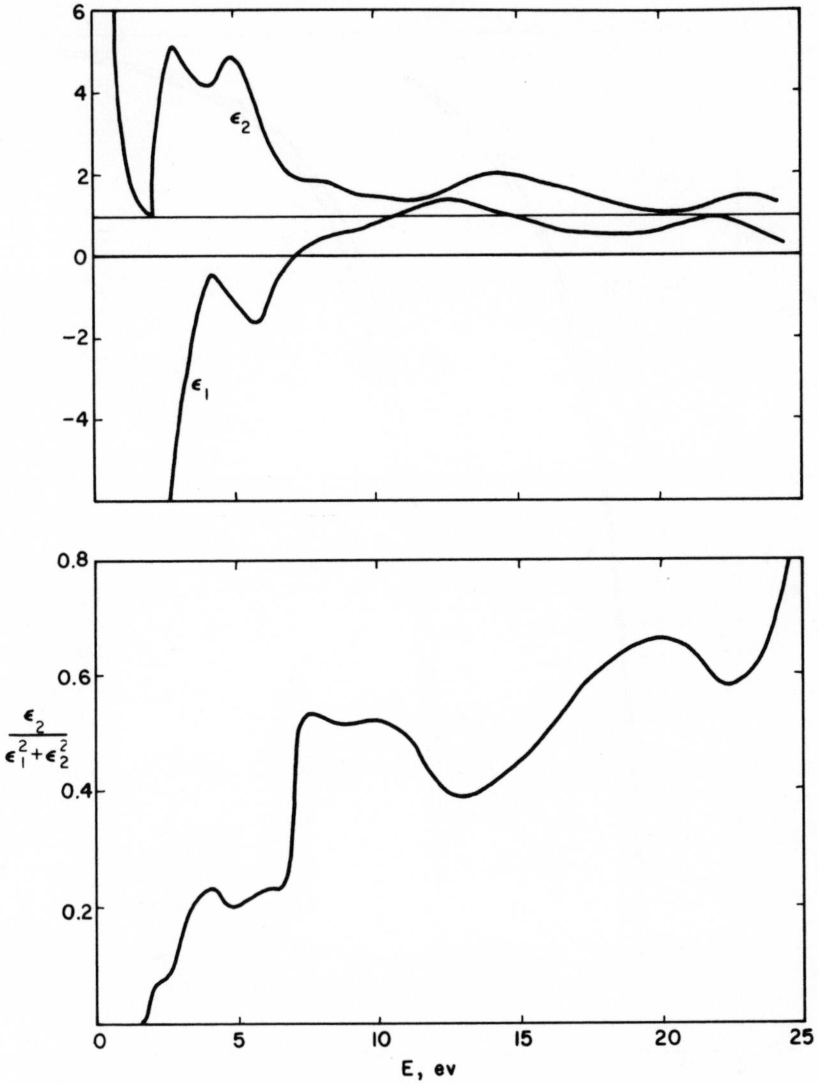

Fig. 4-10. Spectral dependence of the real and imaginary parts of the dielectric constant and the loss function $\varepsilon_2/(\varepsilon_1{}^2 + \varepsilon_2{}^2)$ for Cu. (From H. Ehrenreich and H. R. Phillip.[28])

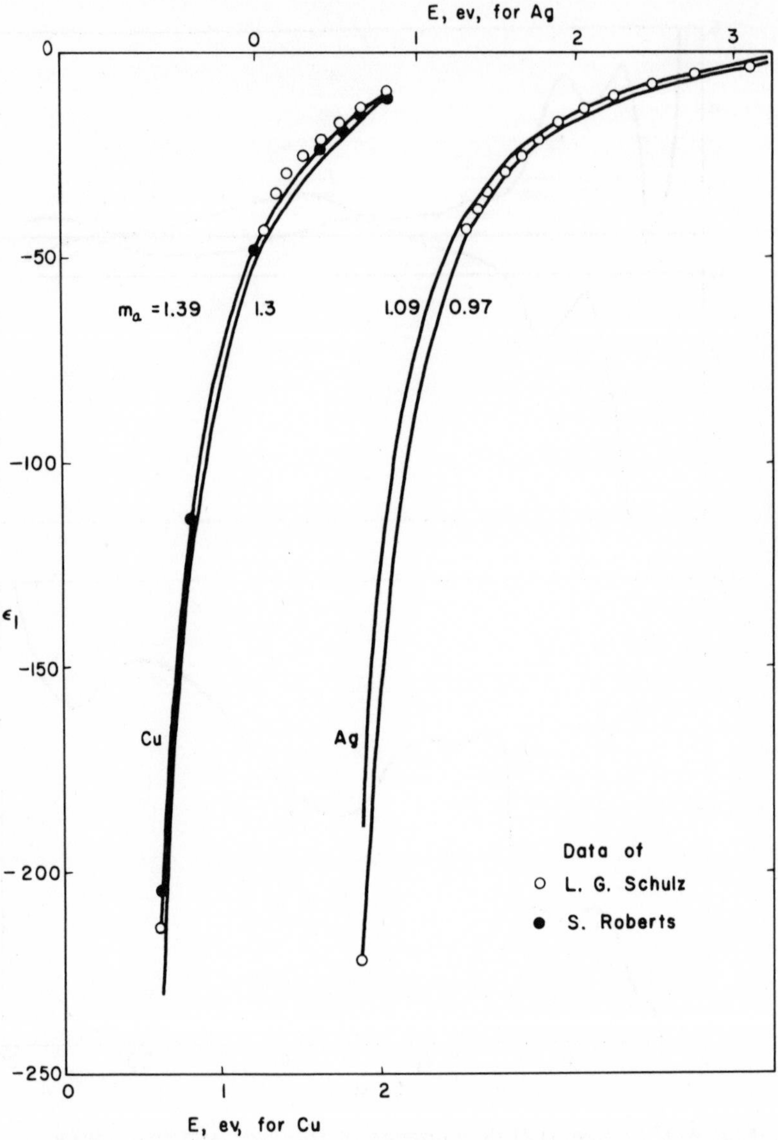

Fig. 4-11. Comparison of experimental and theoretical values of ε_1 for Ag and Cu in the "free-electron" region for several values of the optical mass m*. (From H. Ehrenreich and H. R. Phillip.[28]). The theoretical curve (solid line) is obtained using (4-115a) with $\delta\varepsilon_1^{(b)}$ evaluated from the Kramers-Kronig relations. The points correspond to experimental data of Schultz[33] and Roberts.[34]

energies of 0.62 and 2.5 ev, and the spread between the values is a measure of the accuracy of this method for determining m*.

In Table 4-8 the best average values for m* so obtained are compared with those obtained by Schulz and Roberts from their low-frequency data.

Table 4-8
Comparison of Experimental and Theoretical Values for the Effective Mass of Conduction Electrons in Ag and Cu[a]

Element	EP	Schulz	Roberts	Theory
Ag	1.03 ± 0.06	0.97 ± 0.04		
Cu	1.42 ± 0.05	1.45 ± 0.06	1.44 ± 0.01	1.3 ± 0.1

[a]The experimental values are EP, Ref. 28; Schulz, Ref. 33; and Roberts, Ref. 34. The theoretical value is due to B. Segall [*Phys. Rev.*, 125, 109 (1962)].

It should be remarked that the curves for ε_1 in Fig. 4-11 cannot be fit throughout this frequency range if one takes only the "free-electron" value,

$$\varepsilon_1^{f}(\omega) = 1 - \frac{4\pi N_v e^2}{m^*(\omega^2 + \tau^{-2})}$$

Such an expression is satisfactory only in the very low frequency region; for a consistent account it is necessary that one includes, as well, the interband contributions to $\varepsilon_1(\omega)$, which correspond to an additional frequency-dependent polarizability. Also EP find that $\varepsilon_2(\omega)$ for $\omega \lesssim \omega_i$ cannot be fit with the simple form:

$$\varepsilon_2^{f}(\omega) = \frac{4\pi N_v e^2}{m^* \omega\tau} \; \frac{1}{\omega^2 + \tau^{-2}}$$

where τ is a constant; in other words, the true single-particle damping is frequency-dependent. EP find that τ decreases from its d-c value of 3.7×10^{-14} sec to 1.6×10^{-14} at 3 ev for Ag; while for Cu, it decreases from a d-c value of 3.5×10^{-14} to 1.6×10^{-14} sec at 2 ev.

One can obtain an estimate of the distribution of oscillator strengths for both the intraband and interband transitions by computing the effective number of electrons $n_{eff}(\omega_0)$ defined according to

$$\int_0^{\omega_0} d\omega\ \varepsilon_2(\omega)\omega = \frac{2\pi^2 N n_{eff}(\omega_0)e^2}{m} \tag{4-118}$$

where N is the number of atoms per volume and $n_{eff}(\omega_0)$ is the effective number contributing to optical transitions below an energy of $\hbar\omega_0$. It is clear from the f-sum rule, (4-88), that if one can neglect the contribution to (4-118) from the electrons lying below the d-shells, then the maximum value of $n_{eff}(\omega_0) = 11$ (1 s plus 10 d-shell electrons). Moreover, if $\omega_0 \leq \omega_i$, and $\omega_0\tau >> 1$, then one expects to find $n_{eff}(\omega_0) \approx m/m*$, according to (4-115). The values obtained by EP for $n_{eff}(\omega_0)$ are shown in Fig. 4-12. One sees there the near constancy of $n_{eff}(\omega_0)$ once the intraband contributions have been exhausted, the onset of the interband transitions, and, finally, the rather uniform distribution of interband oscillator strengths over the region extending up to 25 ev.

Perhaps the clearest way of seeing the contribution of the interband transitions to $\varepsilon_1(\omega)$ is to decompose it into a free-electron part, and an interband part, throughout the frequency range of interest. Such a decomposition has been carried out by EP, and is shown in Figs. 4-13 and 4-14 for Ag and Cu. There one sees that in the absence of interband transitions, one would have a zero of $\varepsilon_1(\omega)$ at

$$\omega_p^* = \left(\frac{4\pi N_v e^2}{m^*}\right)^{1/2} = \begin{cases} 9.2 \text{ ev for Ag} \\ 9.3 \text{ ev for Cu} \end{cases}$$

In the case of Ag, the interband transitions cause the zero to be reduced to a value slightly below ω_i (~ 3.9 ev). Since, moreover, $\varepsilon_2 << 1$ in this region, there is a sharp peak in the characteristic energy-loss spectrum at this energy, as may be seen in Fig. 4-9. This loss near ω_i meets all the criteria for plasmon behavior—$\varepsilon_1 << 1$, $\varepsilon_2 << 1$—yet it is little related to the "free-electron" behavior, arising as it does out of the strong, sharp, interband contribution to $\varepsilon_1(\omega)$ at $\omega \cong \omega_i$. The resonance is a mixed, or hybrid, plasma resonance, requiring, as it does, the cooperative behavior of both d and s electrons. Whether such a resonance can occur depends, among other factors, upon the strength and the position of the interband transitions in question. Thus for Cu one sees that the interband transition at ~ 2.1 ev involves, in fact, a larger oscillator strength than the corresponding interband transition at 3.9 ev in Ag; however, because it comes in at a lower frequency, where $\varepsilon_1^{(f)}$ is still quite negative, it is not sufficiently strong to bring $\varepsilon_1(\omega)$ up to zero. As a result, no such hybrid resonance is seen in Cu.

One does see, in Ag, a further peak in Im ε^{-1} at 7.5 ev; it is likely that this represents the free s-electron plasma resonance, which has

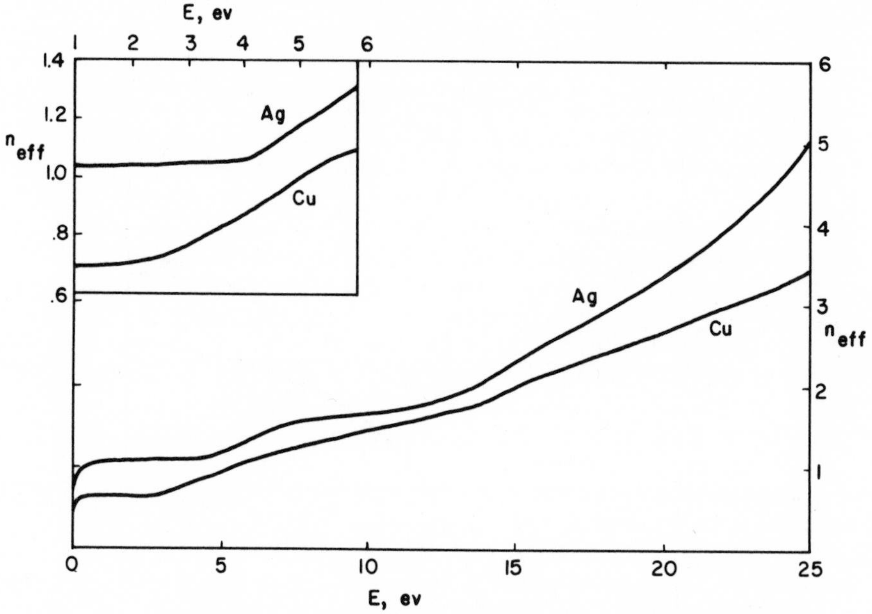

Fig. 4-12. Effective number of electrons per atom vs. E obtained from numerical integration of experimental ε_2 using (4-118). (From H. Ehrenreich and H. R. Phillip.[28])

been pushed down by the d-electron interband transitions. In the same way, one could regard the 7.5 ev peak in Cu as due to a free s-electron plasmon, modified by the d-band transitions. In both cases, since one deals with a two-plasma problem, of coupled d and s electrons, one might expect to find a higher-energy plasmon as well. (The low-energy plasmon can be regarded as associated with an in-phase motion of s vs. d electrons; the high-frequency plasmon, with an out-of-phase motion.) The energy loss at 25 ev in Ag, which Robins[14] has observed, and that at 19.9 ev in Cu, observed for example by Powell,[12] would fit nicely into such a picture. However, in view of the obvious complexity of the structure of the loss spectrum, such remarks can serve only as a qualitative guide in understanding the experimental results. It should also be remarked that complete agreement between the characteristic energy-loss measurements we have mentioned, and the work of EP on Ag and Cu, is not to be expected, since surface plasmons may well play an important role in the characteristic energy-loss experiments.

We consider next the work of Philipp and Ehrenreich[29] on the optical properties of semiconductors possessing the diamond or zinc-blende structure. In Fig. 4-15 we reproduce their results for the

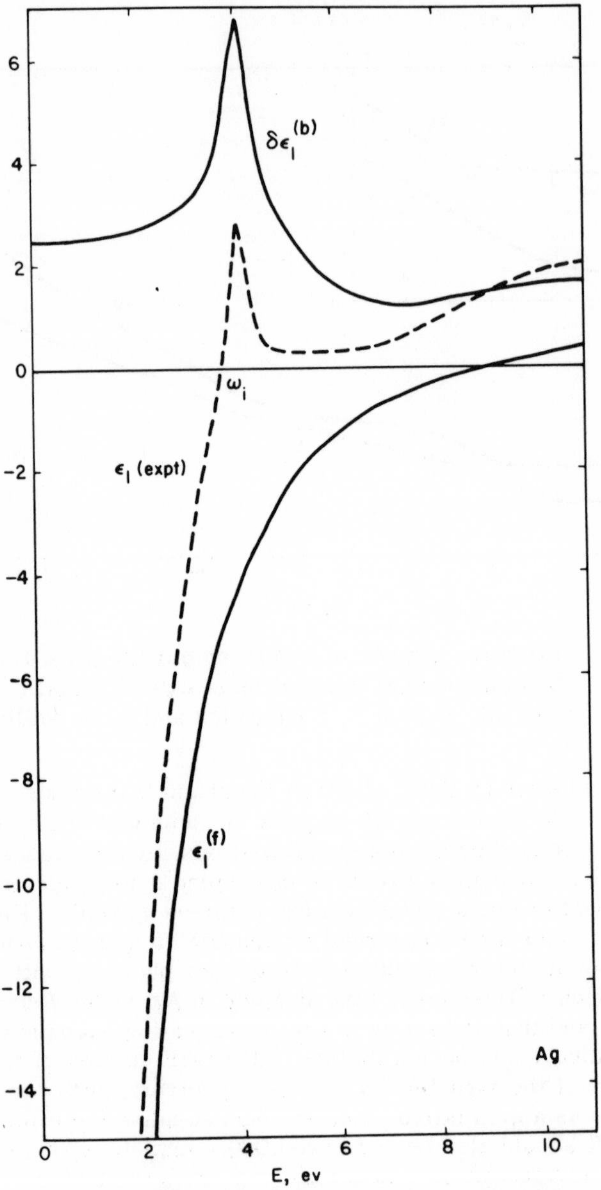

Fig. 4-13. Decomposition of the experimental values of ε_1 for Ag into free and bound contributions $\varepsilon_1^{(f)}$ and $\delta\varepsilon_1^{(b)}$. The threshold energy for interband transitions is indicated by ω_i. (From H. Ehrenreich and H. R. Phillip.[28])

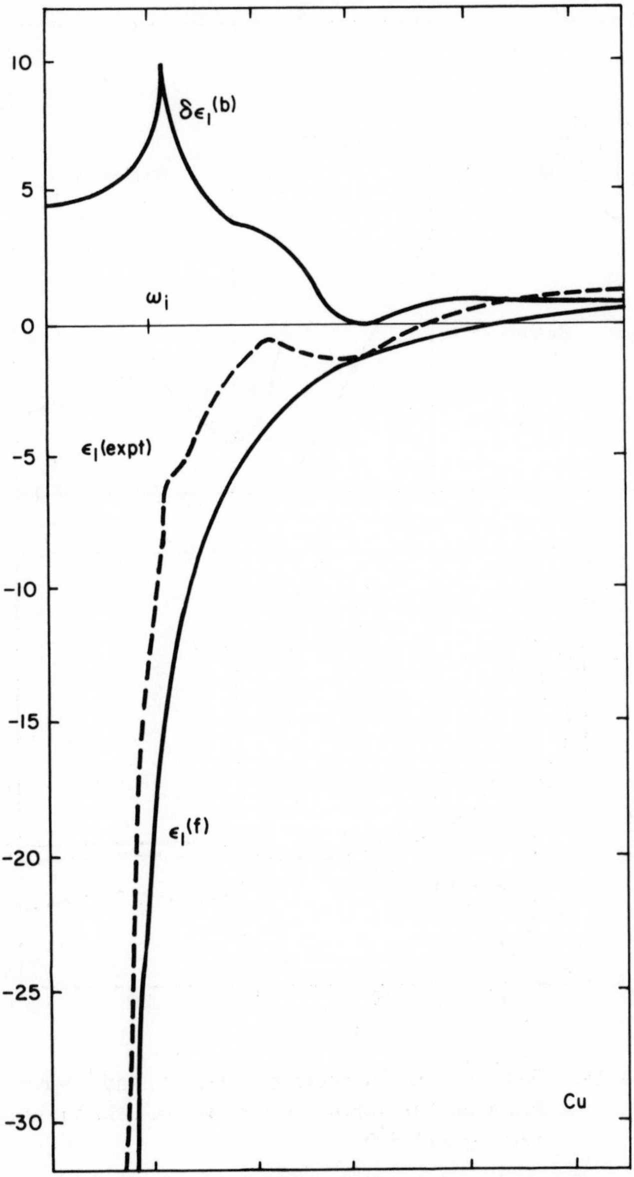

Fig. 4-14. Decomposition of the experimental values of ε_1 for Cu into free and bound contributions $\varepsilon_1^{(f)}$ and $\delta\varepsilon_1^{(b)}$. The threshold energy for interband transitions is indicated by ω_i. (From H. Ehrenreich and H. R. Phillip.[28])

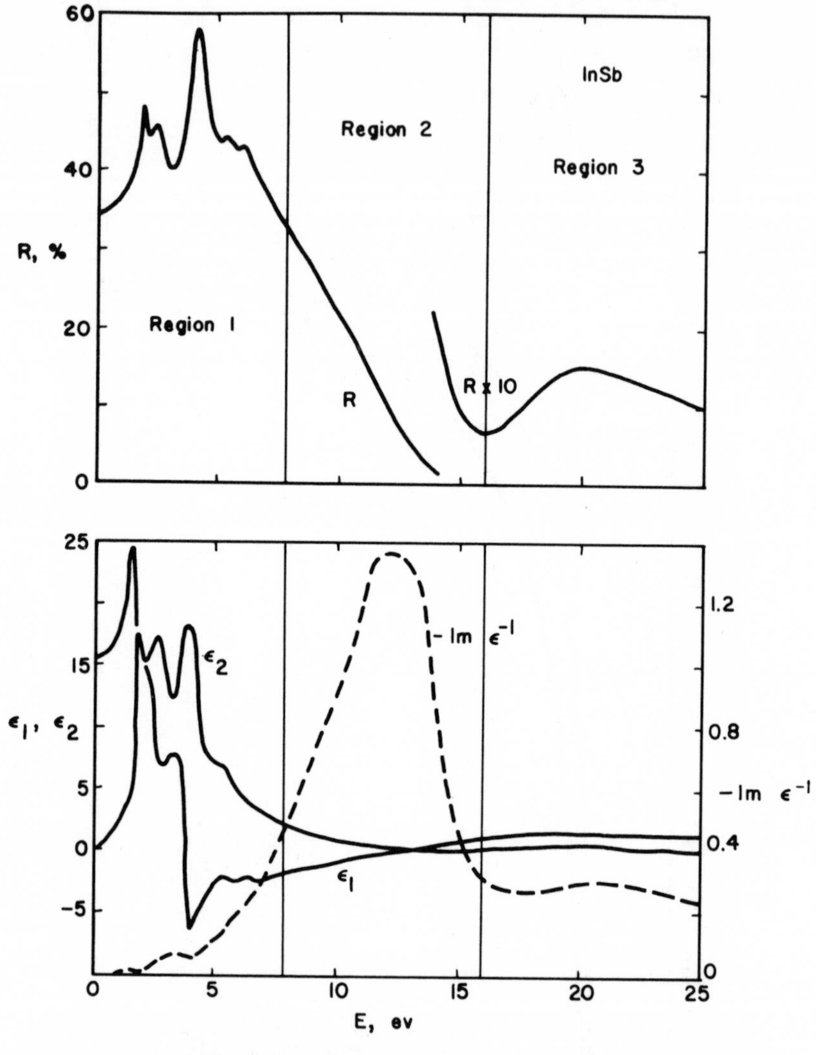

Fig. 4-15. Reflectance, dielectric constant, and energy loss function for InSb. (From H. R. Phillip and H. Ehrenreich.[29])

reflectance and dielectric constants of InSb. Such behavior is characteristic of this group of semiconductors. In region 1 one is observing interband transitions between the valence band and conduction bands; in region 2 one has nearly free-electron-like behavior, while in region 3 one sees the onset of transitions from the d band (where it exists) to the conduction bands. In what follows, we shall confine our attention to the optical properties in regions 2 and 3.

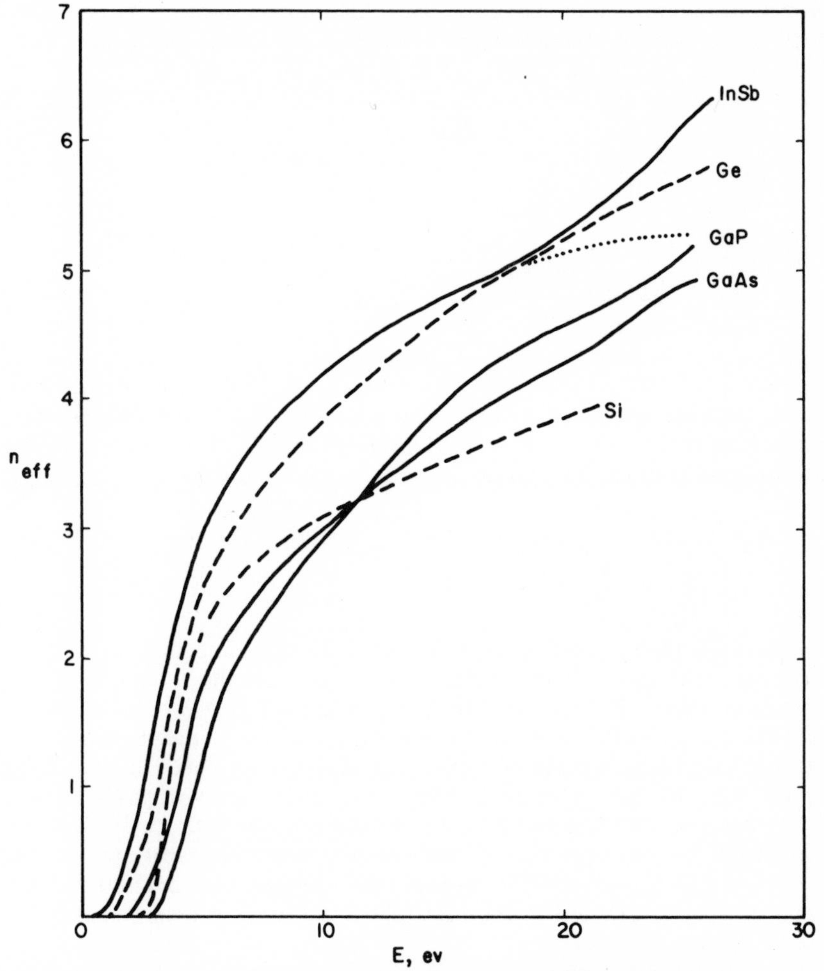

Fig. 4-16. n_{eff} for various semiconductors. (From H. R. Phillip and H. Ehrenreich.[29])

As was the case with Ag and Cu, we may get an idea of the distribution of interband oscillator strengths with energy by plotting $n_{eff}(E)$ as a function of E. (Intraband excitations, of course, now play no role.) The results obtained by PE are shown in Fig. 4-16. The rapid rise of $n_{eff}(E)$ in the region below 10 ev is associated with the valence-electron interband transitions. On the other hand, if only the valence band were important, in the energy range studied, then $n_{eff}(E)$ would saturate at 4. This it appears to do for Si, which is comforting, since there are no nearby lower-lying bands. For the other semiconductors shown, $n_{eff}(E)$ goes beyond 4. This it may do for two reasons. First, because the d band plays a role, the valence electron oscillator strengths are enhanced, as discussed in Sec. 4-1. For a simple two-band model, as discussed there, one has

$$\varepsilon_2(\omega) = \frac{2\pi^2 e^2}{m}\left\{ \sum_{\substack{p \\ \ell > v}} \frac{f_{\ell v}(p)}{\omega_{\ell v}}\, \delta[\omega - \omega_{\ell v}(p)] + \sum_{\substack{p \\ \ell > v}} \frac{f_{\ell d}(p)}{\omega_{\ell d}}\, \delta[\omega - \omega_{\ell d}(p)] \right\} \tag{4-119}$$

Hence, on making use of (4-118), one sees that if ω_0 is such that the transitions from valence electron states to higher states are complete, and yet less than the minimum $\omega_{\ell d}$, then one should have

$$n_{eff}(\omega_0) = \sum_{\substack{p \\ \ell > v}} f_{\ell v}(p) = N_v + \sum_{p} f_{vd}(p) = N_{eff} \tag{4-120}$$

[compare (4-17)]. The second reason for an increase in $n_{eff}(\omega_0)$ is, of course, the onset of interband transitions from the d band to the conduction band. EP have attempted a rough separation of the two effects for the 3-5 compounds by remarking that the break in the $n_{eff}(E)$ curve for these materials could be attributed to an onset of real d-band transitions. In that case, an extrapolation of the smooth part of the curve, such as that indicated by the dotted line for InSb, will yield an estimate of the enhancement of the valence-electron oscillator strength sum from 4 to N_{eff}. As EP remark, the absence of a break for the Ge curve may be attributed to the fact that the d band is considerably deeper in this material.

Further information on the role of the d bands may be obtained by computing the contribution which the various bands make to the static dielectric constant, ε_o. According to the Kramers-Kronig relations, one has

$$\varepsilon_o = 1 + \frac{2}{\pi}\int_0^\infty d\omega\, \frac{\varepsilon_2(\omega)}{\omega} \tag{4-121}$$

One can therefore define an "effective" dielectric constant, which represents a different mean of the interband transitions from that represented by the sum rule, (4-118), according to the relation

$$\varepsilon_{o,eff}(\omega_0) = 1 + \frac{2}{\pi}\int_0^{\omega_0} d\omega\ \frac{\varepsilon_2(\omega)}{\omega} \tag{4-122}$$

If, as is the case for Si, only the valence-electron transitions are important, then $\varepsilon_{o,eff}(\omega_0)$ should saturate at the static value, here 11.6. This it does, as may be seen in Fig. 4-17. On the other hand, for the semiconductors where the d-band polarizability is nonnegligible, one may estimate it by writing

$$\varepsilon_o = \varepsilon_{o,eff}(\omega_0) + \delta\varepsilon_o \tag{4-123}$$

where $\delta\varepsilon_o$ is the d-band polarizability. The values of $\delta\varepsilon_o$ obtained by PE are given in Fig. 4-17.

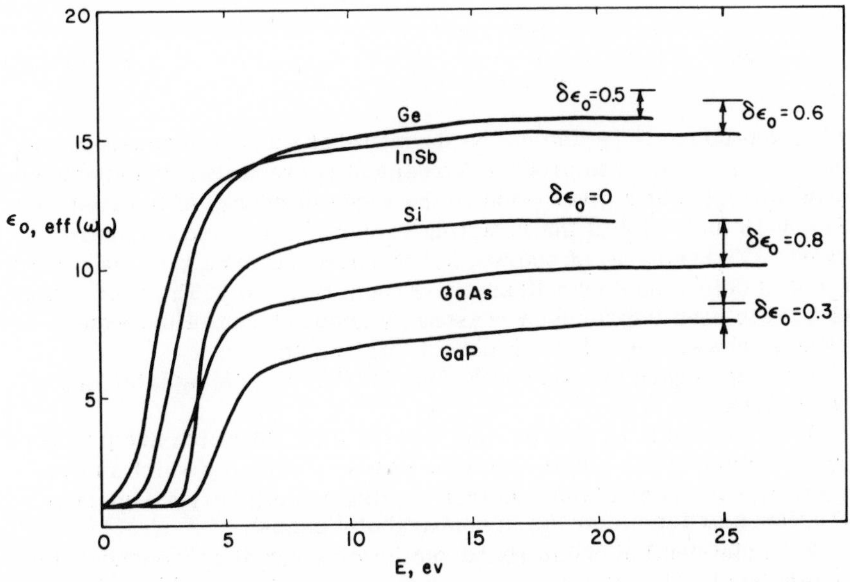

Fig. 4-17. Contributions to the static dielectric constant, according to (4-122). (From H. R. Phillip and H. Ehrenreich.[29])

Consider next the behavior of ε_1 and ε_2 in the "free-electron" region between 10 and 20 ev, say. If the frequency of interest were such that $\omega_{\ell v} < \omega < \omega_{\ell d}$ for all $\omega_{\ell v}$ and $\omega_{\ell d}$ of importance, then throughout this region one would have

$$\varepsilon_1(\omega) = 1 + \delta\varepsilon_o - \frac{4\pi N_{eff} e^2}{m\omega^2}$$
$$\varepsilon_2(\omega) = 0 \qquad (4\text{-}124)$$

[compare (4-42) and (4-43)], where $\delta\varepsilon_0$ is the static d-electron polarizability, and N_{eff} is the "enhanced" sum of valence-electron oscillator strengths, given by (4-120). The value of the plasmon energy, $\omega_{pv}^* = \{4\pi N_{eff} e^2/m[1 + \delta\varepsilon_o]\}^{1/2}$, so obtained, is quoted in Table 4-7. EP find that such an expression does not agree with experiment in detail; that it should not is obvious from Fig. 4-16, where one sees that there are important frequency-dependent contributions to $n_{eff}(E)$ throughout this energy region. EP have attempted to account for these by a simple empirical expression:

$$\varepsilon(\omega) = 1 + \delta\varepsilon_o - \frac{4\pi N_{eff} e^2}{m(\omega + i/\tau)^2} \qquad (4\text{-}125)$$

They determine N_{eff} and $\delta\varepsilon_o$ in the way that we have discussed, and then choose τ so as to produce agreement between theory and experiment for $\varepsilon_2(\omega)$ at a given point in the range of energy of interest. In Fig. 4-18 their plot of the resulting values of $\varepsilon_2(\omega)$ and $\varepsilon_1(\omega)$ are given. [The two are, of course, not independent; once $\varepsilon_2(\omega)$ is chosen, $\varepsilon_1(\omega)$ is determined by a Kramers-Kronig relation.] The expression (4-125) is seen to provide a reasonably good account of the experimental behavior of $\varepsilon_2(\omega)$ throughout this region.

One can regard an expression like (4-125) as arising from one of two causes:

1. Corrections to $\varepsilon(\omega)$ arising outside the RPA which are produced by a damping of the single-particle states—a damping which is presumably due to electron-electron collisions (either via Umklapp processes or for electrons in nonparabolic bands).

2. A distribution of interband oscillator strengths throughout this region, such that a value of $\varepsilon_2(\omega)$ within the RPA resembles closely that obtained from (4-125).

Without detailed calculation of the damping corrections to $\varepsilon(\omega)$, it is difficult to see how one can, a priori, choose one mechanism over the other.

The measurements reported by PE also enable one to make a detailed comparison between the optical determination of $-\operatorname{Im} \varepsilon^{-1}$, and that quantity as measured in a characteristic energy-loss experiment. In making the comparison, PE normalized the energy-loss data in such a way that the peak value of the energy-loss curve was equal to the maximum of $-\operatorname{Im} \varepsilon^{-1}$. In Fig. 4-19, their comparison of the optical data with the energy-loss experiments of Powell[12] for Ge, and

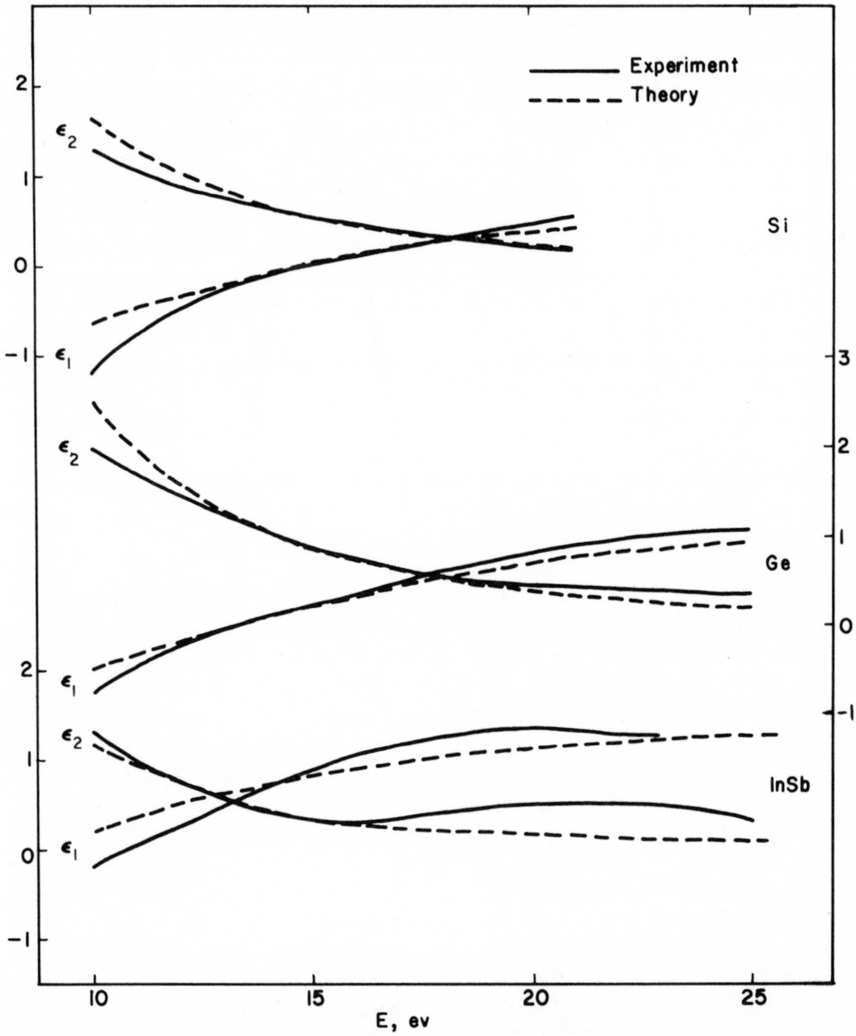

Fig. 4-18. Experimental and theoretical curves of ε_1 and ε_2 for Si, Ge, and InSb. The theoretically determined parameters are $\delta\varepsilon_o = 0$, 0.5, and 0.6, and $\hbar\omega_{pv} = 16.6$, 16.2, and 11.5 ev, respectively, for Si, Ge, and InSb. The adjustable parameter τ is taken to be respectively 1.6, 1.4, and 1.8×10^{-16} sec. (From H. R. Phillip and H. Ehrenreich.[29])

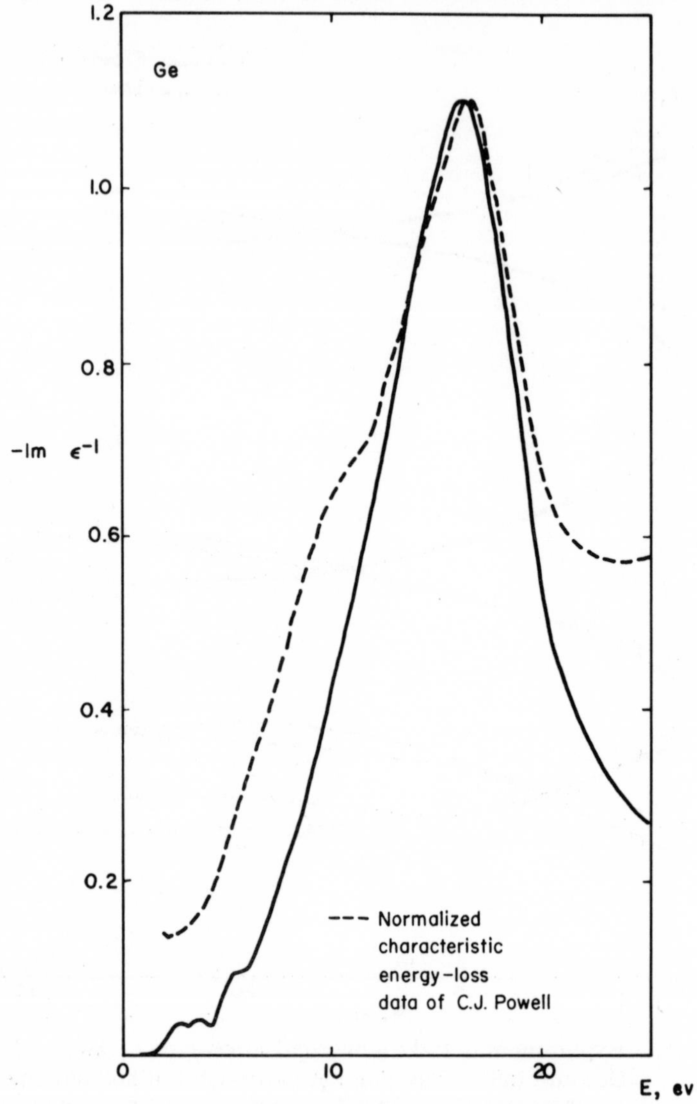

Fig. 4-19. Comparison of energy loss and optical measurements of the energy-loss function. (From H. R. Phillip and H. Ehrenreich.[29])

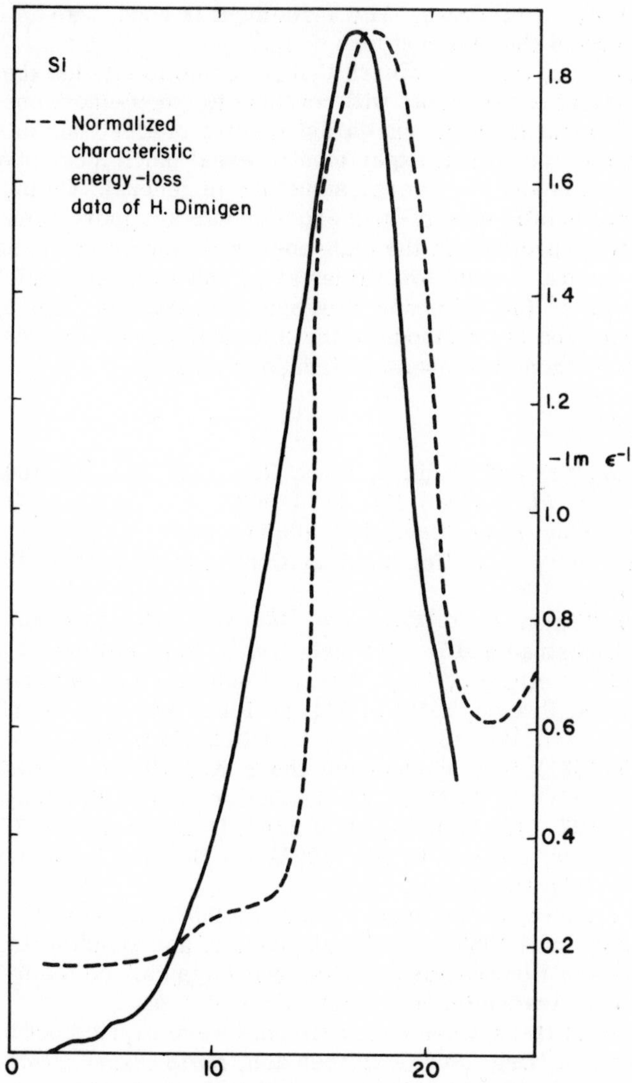

Fig. 4-19. Comparison of energy loss and optical measurements of the energy-loss function. (From H. R. Phillip and H. Ehrenreich[29])—Continued.

Dimigen[36] for Si, is shown. The agreement is good, both as to position and width of the plasmon loss.

In conclusion, we may remark that it seems likely that the energy-loss and optical experiments will continue to complement one another as tools for measuring the excitation spectra of electrons in solids. It is clear that the optical experiments reveal much more about interband transitions and low-energy structure in general. On the other hand, characteristic energy-loss experiments are more sensitive to the excitation spectrum in the high-energy region ($\gtrsim$ 15 ev, say), in which the generally quite low values of ε_1 and ε_2 make it difficult to determine Im $\varepsilon^{-1}(\omega)$ by means of optical experiments. The agreement between the two methods in the intermediate energy region in which both methods are useful is indeed gratifying.

References

1. P. Nozières and D. Pines, *Phys. Rev.*, 109, 741, 762, 1062 (1958).

1a. S. Adler, *Phys. Rev.*, 126, 413 (1962).

1b. D. R. Penn, *Phys. Rev.*, 128, 2093 (1962).

2. N. F. Mott, Proc. Tenth Solvay Congress, R. Stoops, Brussels, 1954.

2a. C. B. Wilson, *Proc. Phys. Soc. (London)*, 76, 481 (1960).

3. M. Glicksman and M. C. Steele, *Phys. Rev. Letters*, 2, 461 (1959); P. Aigrain, Proc. Intern. Conference on Semiconductor Physics, Prague, 1960, p. 224; D. Pines and J. R. Schrieffer, *Phys. Rev.*, 124, 1387 (1961); M. Glicksman, *Phys. Rev.*, 124, 1655 (1961); S. J. Buchsbaum and J. K. Galt, *Phys. Fluids*, 4, 1514 (1961); F. E. Rose, M. T. Taylor, and R. Bowers, *Phys. Rev.*, 127, 1122 (1962); S. Ichimaru, D. Pines, and N. Rostoker, *Phys. Rev. Letters*, 8, 231 (1962). J. Bok and P. Nozières, *Phys. Rev.* (to be published).

4. For a survey of the experimental methods and results in this field up until 1955, see Marton, Leder, and Mandlowitz, in "Advances in Electronics and Electron Physics," edited by L. Marton, Academic, New York, 1955, Vol. 7.

5. The first transmission experiments were carried out by Ruthemann and Lang. See G. Ruthemann, *Naturwissenschaften*, 29, 648 (1941); 30, 142 (1942); *Ann. Physik*, (6) 2, 113 (1948); W. Lang, *Optik*, 3, 233 (1948).

6. The first reflection experiments were carried out by Rudberg, *Proc. Roy. Soc. (London)*, A27, 111 (1930); *Phys. Rev.*, 50, 138 (1936).

6a. D. Pines and D. Bohm, *Phys. Rev.*, 85, 338 (1952).

7. H. Watanabe, *J. Phys. Soc. Japan*, 11, 112 (1956).

8. D. Pines, *Rev. Mod. Phys.*, 28, 184 (1956).

9. P. Nozières and D. Pines, *Phys. Rev.*, 113, 1254 (1959).

10. D. Pines, *Physica*, 26, S103 (1960).

11. C. J. Powell and J. B. Swan, *Phys. Rev.*, 118, 640 (1960).
12. C. J. Powell, *Proc. Phys. Soc. (London)*, 76, 593 (1960).
13. J. L. Robins and J. B. Swan, *Proc. Phys. Soc. (London)*, 76, 857 (1960).
14. J. L. Robins, *Proc. Phys. Soc. (London)*, 78, 1177 (1961).
15. J. L. Robins and P. E. Best, *Proc. Phys. Soc. (London)*, 79, 110 (1962).
16. J. L. Robins, *Proc. Phys. Soc. (London)*, 79, 119 (1962).
17. P. E. Best, *Proc. Phys. Soc. (London)*, 79, 133 (1962).
18. R. H. Ritchie, *Phys. Rev.*, 106, 874 (1957).
19. E. A. Stern and R. A. Ferrell, *Phys. Rev.*, 120, 130 (1960).
20. R. A. Ferrell, *Phys. Rev.*, 107, 450 (1957).
21. R. A. Ferrell, *Phys. Rev.*, 101, 554 (1956).
22. A. W. Blackstock, R. H. Ritchie, and R. D. Birkhoff, *Phys. Rev.*, 100, 1078 (1955).
23. A field-theoretic derivation of this result has been given by V. Ambegoakar and W. Kohn, *Phys. Rev.*, 117, 423 (1960).
24. J. Lindhard, *J. Kgl. Danske Videnskab. Selskab., Mat.-fys. Medd.*, 28, 8 (1954).
25. J. L. Warren and R. A. Ferrell, *Phys. Rev.*, 117, 1252 (1960).
26. J. S. Langer, *Phys. Rev.*, 124, 997 (1961); G. Rickayzen, in "The Many-Body Problem" (Proc. Bergen School of Physics, 1961), edited by C. Fronsdal, Benjamin, New York, 1962, p. 85.
27. D. Bohm and D. Pines, *Phys. Rev.*, 82, 625 (1951).
28. H. Ehrenreich and H. R. Philipp, *Phys. Rev.*, 128, 1622 (1962), hereafter referred to as EP.
29. H. Ehrenreich and H. R. Philipp, Proc. 1962 Exeter Conf. on Semiconductors, *Proc. Phys. Soc. (London)*, to be published; H. R. Philipp and H. Ehrenreich, *Phys. Rev.* (to be published), hereafter referred to as PE.
30. H. Mendlowitz, *J. Opt. Sci. Am.*, 50, 739 (1960).
31. Such a table was first given by R. A. Ferrell, *Phys. Rev.*, 101, 554 (1956).
32. E. A. Taft and H. R. Philipp, *Phys. Rev.*, 121, 1100 (1961).
33. L. G. Schulz, *Suppl. Phil. Mag.*, 6, 102 (1957).
34. S. Roberts, *Phys. Rev.*, 118, 1509 (1960).
35. We shall follow rather closely the analysis presented in Ref. 28.
36. H. Dimigen, *Z. Physik*, 165, 53 (1961).

Problems

4-1 Use the RPA to obtain the dielectric constant, (4-21), for electrons in a periodic array. Work out the form of the density matrix elements, $\left(\rho^{+}_{k\ \nu o}\right)$ in terms of the relevant Bloch wave states.

4-2 Derive the expression (4-28) for the static dielectric constant of a degenerate semiconductor at T = 0. [*Hint*: Consider the long-wavelength behavior of the relevant matrix elements, and use the simplified version of the Pauli principle restrictions, (3-52).]

4-3 Derive the result (4-51) for the dielectric constant appropriate to conduction electrons which obey classical statistics in a semiconductor. Using (4-51) obtain an explicit expression for $\varepsilon(k, 0)$ (4-30), and for the Landau damping of plasma waves in the long-wavelength limit.

4-4 Use the collisionless Boltzmann equation to compute the retarded response of an electron system to a long-wavelength transverse electric field, $E_\perp(k\omega)$. Show that in the limit of $k = 0$ one finds

$$\sigma_\perp(k, 0) = \frac{3\pi N e^2}{4 q k_o}$$

4-5 Use (4-108) to calculate the cross section for plasmon production in the Compton scattering of electromagnetic waves. Design a possible experiment to measure the effect.

4-6 It is sometimes convenient to introduce the spectral function, $g(\omega)$, for the oscillator strengths, f_{on}, which is defined by

$$g(\omega) = \frac{1}{N_v} \sum_n f_{on}\, \delta(\omega - \omega_{no})$$

where N_v is the number of electrons in the band under consideration. Obtain explicit expressions for the f-sum rule, $\varepsilon_1(\omega)$, $\varepsilon_2(\omega)$, and ε_o in terms of $g(\omega)$; discuss the form of $g(\omega)$ which is required in order to fit the results obtained by Phillip and Ehrenreich for silicon in the frequency range 6 to 20 ev.

Chapter 5

ELECTRON-PHONON INTERACTION IN METALS

5-1 BASIC HAMILTONIAN

We now consider the full Hamiltonian for conduction electrons in metals, that is (1-4), in which the effects of both electron-electron and electron-ion interaction on the motion of phonons and electrons is taken into account. The new feature is the interaction of the electrons with the ion displacements, which gives rise to the electron-phonon interaction.

We may write our basic Hamiltonian in the following form:

$$H = \sum_i \frac{p_i^2}{2m} + \sum_{i\alpha} v(\mathbf{r}_i - \mathbf{R}_\alpha) + \frac{1}{2} \sum_{i \neq j} \frac{e^2}{|\mathbf{r}_i - \mathbf{r}_j|} + H_{ph} \tag{5-1}$$

where the second term represents the electron-ion interaction, and

$$H_{ph} = \sum_{k\mu} \frac{p_{k\mu}^{+} p_{k\mu}}{2} + \frac{\Omega_{k\mu}^2}{2} q_{k\mu}^{+} q_{k\mu} \tag{5-2}$$

is the phonon Hamiltonian considered in Chapter 2. We are keeping the harmonic terms in the expansion of the ion-ion interaction, so that we are neglecting phonon-phonon interaction in this chapter. We shall furthermore assume that the ion-ion and ion-electron interactions are pure Coulomb interactions; as we have already mentioned in Chapter 1, we thereby neglect the Pauli principle repulsion associated with the core electrons attached to each ion. In order to eliminate infinities which appear in the separate terms of (5-1) (although not in the sum) we suppose there is subtracted from the electron-ion interaction the interaction of each electron with a uniform positive charge distribution;

from the electron-electron interaction the self-energy of a uniform negative charge distribution; and from the ion-ion interaction the self-energy of a uniform positive charge distribution. The sum of these corrections adds to zero, so that the total system energy is unchanged. Thus the phonon Hamiltonian, H_{ph}, is that of a collection of ions immersed in a uniform background of negative charge, which we have already studied in Chapter 2.

We now treat the electron-ion interaction by expanding about the equilibrium position of the ions, according to

$$\mathbf{R}_\alpha = \mathbf{R}_{o\alpha} + \delta\mathbf{R}_\alpha \tag{5-3}$$

where $\delta\mathbf{R}_\alpha$, the departure from equilibrium, is again taken to be small. The electron-ion interaction then becomes

$$\sum_{i,\alpha} v(\mathbf{r}_i - \mathbf{R}_\alpha) = \sum_{i,\alpha} v(\mathbf{r}_i - \mathbf{R}_{o\alpha}) + \sum_{i,\alpha} \delta\mathbf{R}_\alpha \cdot \nabla v(\mathbf{r}_i - \mathbf{R}_{o\alpha}) \tag{5-4}$$

We are assuming that the form of the interaction of the electron with the ion is not affected by the ion displacement; in other words, $v(\mathbf{r}_i - \mathbf{R}_i)$ does not depend on whether $\mathbf{R}_i = \mathbf{R}_{oi}$ or $\mathbf{R}_{oi} + \delta\mathbf{R}_i$. This is the so-called "rigid ion" model first introduced by Nordheim. We now combine the first term of (5-4) with the electron kinetic energy, and express that part of the Hamiltonian in terms of the Bloch waves for a single electron moving in the periodic static potential of the ions. The Bloch equation is

$$[p^2/2m + v(\mathbf{r})]\, \psi_p(\mathbf{r}) = E_p^B \psi_p(\mathbf{r}) \tag{5-5}$$

where $v(\mathbf{r})$ is the potential of the ions compensated by a uniform negative charge, and may be taken as well to include the periodic Hartree field v_H arising in the electron-electron interaction.

$$v(\mathbf{r}) = \sum_\alpha v(\mathbf{r} - \mathbf{R}_{o\alpha}) + \text{comp. charge} + v_H \tag{5-6}$$

We have used the extended zone scheme, so that p in (5-5) is not necessarily in the first Brillouin zone. As we have seen, the solution for the many-electron Hamiltonian,

$$H_{el} = \sum_i p_i^2/2m + \sum_i v(\mathbf{r}_i) \tag{5-7}$$

can be built up from Slater determinants formed from the one-electron Bloch wave functions,

$$\psi_p(\mathbf{r}) = e^{i\mathbf{k}\cdot\mathbf{r}}\, u_p(\mathbf{r}) \tag{5-8}$$

where $u_p(r)$ is a function with the translational periodicity of the lattice. We shall find it convenient to introduce the second-quantized Bloch wave operators, by regarding $\psi_p(r)$ as a wave field. As discussed in Appendix A we can then replace H_{el}, (5-7), by the appropriate Bloch wave second-quantized Hamiltonian:

$$H_{el} = \sum_p \varepsilon_p^B c_{p\sigma}^+ c_{p\sigma} \tag{5-9}$$

where the $c_{p\sigma}$ and $c_{p\sigma}^+$ act to destroy and create electrons in Bloch wave states specified according to (5-5). They satisfy the usual anti-commutation relations,

$$\{c_{p\sigma}, c_{p'\sigma'}^+\} = \delta_{p,p'}\,\delta_{\sigma,\sigma'}$$

In what follows, we shall suppress the spin indices σ except where necessary for clarity.

Let us now look at the second term of (5-4), which describes the interaction between the electrons and the lattice displacements. We may use the expansion

$$\delta \mathbf{R}_i = \frac{1}{(NM)^{1/2}} \sum_{k\mu} q_{k\mu}\,\varepsilon_{k\mu}\, e^{i\mathbf{k}\cdot\mathbf{R}_{o\alpha}} \tag{5-10}$$

where $\varepsilon_{k\mu}$ is the unit polarization vector, to obtain

$$H_{int} = -\sum_{i\alpha} \delta\mathbf{R}_\alpha \cdot \nabla v(\mathbf{r}_i - \mathbf{R}_{o\alpha})$$

$$= -\frac{1}{(NM)^{1/2}} \sum_{ik\mu\alpha} \varepsilon_{k\mu} \cdot \nabla v(\mathbf{r}_i - \mathbf{R}_{o\alpha})\, q_{k\mu}\, e^{i\mathbf{k}\cdot\mathbf{R}_{o\alpha}} \tag{5-11}$$

We recall that the normal mode coordinate $q_{k\mu}$ may be expressed in terms of phonon creation and annihilation operators, according to

$$q_{k\mu} = \left(\frac{\hbar}{2\Omega_{k\mu}}\right)^{1/2} (a_{k\mu} + a_{-k\mu}^+)$$

so that the kth normal-mode part of (5-11) gives rise to processes in which a phonon of pseudo-momentum $\hbar k$ is absorbed, or one of momentum $-\hbar k$ is emitted. What sort of electron transitions are associated with this mode? We are interested in the matrix elements of H_{int} between two Bloch wave states, ψ_p and $\psi_{p'}$, since only one-electron transitions play a role. We have, on Fourier-analyzing $v(r)$,

$$v(\mathbf{r}) = \sum_{q} v_q \, e^{i\mathbf{q}\cdot\mathbf{r}}$$

the following expression for the matrix element:

$$< \psi_{\mathbf{p}'} | \, H_{int} (\mathbf{k}) | \, \psi_{\mathbf{p}} > \; = \int \frac{d^3 r}{(NM)^{1/2}} \, \psi^{+}_{\mathbf{p}'} (\mathbf{r})$$

$$\times \sum_{q\alpha} i\mathbf{q}\cdot\varepsilon_{k\mu} v_q e^{i\mathbf{q}\cdot\mathbf{r}} e^{-i\mathbf{q}\cdot\mathbf{R}_{o\alpha}} e^{i\mathbf{k}\cdot\mathbf{R}_{o\alpha}} \psi_{\mathbf{p}}(\mathbf{r}) \tag{5-12}$$

Upon making use of the relation (2-5),

$$\sum_{\alpha} e^{i(\mathbf{k}-\mathbf{q})\cdot\mathbf{R}_{o\alpha}} = \sum_{n} N\delta_{\mathbf{q},\mathbf{k}+\mathbf{K}_n}$$

we find

$$< \psi_{\mathbf{p}'} | \, H_{int} (\mathbf{k}) | \, \psi_{\mathbf{p}} > \; = \sum_{n} \frac{i(\mathbf{k}+\mathbf{K}_n)}{(NM)^{1/2}} \cdot \varepsilon_{k\mu} v_{\mathbf{k}+\mathbf{K}_n}$$

$$\times \int d^3 r \; \psi^{+}_{\mathbf{p}'} (\mathbf{r}) \psi_{\mathbf{p}} (\mathbf{r}) e^{i(\mathbf{k}+\mathbf{K}_n)\cdot\mathbf{r}} \tag{5-13}$$

It follows at once that

$$p' = p + k + \mathbf{K}_n \tag{5-14}$$

where $\mathbf{K}_n$ is some reciprocal lattice vector.

At first sight one might think that for a given p and p', there are a large number of reciprocal lattice vectors $\mathbf{K}_n$ which appear in (5-14). In fact, $\mathbf{K}_n$ is unique.. To see this, divide momentum space into polyhedra having the shape of the first Brillouin zone, similarly to the Wigner-Seitz division of the lattice. The reciprocal lattice vectors $\mathbf{K}_n$ reach the centers of each of these polyhedra from the center of the first BZ. Now draw in the vector p - p'. The only nonvanishing terms in the above sum are those for which one of the centers of the polyhedra can be reached by a phonon wave vector k which originates from p - p'. But, since k is restricted to the *first* zone, there is only one k and one $\mathbf{K}_n$ for which

$$p - p' + k = \mathbf{K}_n$$

So, once we have chosen the initial and final states, p, p', the whole sum of terms in H_{int} gives only two contributions, one corresponding to the emission of a phonon - k and the other to the absorption of a phonon k. (Actually, the sum over polarizations brings this up to six terms.) Examination of Fig. 5-1 for the simple square two-dimensional reciprocal lattice will bring out the essentials in the situation.

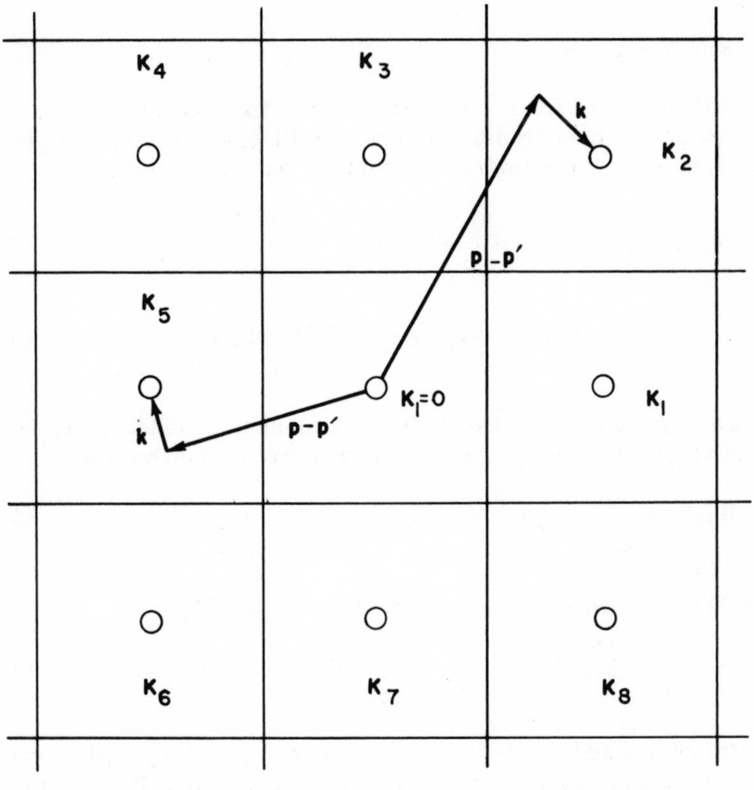

Fig. 5-1. U processes in a simple square lattice.

We observe that the conservation of momentum between initial and final states holds in a generalized sense here. It is convenient to divide the possible transitions into two groups, those for which $K_n = 0$, the "normal processes," and those for which $K_n \neq 0$, the so-called "Umklapp processes[1]:" For processes in which a phonon of pseudomomentum k is destroyed, we have the conservation conditions:

N processes: $p' = p + k$

U processes: $p' = p + k + K_n$

Instead of labeling the transitions by p and p', we can label the transitions by p and k, where k runs over all possible wave vectors. Where k is not in the first zone, one has a U process; the phonon coordinate $q_{k\mu}$ must then correspond to that value of k which lies in the first zone, according to

$$\mathbf{k} = \mathbf{p}' - \mathbf{p} - \mathbf{K}_n$$

We can then regard the kth normal mode of the electron-phonon interaction as inducing transitions between Bloch wave states, $\psi_{\mathbf{p}}(\mathbf{r})$ and $\psi_{\mathbf{p+k}}(\mathbf{r})$, and write the matrix element for such a transition as

$$v^i_{\mathbf{k}\mu} = -\frac{1}{(NM)^{1/2}} \int d^3r \; \psi^+_{\mathbf{p+k}}(\mathbf{r}) \times \left\{ \sum_{\alpha i} \varepsilon_{k\mu} \cdot \nabla v(\mathbf{r}_i - \mathbf{R}_{\alpha o}) e^{i\mathbf{k}\cdot\mathbf{R}_{\alpha o}} \right\} \psi_{\mathbf{p}}(\mathbf{r}) \tag{5-15}$$

where we have assumed that the matrix element is independent of p. We can at once write H_{int} in second-quantized form; we find

$$H_{int} = \sum_{\mathbf{k p}\mu\sigma} v^i_{k\mu} q_{k\mu} c^+_{\mathbf{p+k}\sigma} c_{\mathbf{p}\sigma} = \sum_{\mathbf{k p}\mu} v^i_{k\mu} q_{k\mu} \rho^+_k \tag{5-16}$$

where the electron-density fluctuation ρ_k is, as before,

$$\rho_{\mathbf{k}} = \sum_{\mathbf{q}\sigma} c^+_{\mathbf{q-k}\sigma} c_{\mathbf{q}\sigma} \qquad \rho_{-\mathbf{k}} = \sum_{\mathbf{q}\sigma} c^+_{\mathbf{q}\sigma} c_{\mathbf{q-k}\sigma} = \rho^+_k \tag{5-17}$$

The sum over k and q extend over all values; q_k refers to the reduced vector in the first zone. Note that $(v^i_k)^* = v^i_{-k}$, so that H_{int} is Hermitian.

The other interaction to be considered is the Coulomb interaction between electrons, which may be expressed as

$$H_{coul} = \frac{1}{2} \sum_{k} \mathcal{V}_k \, \rho^+_k \rho_k \tag{5-18}$$

For free electrons, $\mathcal{V}_k = 4\pi e^2/k^2$, as we well know.

Finally, with a neglect of the contribution from the interaction energy for the ions in equilibrium positions, the total Hamiltonian is expressed in the form

$$H = H_{el} + H_{ph} + H_{int} + H_{coul} \tag{5-19}$$

The terms in H are given by (5-9), (5-2), (5-16), and (5-18).

5-2 NEW FEATURES ASSOCIATED WITH THE ELECTRON-PHONON INTERACTION

Consequences of the Electron-Phonon Interaction

What are the consequences of the electron-phonon interaction? Probably that which is most familiar is the scattering of electrons by phonons, which is an important cause of resistance in metals. A second consequence is the absorption of phonons by the electrons; this offers a mechanism for the attenuation of a sound wave, or, in higher order, for thermal resistance in metals. Two other, closely related, phenomena are a shift in one-electron energies and a shift in phonon frequencies, which come about because we deal with a system of *interacting* electrons and phonons. Thus, as an electron moves, it will be surrounded by a co-moving phonon cloud, which acts to alter its properties; one speaks then of the dressed electron (the electron plus its associated phonon cloud) as a quasi-particle; in particular, the electron-phonon interaction will act to change the specific heat of the electron gas. Again the charge disturbance associated with the ionic motion acts to polarize the electron gas; this polarization in turn alters the effective interaction between the ions, and hence changes the phonon frequencies characteristic of the ions immersed in a uniform background of positive charge. Finally, there is introduced a new mechanism of interaction between the electrons; one can picture a given electron as acting to polarize the ions, and this polarization field in turn acting on a second electron. Alternatively, one can view this new interaction as arising from an exchange of virtual phonons. The phonon-induced electron-electron interaction is of great importance in the theory of superconductivity.

It is perhaps helpful to give a representation of these various processes in terms of Feynman diagrams; in fact, one can calculate the various effects with the aid of the appropriate rules for the diagrams in question, but such calculations lie beyond the purview of this book. The basic processes are the following:

1. Electron-phonon scattering: An electron of momentum p absorbs a phonon of momentum k, and is thereby scattered to a state p + k.

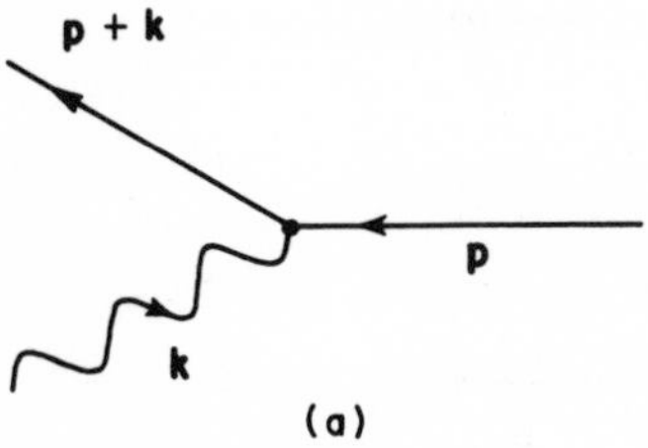

Fig. 5-2a

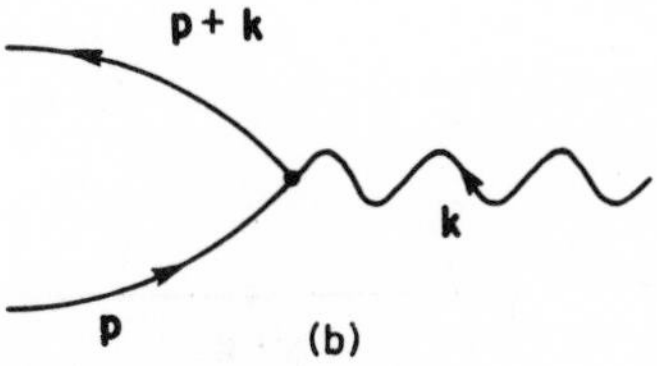

Fig. 5-2b

2. Phonon attenuation (or phonon decay): A phonon of momentum k is absorbed; in the process an electron is scattered from a state of momentum p to a state p + k. Alternatively, one can say that the phonon decays into an electron-hole pair of momentum k.

3. Dressed electrons (an electron plus its phonon cloud): Here we picture an electron of momentum p which virtually emits a phonon of momentum -k and subsequently reabsorbs it. This process is the lowest-order perturbation-theoretic contribution to the virtual phonon cloud about an electron.

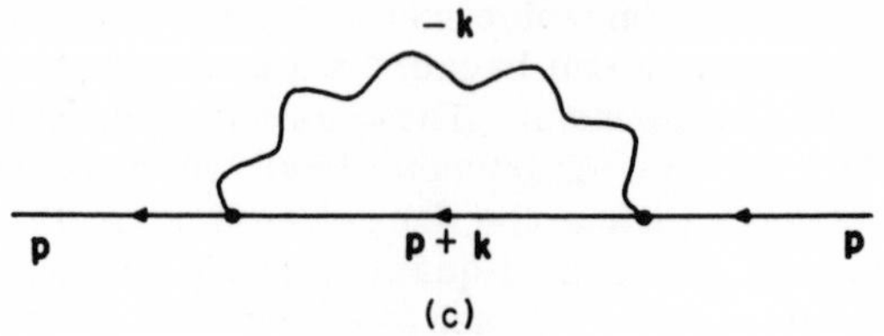

Fig. 5-2c

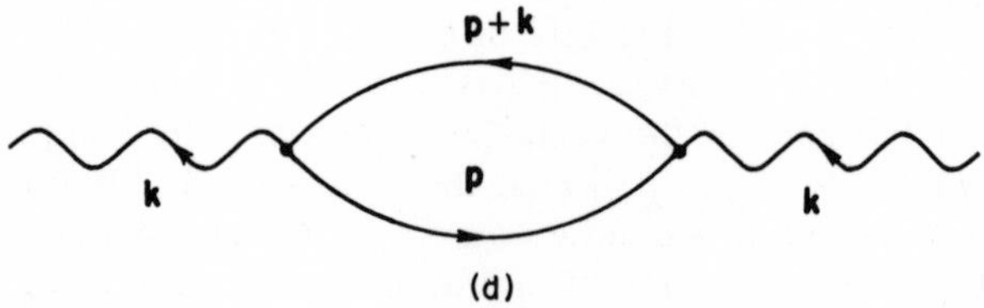

Fig. 5-2d

4. Change in phonon frequencies: A phonon of momentum k decays virtually into an electron-hole pair; subsequently that pair decays in turn into a phonon; such a process corresponds to a polarization of the electron gas.

5. Phonon-induced electron-electron interaction: Two electrons in states p and p' are scattered to states p - k and p' + k via the exchange of a virtual phonon of momentum k.

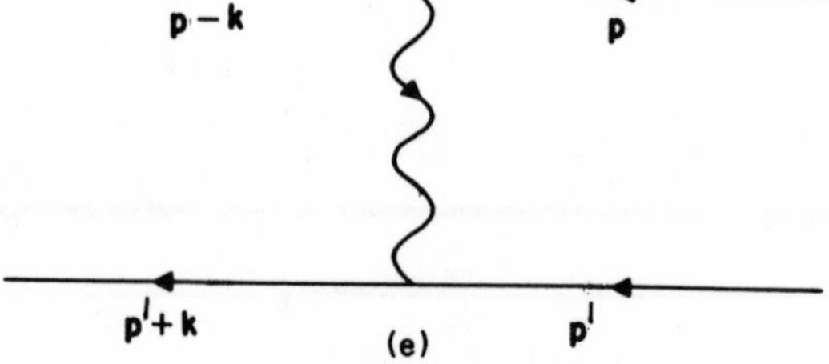

Fig. 5-2e

The alert reader may remark that (1) and (2) represent essentially the same process, while processes (3), (4), and (5) represent possible elaborations of this most elementary process. In the same way one can pass to more-complicated (and higher-order in the perturbation-theoretic hierarchy) processes, such as the scattering of phonons by electrons, etc.

To the extent that perturbation theory is applicable, one may study processes (1) and (2) by application of ordinary second-order time-dependent perturbation theory, and processes (3) through (5) by carrying out a canonical transformation which eliminates, to first order in the electron-phonon coupling, the interaction term H_{int} in (5-19). Such a calculation, in which the electron-electron interaction is neglected, has been carried out by Fröhlich.[2] We shall not go into it here because, in fact, the electron-electron interaction exerts a quite considerable influence on the various processes we have discussed.

Screening

The principal influence of the electron-electron interaction is to *screen* the bare electron-ion and ion-ion interactions present in (5-1). Consider the basic matrix element, v_k^i, which couples the electrons to the phonon field. Very roughly, we can regard the phonon field as representing an external source, coupled to the electron gas by the matrix element v_k^i; as a result of that coupling there is induced a polarization field in the electron gas which alters that coupling, in just the same way as the electrons acted to screen the test charge-electron gas interaction considered in Chapter 3. Because typical phonon frequencies are very low compared with the electronic frequencies of importance (they are of order $\sqrt{m/M}$ the typical electron frequencies), the screening action of the electron gas is very nearly that appropriate to a static external-charge disturbance. Thus the effective electron-phonon interaction is approximately given by the relation

$$v_k^{eff} = \frac{v_k^i}{\varepsilon(k,0)}$$

where $\varepsilon(k, 0)$ is the static wave-number-dependent dielectric constant of the electron gas to a given order of approximation. To put it another way, as an ion moves, it carries with it a co-moving polarization cloud of electrons, which acts to reduce the effective ionic field in the fashion specified above. In similar fashion, the "bare" ion-ion interaction is reduced by the static wave-number-dependent dielectric constant $\varepsilon(k, 0)$; as a result, the effective longitudinal sound-wave frequency is approximately given by

$$\omega_k^2 = \Omega_{k1}^2/\varepsilon(k,0)$$

where Ω_{k1} is the "bare" longitudinal phonon frequency.

In what follows, we shall first consider a version of a simplified calculation of the influence of electron-electron interaction on the electron-phonon interaction matrix element and on the sound-wave frequencies, which is due to Bardeen and the writer.[3] We shall then go on to consider processes (1), (2), (4), and (5), by means of a straightforward generalization of the dielectric constant and equation-of-motion method approach of Chapter 3.

Models for the Electron-Phonon Interaction

Throughout we shall consider a simplified model for the electron-phonon interaction. We shall assume that the longitudinal mode and the two transverse modes are distinct, an approximation which breaks down for short wavelengths and for arbitrary crystal directions (since one cannot hope in general to distinguish between longitudinal and transverse modes). For normal processes, only the longitudinal modes are coupled to the electrons in this approximation; in other words, the coupling of the long-wavelength transverse modes to the electrons only occurs via U processes. Moreover, as far as we carry out explicit calculations, we shall assume a pure Coulomb electron-ion and ion-ion interaction. We may then consider two different approximations for the "bare" ion frequencies, $\Omega_{k\mu}$, and the "bare" electron-ion matrix element, v_k^i.

In the first, the so-called "jellium" model, all effects associated with the periodicity of the ions are neglected. The ions are therefore regarded as a positive ion plasma; the "bare" ion frequencies are then the following:

$$\text{longitudinal modes:}\quad \Omega_{k1} = \Omega_p = (4\pi N Z^2 e^2/M)^{1/2}$$

$$\text{transverse modes:}\quad \Omega_{k\perp} = 0$$

where Ω_p is the ionic plasma frequency appropriate for the free ions of charge Z, mass M, immersed in a uniform background of negative charge. (There is no resistance to shear, hence the transverse frequencies vanish.) The "bare" electron-ion matrix element v_k^i is obtained from (5-15); on substituting plane waves for the electron states and $v(\mathbf{r}_i - \mathbf{R}_{\alpha o}) = e^2/|\mathbf{r}_i - \mathbf{R}_{\alpha o}|$, one finds readily that

$$v_k^i \cong -i(4\pi Z e^2/k)(N/M)^{1/2} \qquad (5\text{-}20)$$

A second model for which explicit calculations can be carried out involves keeping the effects of ionic periodicity, but again assuming the electron-ion and ion-ion interactions are purely Coulombic in nature. In this model one will have transverse lattice vibrations, the frequencies of which can be calculated directly, as we have seen in Sec. 2-2. We recall that the general character of the results for the "bare" ion frequencies can be understood by application of the sum rule, (2-62),

$$\sum_{\mu} \Omega_{k\mu}^2 = \Omega_p^2$$

For small k, the longitudinal mode frequency will be

$$\Omega_{k1}^2 = \Omega_p^2 - s_1^2 k^2$$

since at long wavelengths the two transverse mode frequencies will be proportional to k. The general character of the dispersion relation for $\Omega_{k\mu}$ as calculated in Refs. 4 and 5, was shown in Fig. 2-2. In this second model, moreover, there will be important departures of the v_k^i from the form (5-20), departures due to the influence of the periodic ionic potential on the electronic motion. We shall return to these in Sec. 5-7.

5-3 GENERAL PHYSICAL PICTURE

Let us carry out a simplified calculation of the influence of electron interactions on the longitudinal sound-wave frequencies and the matrix element for the electron-phonon interaction. We therefore drop the suffix μ in dealing with the lattice modes; q_k henceforth refers to the longitudinal lattice mode. Our basic electron-ion interaction is then given by

$$H_{int} = \sum_k v_k^i q_k \rho_k^+$$

As we have remarked, we may regard the effective matrix element for the electron lattice interaction, v_k^{eff}, as made up of two parts,

$$v_k^{eff} = v_k^i + v_k^{\rho} \qquad (5\text{-}21)$$

where v_k^{ρ} represents the contribution to the interaction arising from the electron polarization induced by the ionic motion. The first calculation of v_k^{ρ} was carried out by Bardeen in 1937,[6] in what was perhaps the first use of a self-consistent field approximation, or RPA, to treat the screening action of the electron gas. A Fermi-Thomas calculation of v_k^{ρ} has been given by Bardeen and the writer[3]; here we shall give an intuitive derivation closely related to the dielectric approach to screening developed in Chapter 3.

If, for simplicity, we regard the ionic motion as introducing a static disturbance in the electron gas (since, as we have mentioned, ionic frequencies are of order $\sqrt{m/M}$ compared to electronic frequencies) then by comparison with the macroscopic equations of Chapter 3 it is clear that Poisson's equation reads

$$k^2 \varphi_k^{ind} = k^2 v_k^{\rho} q_k = 4\pi e^2 \delta\rho_k \tag{5-22}$$

where φ_k^{ind} is the potential and $\delta\rho_k$ is the density fluctuation, induced by the sound wave of amplitude q_k. Moreover, the total potential acting on the electrons is given by

$$\varphi_k = \varphi_k^{ext} + \varphi_k^{ind} = \left(v_k^i + v_k^{\rho}\right) q_k = v_k^{eff} q_k = \varphi_k^{ext}/\varepsilon(k, 0) \tag{5-23}$$

the last equality coming from the definition of the static dielectric constant [compare (3-104)]. Hence we can write

$$v_k^{eff} = v_k^i/\varepsilon(k, 0) \tag{5-24}$$

so that the screening action of the electrons can, in this approximation, be expressed in terms of the static dielectric constant, $\varepsilon(k, 0)$.

To obtain the modification of the ionic frequencies, we write the equation of motion for the kth normal mode of the lattice:

$$\ddot{q}_k + \Omega_k^2 q_k = - v_{-k}^i \rho_k \tag{5-25}$$

a result that follows directly from (5-19). If we now regard ρ_k as made up of two parts,

$$\rho_k = \rho_k^o + \delta\rho_k \tag{5-26}$$

where $\delta\rho_k$ is, as before, the density fluctuation induced by the sound wave of amplitude q_k, then on using (5-22), we can write

$$\ddot{q}_k + \omega_k^2 q_k = - v_{-k}^i \rho_k^o \tag{5-27}$$

where the new sound-wave frequency is given by

$$\omega_k^2 = \Omega_k^2 + (k^2/4\pi e^2)\, v_{-k}^i v_k^{\rho} \tag{5-28}$$

An alternative form of (5-28) may be obtained on making use of (5-21) and (5-24); we find

$$\omega_k^2 = \Omega_k^2 - \frac{k^2}{4\pi e^2} \left(v_k^i\right)^2 \left[1 - \frac{1}{\varepsilon(k, 0)}\right] \tag{5-29}$$

or

$$\omega_k^2 = \Omega_k^2 - \Omega_a^2 + \Omega_a^2/\varepsilon(k, 0) \tag{5-30}$$

with the definition

$$\Omega_a^2 = (k^2/4\pi e^2)\left(v_k^i\right)^2 \tag{5-31}$$

Suppose we now consider the "jellium" model for the ions. We then have

$$\Omega_k^2 = \Omega_p^2 = \Omega_a^2$$

and hence

$$\omega_k^2 = \frac{\Omega_p^2}{\varepsilon(k,0)} \tag{5-32}$$

If we now make the RPA for $\varepsilon(k, 0)$, we have in the limit of long wavelengths from (3-72a),

$$\varepsilon_{RPA}(k,0) = 1 + \frac{k_{FT}^2}{k^2} \cong \frac{3\omega_p^2}{k^2 v_o^2}$$

a result equivalent to the Fermi-Thomas approximation. The phonon frequencies are, therefore,

$$\omega_k^2 = \frac{\Omega_p^2 k^2 v_o^2}{3\omega_p^2} = \frac{Z}{3}\frac{m}{M} k^2 v_o^2 \tag{5-33a}$$

This result for the longitudinal sound velocity,

$$s_{RPA} = \left(\frac{Z}{3}\frac{m}{M}\right)^{1/2} v_o \tag{5-33b}$$

was first obtained by Bohm and Staver.[7,8] It gives a good qualitative and a fair quantitative account of the experimentally observed sound velocities in metals. We remark on the very important role played by the electrons, which in screening the ionic motion act to reduce the long-wavelength longitudinal sound-wave frequency from $\sim \Omega_p$ to sk. Moreover, the effective matrix element for the coupling of an electron to a long-wavelength phonon is now

$$v_k^{eff} \cong \frac{k^2}{k_{FT}^2} v_k^i \cong -i\left(\frac{4\pi Z e^2 k}{k_{FT}^2}\right)\left(\frac{N}{M}\right)^{1/2}$$

and is proportional to k rather than its inverse.

5-4 PHONON FREQUENCIES AND EFFECTIVE ELECTRON-ELECTRON INTERACTION

The RPA for the Coupled Electron-Ion System

In Chapter 3 we have discussed the way in which the longitudinal wave-vector and frequency-dependent dielectric constant $\varepsilon(k\omega)$ serves as a simple unifying concept for theories of the electron gas; indeed a knowledge of $\varepsilon(k\omega)$ permits one to obtain directly the various properties of an interacting electron system. We now extend the dielectric formulation to the problem of a system of electrons and ions interacting with one another through Coulomb interactions only.

A formal extension of the dielectric-constant approach to the electron *and* ion system may be carried out by means of the definition

$$\frac{1}{\varepsilon_{tot}(k\omega)} - 1 = - \frac{e\langle \rho(k\omega) - ZR(k\omega)\rangle}{z\rho_{ext}(k\omega)} \tag{5-34}$$

where $z\rho_{ext}(k\omega)$ is, as before, the oscillating test charge which may be introduced to define and calculate $\varepsilon_{tot}(k\omega)$; $\langle\rho(k\omega)\rangle$ and $\langle R(k\omega)\rangle$ are the induced density fluctuations of electrons and ions, respectively, and the average is over the states of the system in the presence of the test charge. The definition (5-34) is made, of course, in accordance with the macroscopic laws of the electrodynamics. The dielectric constant defined by (5-35) is that appropriate to the coupling of the electrons and ions to a weak external longitudinal field; thus the interaction of the electron and ion density fluctuations with the external test charge is taken to be

$$H_{ext} = \lim_{\delta \to 0} - \frac{4\pi e z}{k^2} \rho_{ext}(k\omega) \left\{\rho_k^+ - ZR_k^+\right\} e^{-i\omega t} e^{\delta t} + \text{c.c.} \tag{5-35a}$$

where the ion-density fluctuation is given by

$$R_k^+ = \sum_i e^{+ik\cdot(R_{oi}+\delta R_i)} = \sum_i e^{+ik\cdot R_{oi}} (1 + ik\cdot\delta R_i + \ldots)$$

$$= \sum_{ik'\mu} e^{ik\cdot R_{oi}} \frac{ik\cdot\varepsilon_{k'\mu}}{(NM)^{1/2}} q_{k'\mu}^+ e^{-ik'\cdot R_{oi}} + \sum_i e^{ik\cdot R_{oi}}$$

$$= i\left(\frac{N}{M}\right)^{1/2} \sum_{k\mu} k\cdot\varepsilon_{k+K_n\mu} q_{k\mu}^+ + \sum_i e^{ik\cdot R_{oi}} \tag{5-35b}$$

In (5-35b) we have kept only the linear "harmonic" term, and have made use of the expansion (5-10) for δR_i, and the orthogonality relation, (2-45). The reciprocal lattice vector appearing in (5-35a) is that required to bring the wave vector k back inside the first Brillouin zone if k happens to lie outside it, i.e., $k \geq k_{max}$.

We see once more in (5-35b) that if k is within the first Brillouin zone, and one can separate the phonon modes into one longitudinal and two transverse modes, transverse modes play no role in determining the ion-density fluctuation. Moreover, for any finite frequency disturbance, the periodic part of R_k^+ will play no role. If we neglect transverse phonons, we may write

$$R_k^+ = +i\left(\frac{N}{M}\right)^{1/2}\left\{(\mathbf{k}+\mathbf{K}_n)\cdot\mathbf{k}/|\mathbf{k}+\mathbf{K}_n|\right\} q_k^+$$

so that H_{ext} takes the form

$$H_{ext} = \lim_{\delta\to 0} z\rho_{ext}(k\omega)\left\{-\frac{4\pi e}{k^2}\rho_k^+ + v_{-k}^{ext} q_k^+\right\} \qquad \text{(5-35c)}$$

where

$$v_{-k}^{ext} = +\frac{4\pi e}{k^2}\, i\left(\frac{NZ^2}{M}\right)^{1/2}\left\{\frac{k}{\mathbf{k}\cdot(\mathbf{k}+\mathbf{K}_n)/|\mathbf{k}+\mathbf{K}_n|}\right\}$$

One can, for the present system, define yet another dielectric constant $\varepsilon_{eff}(k\omega)$ which measures the effective interaction between a pair of electrons in the system. This will differ from (5-34), because as we have seen, the coupling between an electron density fluctuation, ρ_k, and the phonon in the metals is not given by

$$v_{-k}^{ext}\, q_k^+\rho_k$$

but rather by

$$v_{-k}^{i}\, q_k^+\rho_k$$

The difference between v_{-k}^i and v_{-k}^{ext} is a consequence of the influence of the *static* periodic field of the ions on the electrons in the metal. One can, in principle, take this into account, through v_k^i; by definition such periodic effects play no role in the coupling of an external longitudinal field to the phonons. It is this second dielectric constant, $\varepsilon_{eff}(k\omega)$, which will interest us here, since we are especially interested in the effective electron interaction. It, too, is defined by (5-34); the difference is that (5-35c) is replaced by

$$H_{ext} = \lim_{\delta \to 0} z\rho_{ext}(k\omega) \quad -\left\{\frac{4\pi e}{k^2}\rho_k^+ + v_{-k}^i q_k^+\right\} \qquad (5\text{-}35d)$$

The result which one obtains for $\varepsilon_{eff}(k\omega)$ in the RPA is the following[9]:

$$\varepsilon_{eff}(k\omega) = 1 + 4\pi\alpha_{RPA}(k\omega) - \frac{\Omega_a^2}{\omega^2 + \Omega_k^2 - \Omega_a^2} \qquad (5\text{-}36)$$

where $4\pi\alpha_{RPA}(k\omega)$ is the electronic polarizability; Ω_k is, as before, the "bare" longitudinal phonon frequency; and Ω_a is defined by (5-31). In this calculation, the role played by U processes is neglected; however, the effects of lattice periodicity on both Ω_k and Ω_a may be taken into account.

The result, (5-36), can be obtained by direct generalization of the methods of Chapter 3 and that calculation is given as a problem at the end of the chapter. Here we shall present a slightly different "derivation," in which we determine directly the frequency of oscillation ω_k for the longitudinal collective modes. If we then take that to be equivalent to

$$\varepsilon(k\omega) = 0$$

we shall obtain thereby our desired expression for $\varepsilon(k\omega)$, (5-36).

Let us therefore study the equation of motion for an electron-hole pair: $\rho(\mathbf{kp}) = c_{\mathbf{p}}^+ c_{\mathbf{p+k}}$. The procedure is similar to that followed in Chapter 3, except for the fact that we have in the Hamiltonian the terms arising from the presence of the lattice vibrations and that we need not consider the presence of an external test charge. We seek an oscillatory solution of the form

$$[\rho(\mathbf{kp}), H] = \hbar\omega_k \rho(\mathbf{kp}) \qquad (5\text{-}37)$$

since if the density fluctuation of the system is to oscillate at frequency ω_k, each electron-hole pair must likewise do so. We evaluate the commutator in (5-37) by making the RPA; that is, in following the motion of an electron-hole pair of momentum $-\mathbf{k}$, we keep only the $-\mathbf{k}^{th}$ component of the electron-electron and electron-phonon interactions. It is left as an exercise for the reader to show that one thereby obtains

$$\hbar\omega_k \rho(\mathbf{kp}) = \hbar\omega(\mathbf{kp})\rho(\mathbf{kp}) - \mathcal{V}_k(n_{\mathbf{p}} - n_{\mathbf{p+k}})\rho_k - v_k^i q_k (n_{\mathbf{p}} - n_{\mathbf{p+k}}) \qquad (5\text{-}38a)$$

We can write this equation as

$$\rho(\mathbf{kp}) = -\frac{(n_\mathbf{p} - n_{\mathbf{p}+\mathbf{k}})}{\hbar(\omega_k - \omega(\mathbf{kp}) + i\delta)}\left\{\mathcal{V}_k \rho_k + v_k^i q_k\right\} \tag{5-38b}$$

where the small positive imaginary part in the denominator corresponds to a choice of retarded boundary condition in our computation of the motion of an electron-hole pair in the presence of the lattice vibrations.

We sum (5-38b) over all states p, to obtain an equation for the density fluctuation,

$$\rho_k = -4\pi\alpha_{\text{RPA}}(k\omega)\rho_k - \frac{v_k^i}{\mathcal{V}_k} 4\pi\alpha_{\text{RPA}}(k\omega) q_k \tag{5-39a}$$

which may be written

$$\mathcal{V}_k \rho_k = -v_k^i \frac{4\pi\alpha_{\text{RPA}}(k\omega)}{1 + 4\pi\alpha_{\text{RPA}}(k\omega)} q_k \tag{5-39b}$$

Here we have introduced the RPA electronic polarizability by

$$4\pi\alpha_{\text{RPA}}(k\omega) = \mathcal{V}_k \sum_p \frac{n_p - n_{p+k}}{\hbar\omega - (\varepsilon_p - \varepsilon_{p+k}) + i\delta} \tag{5-40}$$

[One is free to regard the one-electron energies in (5-40) as Bloch excitation energies, if one likes. However, since we shall not carry out any explicit Bloch wave calculations, we simply take the energies appropriate to free electrons.] The small positive imaginary part in the denominator arises from our choice of the retarded boundary condition. The amplitude q_k of the lattice vibration obeys a simple equation of motion like (5-25):

$$\ddot{q}_k + \Omega_k^2 q_k = -v_{-k}^i \rho_k = -(\omega^2 - \Omega_k^2) q_k \tag{5-41}$$

On comparing (5-39) with (5-41), we see that the two equations are consistent only if

$$\omega^2 = \Omega_k^2 - \frac{\Omega_a^2 4\pi\alpha_{\text{RPA}}(k\omega)}{1 + 4\pi\alpha_{\text{RPA}}(k\omega)} \tag{5-42}$$

which is our desired dispersion relation for the longitudinal mode of the coupled electron-ion system [Ω_a has been defined by (5-31)]. It is possible to rewrite the dispersion relation as

$$1 + 4\pi\alpha_{\text{RPA}}(k\omega) - \frac{\Omega_a^2}{\omega^2 - \Omega_k^2 + \Omega_a^2} = 0 \tag{5-43}$$

We may thus conclude that the dielectric constant for the system is given by (5-36).

This result could have been obtained from the even simpler considerations, Sec. 5-3. We remark that the dispersion relation (5-42), is identical to that of (5-29) if one allows for the proper frequency dependence of the electronic polarizability in (5-29). Thus it is clear that the screening action of the electrons discussed in Sec. 5-3, for instance, is naturally built in these calculations. We also note that (3-28) to (3-30) of Ref. 3 are readily obtained from the present results.

Phonon Dispersion Relation for "Jellium"

Let us consider the solutions of dispersion relation (5-43) for the "jellium" model of ionic behavior. As we have remarked earlier, in this model one neglects all effects of periodicity; one has then

$$\Omega_k^2 = \Omega_a^2 = \Omega_p^2 = 4\pi NZ^2e^2/M$$

There are two branches to the solution for the dispersion relation. The first is the high-frequency branch; we have already considered the plasmon solution. The electronic polarizability is expanded as $-\omega_p^2/\omega^2 + 0\,(k^2\langle v^2\rangle/\omega^2)$ and the ions act to shift the plasmon frequency from ω_p to $(\omega_p^2 + \Omega_p^2)^{1/2}$, a correction of order $(m/M)^{1/2}$. This mode is an "optical" mode (in analogy to the theory of longitudinal modes in polar crystals) in which the electrons and ions oscillate out of phase.

The second branch is a low-frequency acoustic mode, in which the electrons follow the motion of the ions. For low frequencies and long wavelengths, the electronic polarizability becomes

$$4\pi\alpha_{\text{RPA}}(k\omega) \cong k_{FT}^2/k^2 + i\,\frac{\pi}{2}\left(\frac{k_{FT}^2}{k^2}\right)\frac{\omega}{kv_o} \qquad \omega \ll kv_o$$

The "jellium" dispersion relation is then

$$1 = \left(k_{FT}^2/k^2\right) + i\,\frac{\pi}{2}\left(\frac{k_{FT}^2}{k^2}\right)\frac{\omega}{kv_o} - \frac{\Omega_p^2}{\omega^2} = 0$$

We search for a solution of the form $\omega = \omega_1 - i\omega_2$; we obtain

$$\omega_1^2 = \frac{\Omega_p^2}{1 + (k_{FT}/k)^2} \cong k^2(\Omega_p/k_{FT})^2 = k^2 \frac{Zm}{3M} v_o^2 = k^2 s_{RPA}^2 \tag{5-44}$$

$$\frac{\omega_2}{\omega_1} = \frac{\pi}{4} \frac{\omega_1}{kv_o} = \frac{\pi}{4} \left(\frac{Zm}{3M}\right)^{1/2} \tag{5-45}$$

The result (5-44) for the real part of the phonon frequency is identical with our previous result, (5-33b); we note that the condition $\omega \ll kv_o$ is clearly satisfied.

The imaginary part of the phonon frequency arises because of the possibility of a phonon decaying into an electron-hole pair. One can thus look upon this phenomenon as Landau damping of the phonons, analogous to the similar phenomenon for the plasmons. There is no lack of low-energy electron-hole pairs; the damping is small because of the "mismatch" between typical electron frequencies, kv_o, and typical phonon frequencies, ks. One measures ω_2 directly in an ultrasonic attenuation experiment, and the experimental results are in good qualitative agreement with the simple theory.

The Phonon Dispersion Relation for Simple Metals

The longitudinal phonon dispersion relation for simple metals will not differ greatly from (5-42). There are three corrections which need to be considered: (1) the modification of the RPA in treating the electron response to ionic motion, (2) the role of U processes, and (3) the departure of the bare ion-ion interaction from a pure Coulomb force law.

As to the first correction, a field-theoretic calculation shows that (5-42) provides a correct treatment of electron response to order $(m/M)^{1/2}$, if in place of $4\pi\alpha_{RPA}(k\omega)$ one takes $4\pi\alpha(k\omega)$ to be the *exact* electronic polarizability, including the changes brought about by the periodic ion potential as well as those due to modifications in the free-electron RPA polarizability.[9]

The non-Coulombic aspect of the bare ion-ion interaction can, in principle, be taken into account in a proper calculation of the bare ion frequencies Ω_k. A possible approximate method of doing this is to assume that the sum rule (2-62) is, in fact, little modified by the departure from Coulombicity. Hence, if one used the sum rule together with the experimentally determined transverse sound-wave frequencies, one can arrive at an accurate initial bare longitudinal frequency, Ω_k.

It is also not difficult to write down a formal expression which includes the role of U processes in determining the sound-wave frequencies. As shown in Ref. 3, one need simply replace (5-41) by

$$\ddot{q}_k + \Omega_k^2 q_k = - \mathcal{S}\, v_{-k}^i \rho_k$$

where $\mathcal{S}$ denotes the sum over all extended-zone wave vectors k which correspond to a phonon wave vector k in the first Brillouin zone. Thus

$$\mathcal{S}\, v_{-k}^i \rho_k = \sum_{\mathbf{K}_n} v_{-(\mathbf{k}+\mathbf{K}_n)}^i \rho_{\mathbf{k}+\mathbf{K}_n} \tag{5-46a}$$

where, on the right-hand side of (5-46a), k is understood to be in the first Brillouin zone. The modified phonon dispersion relation is then

$$\omega_k^2 = \Omega_k^2 - \mathcal{S}\, \frac{\Omega_a^2 4\pi\alpha(k\omega)}{1 + 4\pi\alpha(k\omega)} \tag{5-46b}$$

where all the three corrections discussed above have been incorporated.

It is instructive to study (5-46b) in the long-wavelength limit. In this limit, the corrections due to U processes can safely be neglected in first approximation. The corrections due to lattice periodicity can be expressed as follows:

$$\Omega_k^2 = \Omega_p^2 - s_1^2 k^2 \tag{5-47a}$$

$$\Omega_a^2 = \Omega_p^2 - s_2^2 k^2 \tag{5-47b}$$

We have already considered (5-47a); the result (5-47b) follows from detailed examination of periodicity corrections to v_k^i, of the kind considered by Bardeen, which will be discussed in Sec. 5-7. On substituting (5-47a) and (5-47b) into (5-46b), and keeping terms of order k^2, one finds

$$\omega_k^2 = s_+^2 k^2 + \frac{\Omega_p^2}{1 + 4\pi\alpha(k\omega)} \tag{5-48}$$

where

$$s_+^2 = s_2^2 - s_1^2$$

Let us now consider the solution

$$\omega_k = \omega_1 - i\omega_2$$

of this dispersion relation. If we write

$$4\pi\alpha(k\,0) = \omega_p^2/s_-^2k^2 \tag{5-49a}$$

we have

$$\omega_1^2 = \left\{ s_+^2 + \left(\frac{mZ}{M}\right) s_-^2 \right\} k^2 = s^2k^2 \tag{5-49b}$$

where s is the longitudinal sound velocity. The quantity, s_-, in (5-49a), may be identified with the macroscopic sound velocity for the electron system, defined according to

$$s_- = \left(\frac{1}{\kappa m N}\right)^{1/2}$$

where κ is the compressibility of the electron system. A proof of (5-49a) based on the Landau-Fermi liquid theory has been given by Nozières[10]; the generalization of this proof to a system of electrons moving in a periodic lattice potential is likely to prove straightforward, but has not yet been carried out. We remark that the condition for stability of the phonons is

$$s_+^2 \geq -\left(\frac{mZ}{M}\right) s_-^2 \tag{5-49c}$$

which places a limit on the strength of the electron-phonon coupling, v_k^i. We note, too, that s_+^2 is inversely proportional to M (as may be seen from the dispersion relation for Ω_k and the definition of Ω_a), so that s is inversely proportional to $M^{1/2}$, as it should be.

It would now seem feasible to use (5-46b) and (5-48) for a calculation, from first principles, of the phonon spectra of simple metals. The calculation is of considerable interest since, as we have seen in Chapter 2, experimental measurements of such phonon spectra now exist. Probably the most difficult quantity to calculate is v_k^i. As we shall see in Sec. 5-7, calculations of this quantity have been carried out by Bardeen[6] for monovalent metals. Bardeen and the writer[3] have used these results to determine the long-wavelength phonon behavior in sodium. At long wavelengths, the comparison between theory and experiment is facilitated if one considers not ω_k^2 but rather $\Sigma_\mu \omega_{k\mu}^2$. In the long-wavelength limit, one has

$$\lim_{k\to 0} \Sigma_\mu \omega_{k\mu}^2 = k^2(C_{11} + 2C_{44})/NM \tag{5-50a}$$

where C_{11} and C_{44} are the appropriate elastic constants. Moreover, since the long-wavelength sound waves are not affected by U processes to first approximation, one has also

$$\lim_{k \to 0} \Sigma_\mu \omega_{k\mu}^2 = \Sigma_\mu \Omega_{k\mu}^2 - \Omega_a^2 + \frac{\Omega_p^2}{4\pi\alpha(k, 0)} \tag{5-50b}$$

On making use of (5-47b) and (5-49a), we may write

$$s_2^2 + \frac{Zm}{M} s_-^2 = C_{11} + 2C_{44}/NM$$

If one takes the Bardeen calculation of s_2^2 and the free-electron RPA value of s_-^2, $v_o^2/3$, one finds an agreement between theory and experiment for sodium of some 10 per cent. The extent of this agreement would seem to indicate that both the Bardeen approximation and the RPA work rather well in this case.

The imaginary part of the phonon frequency is given by

$$\frac{\omega_2}{\omega_1} = - \frac{\Omega_p^2}{2\omega_1^2} \operatorname{Im} \frac{1}{\varepsilon(k, \omega_1)} \tag{5-51a}$$

Thus phonon damping as a result of phonon-electron interaction is simply proportional to Im $1/\varepsilon(k, \omega_1)$, and offers a way to measure this quantity directly. In the approximation in which the effects of periodicity can be neglected, one can calculate Im $1/\varepsilon(k, \omega_1)$ *exactly* using the Fermi liquid theory. The result is[10a]:

$$- \operatorname{Im} \frac{1}{\varepsilon(k, \omega_1)} = \frac{\varepsilon_2(k, \omega_1)}{\varepsilon_1(k, 0)^2} = \frac{\pi}{2} \left(\frac{\omega_1 k_o k}{3m\omega_p^2} \right) \tag{5-51b}$$

to lowest order in k^2 and (m/M); the corresponding expression for phonon damping is

$$\frac{\omega_2}{\omega_1} = \frac{\pi}{4} \left(\frac{mZ}{3M} \right)^{1/2} \frac{s_{RPA}}{s} \tag{5-51c}$$

where s is the exact sound velocity, and s_{RPA} the RPA result (5-44). We note, too, that phonon damping at any wavelength is given by

$$\frac{\omega_2}{\omega_1} = - \mathcal{S} \left\{ \frac{\Omega_a^2(k)}{\omega_1^2} \operatorname{Im} \frac{1}{\varepsilon(k, \omega_1)} \right\} \tag{5-51d}$$

Phonon Anomalies

Kohn[11] has pointed out that there will exist certain anomalies in the phonon spectra which are caused by corresponding anomalies in the static dielectric constant of an electron system. To see how these come about, let us use (5-31) and (5-46b) to write the real part of the phonon dispersion relation in the following way:

$$\omega_1^2(k) = \Omega_k^2 - \sum_{\mathbf{K}_n} \left(v^i_{\mathbf{k}+\mathbf{K}_n}\right) \frac{(\mathbf{k}+\mathbf{K}_n)^2}{4\pi e^2} \left\{1 - \frac{1}{\varepsilon(\mathbf{k}+\mathbf{K}_n, 0)}\right\} \tag{5-52}$$

We now recall, from Sec. 3-6, the anomalous behavior of the static wave-vector-dependent dielectric constant $\varepsilon(k, 0)$; we saw that in the RPA, $\varepsilon_{RPA}(k, 0)$ possessed a logarithmic singularity such that

$$\left\{\nabla_k \varepsilon_{RPA}(k, 0)\right\}_{k=2k_o} = \infty$$

The origin of this singularity is the sharpness of the Fermi surface; if the Fermi surface is sharp one will have a different contribution to $\varepsilon_{RPA}(k, 0)$ from quasi-particle pair excitation when $k > 2k_o$, since for such momentum transfers it is no longer possible to excite an electron-hole pair on the Fermi surface. Thus one expects that the singularity will be characteristic of all normal (i.e., nonsuperconducting) fermion systems, and is not simply characteristic of the RPA.

From (5-52) it follows directly that there is a corresponding anomaly in the phonon spectrum; for those wave vectors $\mathbf{k}$ such that

$$|\mathbf{k} + \mathbf{K}_n| = 2k_o$$

one expects that

$$\nabla_{\mathbf{k}} \omega_{\mathbf{k}} = \infty$$

Actually the phonon anomaly is slightly displaced, since what really appears in (5-52) is $\varepsilon(\mathbf{k} + \mathbf{K}_n, \omega_1)$; this displacement is, however, negligible, being of order m/M. Kohn concluded, therefore, that it was possible to observe images of the Fermi surface in the phonon spectra of metals. Such images have now been observed for lead by Brockhouse et al.[12] Corresponding images have not been seen for sodium. This result is not difficult to understand; we see in (5-52) that the strength of the anomaly depends sensitively on the strength of the bare matrix element for electron-phonon interaction, v_k^i. Sodium is a metal in which the phonon-electron coupling is comparatively weak; in lead the coupling is strong, so the anomaly is observable.

Effective Electron-Electron Interaction

We next consider the effective interaction between electrons in simple metals. As was the case for the free-electron gas considered in Sec. 3-5 the interaction is screened by the appropriate frequency and wave-vector-dependent dielectric constant. The situation is pictured in Fig. 5-3; the effective matrix element for scattering a pair of electrons from the states p and q to states p + k, q - k is given by[12a]

$$\mathcal{V}_k^{eff} = \mathcal{V}_k/\varepsilon_{eff}[k, \omega(p,k)] \tag{5-53}$$

where

$$\omega(p,k) = (\varepsilon_{p+k} - \varepsilon_p)/\hbar$$

and $\varepsilon_{eff}(k\omega)$, which includes the modification in $\varepsilon(k\omega)$ brought about by the phonons, is given by (5-36).

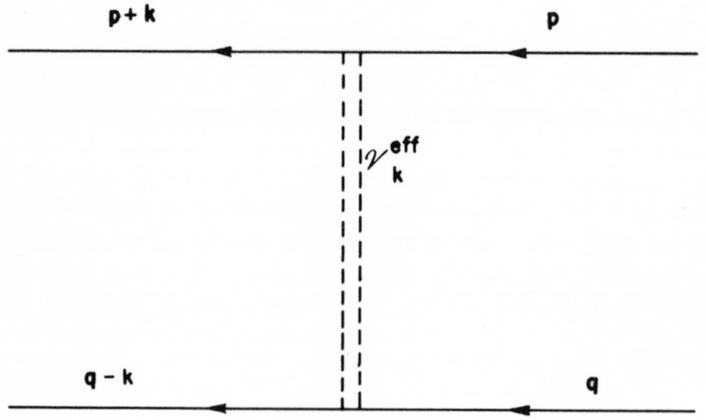

Fig. 5-3

An equivalent way of expressing this effective interaction is to consider the modified electron-electron interaction Hamiltonian,

$$H_2 = \frac{1}{2}\sum \mathcal{V}_k \rho_{-k}\rho_k{}^s$$

in which one of the density-fluctuation operators is replaced by the corresponding screened one, ρ_k^s, defined according to

$$\left(\rho_k{}^s\right)_{no} = (\rho_k)_{no}/\varepsilon_{eff}(k, \omega_{no})$$

We shall be particularly interested in the effective low-frequency interaction between the electrons. As one might expect, it is only for excitation frequencies comparable to, or less than, the phonon frequencies of interest that the phonon contribution to the electron-electron interaction is at all appreciable. [At larger frequencies the ions are simply not able to follow the electron motion, so that $\varepsilon_{tot}(k, \omega_{no})$ reduces to its value for electron-electron interaction only.] Moreover, since a typical phonon frequency, sk, is of order $(m/M)^{1/2}$ times a typical electron frequency, kv_o, it follows that one can, to a quite satisfactory degree of approximation, replace $4\pi\alpha_{RPA}(k\omega)$ by the static electronic polarizability, $4\pi\alpha_{RPA}(k\,0)$.

In calculating $\varepsilon(k\omega)$ let us, for the moment, neglect the role played by U processes. In that case, the dielectric constant is given by (5-36); if we make use of the phonon dispersion relation, (5-42), we may write

$$\varepsilon_{eff}(k, \omega) = [1 + 4\pi\alpha_{RPA}(k, 0)] \frac{\omega^2 - \omega_k^2}{\omega^2 - \Omega_k^2 + \Omega_a^2} \qquad \omega << kv_o$$

or

$$\frac{1}{\varepsilon_{eff}(k, \omega)} = \frac{1}{1 + 4\pi\alpha_{RPA}(k, 0)} \left[1 + \frac{\omega_k^2 + \Omega_a^2 - \Omega_k^2}{\omega^2 - \omega_k^2} \right] \qquad \text{(5-54a)}$$

With the aid of (5-54a) and (5-43) we may write the effective "low-frequency" interaction between electrons in the following way:

$$\frac{\mathscr{V}_k}{\varepsilon_{eff}(k\omega)} = \frac{\mathscr{V}_k}{1 + 4\pi\alpha_{RPA}(k,0)} + \frac{\{v_k^i/(1 + 4\pi\alpha_{RPA}(k,0)\}^2}{\omega^2 - \omega_k^2}$$

$$= \frac{\mathscr{V}_k}{1 + 4\pi\alpha_{RPA}(k, 0)} + \frac{(v_k^{eff})^2}{\omega^2 - \omega_k^2} \qquad \text{(5-54b)}$$

where

$$v_k^{eff} = v_k^i/[1 + 4\pi\alpha_{RPA}(k, 0)] \qquad \text{(5-55a)}$$

is the effective screened electron-ion interaction in the RPA. We see in (5-54b) the usual separation (compare Ref. 3) of the effective electron interaction into two terms: the first corresponds to the usual screened Coulomb interaction; the second may be regarded as representing the effect of phonon exchange.

We see that the phonon-induced electron-electron interaction is attractive when the change of electron energy, $\hbar\omega(p,k) = (\varepsilon_{p+k} - \varepsilon_p)$, is less than the phonon energy, $\hbar\omega_k$. It becomes repulsive for $\omega(p,k) > \omega_k$. Moreover, it is immediately clear from (5-54a) that for $\omega(p,k) >> \omega_k$ the phonon contribution to $\varepsilon(k\omega)$ becomes negligible in accordance with our expectations. The attractive part of the phonon-induced interaction is of very great importance, because, as

Bardeen, Cooper, and Schrieffer have shown, it may give rise to superconductivity.[13] We can only present a qualitative discussion of the possibility of superconductivity; the criterion for superconductivity depends, in fact, upon the existence of a nontrivial solution of the BCS integral equation for the energy gap,[12a] and such considerations lie well beyond the scope of this book. We therefore content ourselves with the remark that, in general, an attractive interaction favors superconductivity, while a repulsive interaction opposes it, and that one must therefore consider the delicate interplay between the repulsive and attractive parts of the interaction, (5-54b), in some detail.

For the jellium model of ionic behavior we find

$$\frac{1}{\varepsilon_{eff}(k\omega)} = \frac{1}{1 + 4\pi\alpha_{RPA}(k,0)}\left\{1 + \frac{\omega_k^2}{\omega^2 - \omega_k^2}\right\}$$

$$= \frac{\omega^2}{\omega^2 - \omega_k^2}\left\{\frac{1}{1 + 4\pi\alpha_{RPA}(k,0)}\right\} \tag{5-55b}$$

In this model, the attractive phonon-inducted interaction for zero excitation frequency just compensates the repulsive screened interaction; for frequencies less than ω_k the interaction is attractive, for frequencies greater than ω_k the interaction is repulsive. From the standpoint of the BCS theory, the jellium model would lead one to conclude that all metals superconduct.

Let us consider next the more realistic model for the phonon frequencies and electron-phonon interaction. In the limit of zero excitation frequency (5-54) becomes

$$\frac{1}{\varepsilon_{eff}(k,0)} = \frac{1}{1 + 4\pi\alpha_{RPA}(k,0)}\left\{\frac{\Omega_k^2 - \Omega_a^2}{\omega_k^2}\right\}$$

Thus the effective static interaction is positive provided $\Omega_k^2 > \Omega_a^2$. This requirement, which means that periodicity is more effective in reducing v_k^i than in reducing the "bare" phonon frequencies Ω_p, appears to be well satisfied in the cases of the monovalent metals for which specific calculations have been carried out. If we assume that it is valid in general, the effective electron interaction possesses the following character as a function of the excitation frequency, ω:

$0 \leq \omega^2 \leq \Omega_k^2 - \Omega_a^2$	repulsive
$\Omega_k^2 - \Omega_a^2 \leq \omega^2 \leq \omega_k^2$	attractive
$\omega_k^2 \leq \omega^2$	repulsive

We remark that whether the repulsive or attractive domain is more important is thus clearly seen to depend on the role played by the periodicity corrections.

Finally we consider the role played by "Umklap processes" in determining the effective electron-electron interaction. We first remark that if one is to have a phonon-induced short-range electron-electron interaction corresponding to momentum transfers greater than k_{max} (k_{max} being the maximum phonon wave vector), it is necessary that one take U processes into account. It is not in fact difficult to do so. It is left as a problem for the reader to show that the modified electron-electron interaction in the RPA is given by

$$\frac{\mathcal{V}_k}{\varepsilon_{eff}(k\,\omega)} = \frac{\mathcal{V}_k}{1 + 4\pi\alpha_{RPA}(k, 0)} + \frac{\left(V_k^{eff}\right)^2}{\omega^2 - \omega_k^2} \tag{5-56}$$

where if k lies outside the first Brillouin zone, it is to be understood that ω_k refers to the frequency of the appropriate phonon, of wave vector $\mathbf{k} + \mathbf{K}_n$, which has a wave vector inside the first Brillouin zone. Such U processes undoubtedly play an important role in determining both the criterion for superconductivity and the size of the effective matrix elements that appear in the BCS theory.[13a]

5-5 THE APPROACH TO EQUILIBRIUM OF A COUPLED ELECTRON-PHONON SYSTEM

The Coupled Boltzmann Equations

In this section we consider the set of coupled equations which describe the approach to equilibrium of a system of interacting electrons and phonons. We assume that the problems considered in the previous section, which involve essentially the *virtual* electron-phonon and electron-electron interactions, have been solved. Thus we assume the existence of an effective screened matrix element for electron-phonon interaction, and go on to consider the *real* energy-conserving processes which couple electrons and phonons. The approach we adopt is a heuristic one; we assume, without proof, that the correct coupled equations can be obtained by application of standard first-order time-dependent perturbation theory.[14] The equations so obtained are interesting in themselves; they also serve to prepare the way for a calculation of the conductivity of simple metals.

We begin by writing the "effective" electron-phonon interaction in the following way:

$$H_{int} = \sum_{pp'k} M(p'p;k\mu)\,(a_{\mathbf{k}\mu} + a^+_{-\mathbf{k}\mu})\,c^+_{\mathbf{p}'}c_{\mathbf{p}} \tag{5-57}$$

Here $M(p'p; k\mu)$ is the matrix element for the scattering of an electron from a state p to p' with absorption of a phonon of pseudo-momentum $\hbar k$ or emission of a phonon of momentum $-\hbar k$. On comparing (5-57) with (5-16) and (5-55), we remark that

$$M(p'p; k\mu) = v_k^i/\varepsilon_{RPA}(k, 0)\left(\frac{\hbar}{2\omega_k}\right)^{1/2} \tag{5-58}$$

if we confine our attention to longitudinal phonons and, further, assume that the screening of the electron-ion interaction is adequately described by the electron static wave-number-dependent dielectric constant. This last assumption is not in general true, as a detailed field-theoretic calculation shows.[9]

According to the standard first-order time-dependent perturbation theory, the time rate of a transition from an initial state I to a final state F is given by

$$W(F, I) = \frac{2\pi}{\hbar}\left|\langle F | H_{int} | I\rangle\right|^2 D_F(E_I)$$

where $D_F(E_I)$ denotes the density of the final states. Before going into the calculation of the transition rate, let us consider the density of the final states in more detail. As is well known, if one waits for a sufficiently long time, $D_F(E_I)$ is approximately expressed by the δ function,

$$D_F(E_I) = \delta(E_F - E_I) \tag{5-59}$$

This is the precise statement of the energy-conservation law; for finite times, however, the energy conservation holds only approximately, a statement that directly follows from the uncertainty principle.

How long must one wait for (5-59) to be valid? At first sight one might expect that the temperature variation of the electron distribution function, $f(p, E)$, plays a role in determining the time interval of importance; that is, one might expect that one needs a time which is long enough to guarantee energy conservation with an accuracy better than κT:

$$t \gg \hbar/\kappa T$$

Such however is not the case; more careful investigation[13,134,14a] shows that this rather stringent requirement can be replaced by the requirement

$$t \gg \hbar/\varepsilon_F$$

i.e., the time t must be long compared to the "Pauli principle" smearing of the Fermi distribution, instead of the "temperature" smearing represented by $\hbar/\kappa T$.

On the other hand, the time t must not be taken longer than the time between collisions, as the simple first-order theory is incapable of treating the transition rates beyond the first collision. The time between collisions may be approximately represented by a relaxation time τ. We then have the two criteria

$$\tau \gg t \gg \hbar/\varepsilon_F$$

Let us now adopt a semiclassical approach and study the time-dependent behavior of the distribution function for the electrons, $2f(p, t)$. The factor 2 takes care of the sum over spin orientations. We likewise introduce $N_{k\mu}(t)$, the number of phonons with momentum $\hbar k$ and polarization μ. With no external fields and no electron-phonon interaction, $f(p, t)$ takes the well-known form characteristic of the Fermi distribution,

$$f(p,t) = f^\circ(p) = \frac{1}{e^{\beta(\varepsilon_p - \varepsilon_o)} + 1} \tag{5-60}$$

We wish to calculate the time rate of change of the distribution functions due to the interaction. There will be four terms in the expression for $\partial f/\partial t$, corresponding to the following processes:

1. Create one phonon of momentum $k = p' - p + K_n$ and transfer an electron from p' to p:

$$\left\{\frac{\partial f(p,t)}{\partial t}\right\}_1 = \frac{2\pi}{\hbar} \sum_{p'\mu} \delta(\varepsilon_{p'} - \varepsilon_p - h\omega_{k\mu})\,(N_{k\mu} + 1)$$

$$\times\, |M(p, p'; -k, \mu)|^2\, f(p')\,[1 - f(p)] \tag{5-61a}$$

We have assumed that the restrictions on the time between collisions, which allow the use of a δ function, are satisfied. The factor $f(p')$ $[1 - f(p)]$ in (5-61a) takes care of the restriction coming from the Pauli principle.

2. Destroy one phonon of momentum $-k$ and transfer an electron from p' to p:

$$\left(\frac{\partial f}{\partial t}\right)_2 = \frac{2\pi}{\hbar} \sum_{p'\mu} \delta(\varepsilon_{p'} - \varepsilon_p + \hbar\omega_{-k\mu})\, N_{-k\mu}$$

$$\times\, |M(p, p'; -k, \mu)|^2\, f(p')\,[1 - f(p)] \tag{5-61b}$$

3. Create one phonon of momentum - k and transfer an electron from p to p':

$$\left(\frac{\partial f}{\partial t}\right)_3 = -\frac{2\pi}{\hbar}\sum_{p'\mu} \delta(\varepsilon_{p'} - \varepsilon_p + \hbar\omega_{-k\mu})\,(N_{-k\mu} + 1)$$

$$\times\, |M(p', p; k, \mu)|^2 f(p)\,[1 - f(p')] \qquad (5\text{-}61c)$$

4. Destroy one phonon of momentum k and transfer an electron from p to p':

$$\left(\frac{\partial f}{\partial t}\right)_4 = -\frac{2\pi}{\hbar}\sum_{p'\mu} \delta(\varepsilon_{p'} - \varepsilon_p - \hbar\omega_{k\mu})\,N_{k\mu}$$

$$\times\, |M(p', p'; k, \mu)|^2 f(p)\,[1 - f(p')] \qquad (5\text{-}61d)$$

It is possible to show that

$$M(p, p'; -k, \mu) = M^*(p', p; k, \mu) \qquad (5\text{-}62)$$

It must also be understood that in all the above formalism the frequencies $\omega_{k\mu}$ and $\omega_{-k\mu}$ are positive quantities, so that a phonon carries a positive amount of energy. The sum over the states p' in (5-61a) and (5-61d) are effective only for those states for which $\varepsilon_{p'} > \varepsilon_p$; in (5-61b) and (5-61c), $\varepsilon_p > \varepsilon_{p'}$. With the aid of these relations, we sum all the four contributions to obtain the net time rate of change in the electron distribution function:

$$\frac{\partial f(p)}{\partial t} = \frac{2\pi}{\hbar}\sum_{p'\mu} |M(p', p; k, \mu)|^2 \Big\{\delta(\varepsilon_{p'} - \varepsilon_p + \hbar\omega_{-k\mu})$$

$$\times \Big[N_{-k\mu}\,[f(p') - f(p)] - f(p)\,[1 - f(p')]\Big]$$

$$+\, \delta(\varepsilon_{p'} - \varepsilon_p - \hbar\omega_{k\mu})\Big[N_{k\mu}\,[f(p') - f(p)] + f(p')\,[1 - f(p)]\Big]\Big\} \qquad (5\text{-}63a)$$

Similarly, the Boltzmann equation for the phonon distribution derives from processes (1) and (4); with a factor of two for spins one finds

$$\frac{\partial N_{k\mu}}{\partial t} = \frac{4\pi}{\hbar}\sum_{p} \delta(\varepsilon_{p'} - \varepsilon_p - \hbar\omega_{k\mu})\,|M(p', p; k, \mu)|^2 \Big\{N_{k\mu}[f(p') - f(p)]$$

$$+\, f(p')\,[1 - f(p)]\Big\} \qquad (5\text{-}64)$$

The result (5-63a) is somewhat awkward in its form. It is possible to attain a slight formal simplification by artificially allowing negative values of μ and defining[15]

$$\omega_{-k,\mu} = -\ \omega_{k,-\mu}$$

$$N_{-k,\mu} = -\ (N_{k,-\mu} + 1)$$

It must be remembered clearly that in this definition $\omega_{k\mu}$ and $N_{k\mu}$ become negative when μ takes on values -1, -2, -3. By means of this device, we rewrite (5-63a) as

$$\frac{\partial f(p)}{\partial t} = \frac{2\pi}{\hbar} \sum_{p'\mu} |M(p', p; k, \mu)|^2 \delta(\varepsilon_{p'} - \varepsilon_p - \hbar\omega_{k\mu}) \Big\{ N_{k\mu}[f(p') - f(p)] + f(p')\,[1 - f(p)] \Big\} \tag{5-63b}$$

Here the sum over μ extends to negative values as well as to positive ones.

One can arrive at several consequences of physical importance from the formulation discussed above. The first point we wish to take up concerns the equilibrium solution. Remark that processes (1) and (4), or (2) and (3), form inverse processes to each other; in equilibrium the principle of detailed balancing must apply and thus

$$\frac{N_{k\mu}}{N_{k\mu} + 1} = \frac{N_{-k\mu} + 1}{N_{-k\mu}} = \frac{1 - f(p)}{f(p)}\ \frac{f(p')}{1 - f(p')}$$

Taking the equilibrium distribution (5-60) for f, or

$$\frac{f(p)}{1 - f(p)} = e^{-\beta(\varepsilon_p - \varepsilon_o)}$$

we obtain, with the aid of the δ functions which guarantee energy conservation,

$$N^o_{k\mu} = \frac{1}{e^{\beta\hbar\omega_{k\mu}} - 1} \tag{5-65}$$

This is the equilibrium distribution function for the phonons.

The Phonon Boltzmann Equation

It is instructive to consider the phonon Boltzmann equation in more detail.[16] We begin by rewriting the right-hand side of (5-64) as

$$\frac{\partial N_{k\mu}}{\partial t} = -(B - C)N_{k\mu} + A \tag{5-66}$$

where $-BN_{k\mu}$ comes from the phonon absorption process given by (5-61d), $CN_{k\mu}$ means the induced emission, and A represents the spontaneous emission of phonons; $CN_{k\mu} + A$ is given by (5-61a). From (5-64) and (5-66), we have

$$C - B = \frac{4\pi}{\hbar}\sum_{p} |M(p', p; k, \mu)|^2 \left[f(p') - f(p)\right] \delta(\varepsilon_{p'} - \varepsilon_p - \hbar\omega_{k\mu})$$

$$= \frac{4}{\hbar}\sum_{p} |M(p', p; k, \mu)|^2 \, \text{Im} \, \frac{f(p') - f(p)}{\varepsilon_{p'} - \varepsilon_p - \hbar\omega_{k\mu} - i|\delta|} \tag{5-67}$$

We now make an explicit connection between the Boltzmann equation and the dielectric formulation discussed in the previous section. For simplicity we adopt the jellium model, and, further, make the RPA. In this approximation the only nonvanishing matrix element is that for longitudinal phonons. It is, from (5-58) and (5-20),

$$M(p', p; k) = -i\left(\frac{\hbar N}{2M\omega_k}\right)^{1/2} \frac{4\pi Ze^2}{k\,\varepsilon_{RPA}(k, 0)} \tag{5-68}$$

where, as usual,

$$\varepsilon_{RPA}(k, 0) \cong 1 + k_{FT}^2/k^2 \tag{5-69}$$

We also have the relation

$$n(p) = 2f(p)$$

by taking the spin sum into account. With the aid of these expressions, we can rewrite (C - B) in (5-67) as

$$C - B = -\sum_{p} \frac{N}{M\omega_k}\left[\frac{4\pi Ze^2}{\varepsilon_{RPA}(k, 0)}\right]^2 \frac{1}{k^2} \, \text{Im} \, \frac{n(p+k) - n(p)}{\hbar\omega_k - \left[\varepsilon_{p+k} - \varepsilon_p\right] + i\delta}$$

$$= -\frac{4\pi NZ^2e^2}{M\omega_k[\varepsilon_{RPA}(k, 0)]^2} \, \text{Im} \left[4\pi\alpha_-(k, \omega_k)\right]$$

$$= -\frac{\omega_k}{\varepsilon_{RPA}(k, 0)} \, \text{Im} \left[4\pi\alpha_-(k, \omega_k)\right] = 2\gamma_k \tag{5-70}$$

Here we have used (5-51a) and the relation

$$\omega_k^2 = \Omega_p^2/\varepsilon_{RPA}(k, 0) = \frac{4\pi N(Ze)^2}{M\varepsilon_{RPA}(k, 0)}$$

The γ_k is the damping rate of the phonon, which is given from the solution to the dispersion relation

$$\varepsilon(k, \omega + i\gamma) = 0$$

or

$$1 + 4\pi\alpha_-(k, \omega + i\gamma) - \frac{\Omega_p^2}{(\omega + i\gamma)^2} = 0$$

We thus write (5-66) as

$$\frac{\partial N_k}{\partial t} = 2\gamma_k N_k + \text{(spontaneous emission term)} \tag{5-71}$$

The factor of 2 in the first term of the right-hand side possesses a further physical interpretation. We remark that the γ_k obtained from the dispersion relation gives the damping rate of the *amplitude* of the lattice vibration; the factor of 2 must thus appear in order to describe the time rate of change in the phonon number, which is closely connected with the energy contained in the particular phonon mode.

We thus see that the phonon-electron equilibrium comes about as a result of two competing processes:

1. Phonon damping, at a rate specified by (5-70).
2. Phonon growth, as a result of the spontaneous emission of phonons, at a rate specified by (5-61a).

The spontaneous-emission term possesses a simple physical interpretation. It corresponds to Čerenkov radiation of phonons by electrons moving at a speed greater than the sound velocity, s. In fact, one can calculate it by direct application of the dielectric formulation developed for the energy-loss problem in Chapter 3; the calculation is left as a problem for the reader. We also remark that for some electron distribution functions (which are not physically realizable for metals, but are possible for semiconductors or for classical plasmas), the damping rate γ_k may turn out to have the opposite sign—and hence correspond to phonon growth. In that case (5-63) and (5-64) do not possess an equilibrium solution within the approximations considered here, and one has a case of an *instability* associated with the growing phonon waves.

Simple Solutions of the Coupled Equations

Let us further seek for a solution to the Boltzmann equations, (5-63) and (5-64).[16a] We define (suppressing subscripts when obvious)

$$E = \beta(\varepsilon_p - \varepsilon_o) \qquad \gamma = \beta\hbar\omega$$

and take for the distribution functions

$$f(p) = f^\circ - g(p)\,\frac{\partial f^\circ}{\partial E} = f^\circ(p) + \beta\,\frac{g(p)}{(1 + e^E)\,(1 + e^{-E})} \tag{5-72a}$$

$$N_{k\mu} = N^\circ - G(k)\,\frac{\partial N^\circ}{\partial(\hbar\omega_{k\mu})} = N^\circ(k\mu) + \beta\,\frac{G(k)}{(e^\gamma - 1)\,(1 - e^{-\gamma})} \tag{5-72b}$$

where N° is the equilibrium phonon distribution (5-65). We then have for the Boltzmann equations, (5-63b) and (5-64),

$$\frac{\partial f}{\partial t} = \frac{2\pi\beta}{\hbar}\sum_{p'\mu} |M(p',p;k,\mu)|^2\,\delta(E' - E - h\omega)\,\frac{g' - g - G}{(e^E + 1)\,(1 + e^{-E})\,(e^\gamma + 1)} \tag{5-73}$$

$$\frac{\partial N}{\partial t} = \frac{4\pi\beta}{\hbar}\sum_{p} |M(p',p;k,\mu)|^2\,\delta(E' - E - \hbar\omega)\,\frac{g' - g - G}{(e^E + 1)\,(1 + e^{-E})\,(e^\gamma - 1)} \tag{5-74}$$

We are using the notation $g' = g(p')$, $g = g(p)$, etc.

We now examine three possibilities:

1. We obtain an equilibrium solution with

$$g = \text{constant} \qquad G = 0$$

This corresponds to a change in the total number of electrons; the transport equation is invariant under a change in the total number of electrons.

2. Another solution obtains by letting

$$g = \lambda E \qquad G = \lambda\hbar\omega$$

This simply corresponds to a change in the temperature. The time derivatives vanish because the δ function requires that

$$g' = g + G$$

3. Assume that there are no U processes. Then if we take

$$g(p) = \lambda p_x \qquad G(k) = \lambda k_x$$

the conservation of momentum, which requires $p' = p + k$, now guarantees

$$g' - g - G = 0$$

So we get a solution representing a net current in the system without the application of an external field. *Without the U processes, the conductivity would be infinite if we have only electron-phonon interactions.* (If there are frequent phonon-phonon collisions, the momentum would be degraded in these processes, so that N processes could contribute to the resistance.)

5-6 HIGH-TEMPERATURE CONDUCTIVITY

For temperatures well above the characteristic temperature of Debye, the formula for the conductivity may be written in the Drude-Lorentz-Sommerfeld form[15,17]:

$$\sigma = \left(ne^2/\hbar k_0\right)v_0\tau$$

where n is the number of valence electrons per unit volume, v_0 is the group velocity of an electron in a state k_0 at the top of the Fermi distribution, and τ is the relaxation time of an electron in that state.

To get a relaxation out of our formalism, we have to make several simplifications:

1. We assume that the temperature is higher than the Debye temperature for the phonons: $T > \theta_D$. This means that we can assume classical statistics for the phonons. For example,

$$N^{\circ}_{k\mu} = \frac{1}{e^{\gamma} - 1} = \frac{1}{e^{\beta\hbar\omega} - 1} \cong \frac{\kappa T}{\hbar\omega_{k\mu}} \tag{5-75}$$

2. We assume that the phonons are in equilibrium and take $G = 0$. A more precise statement of this assumption involves a comparison of the relaxation times for electron-phonon and phonon-phonon collisions:

$$\tau_{\text{phonon-phonon}} \ll \tau_{\text{phonon-electron}}$$

Physically, this means that the phonons "collide" many times between each interaction with the electrons, and hence are always able to maintain equilibrium.

3. Since the exclusion principle requires that only electrons on the Fermi surface interact, the collisions will all be elastic to a high degree of approximation:

$$\varepsilon' - \varepsilon = \hbar\omega \cong 0 \qquad \varepsilon, \varepsilon' >> \hbar\omega$$

Having made these assumptions, we need concern ourselves only with the Boltzmann equation for the electrons. This now simplifies considerably:

$$\frac{\partial f}{\partial t} = -\frac{2\pi}{\hbar} \sum_{p'\mu} |M(p',p;k,\mu)|^2 \delta(E - E')(g' - g)\left(\frac{\kappa T}{\hbar\omega}\right)\frac{\partial f^\circ}{\partial E}$$

The usual definition of the relaxation time is made so that the approach to equilibrium is governed by

$$f - f^\circ = (f_{\text{initial}} - f^\circ)e^{-t/\tau}$$

or

$$\frac{\partial f}{\partial t} = -\frac{f - f^\circ}{\tau} = g\frac{1}{\tau}\frac{\partial f^\circ}{\partial E}$$

Therefore we obtain the following expression for the relaxation time:

$$\frac{1}{\tau} = \frac{2\pi}{\hbar} \sum_{p'\mu} |M(p',p;k,\mu)|^2 \, \delta(E - E')\left(\frac{\kappa T}{\hbar\omega}\right)\left(1 - \frac{g'}{g}\right)$$

This can be further simplified when we note that in the presence of an external electric field **F** in the x direction, g has the form

$$g = ev_x F\tau$$

Furthermore, we assume here that the energies are correctly given by the effective-mass approximation

$$\varepsilon_p^* = \frac{\hbar^2 p^2}{2m^*} \tag{5-76}$$

Then

$$1 - \frac{g'}{g} = 1 - \frac{p_x'}{p_x}$$

We also assume that $|M(p', p; k, \mu)|^2$ depends only on (1) the magnitude of p (which must now be the same as the magnitude of p'); and (2) the angle between p and p'.

Let us define M(p', p) by

$$2|M(p',p)|^2 = \sum_{\mu} \frac{\kappa T}{\hbar\omega} |M(p',p; k, \mu)|^2 \tag{5-77}$$

To simplify our calculations, we neglect the transverse waves and take only the terms with $\mu = \pm 1$; these two terms will yield the same contribution. Then we have for the relaxation time

$$\frac{1}{\tau} = \frac{2\pi}{\hbar} 2 \sum_{p'} |M(p',p)|^2 \delta(E - E')[1 - (p' \cdot \mathbf{F}/p \cdot \mathbf{F})]$$

We next change the sum to an integral over p'. It is most convenient to choose the z axis in the direction of p. Then (letting **F** lie in the xz plane) (see Fig. 5-4),

$$\cos(p, \mathbf{F}) = \cos\alpha$$

$$\cos(p', \mathbf{F}) = \cos\alpha \cos\theta + \sin\alpha \sin\theta \cos\varphi$$

$$\frac{p' \cdot \mathbf{F}}{p \cdot \mathbf{F}} = \cos\theta + \tan\alpha \sin\theta \cos\varphi$$

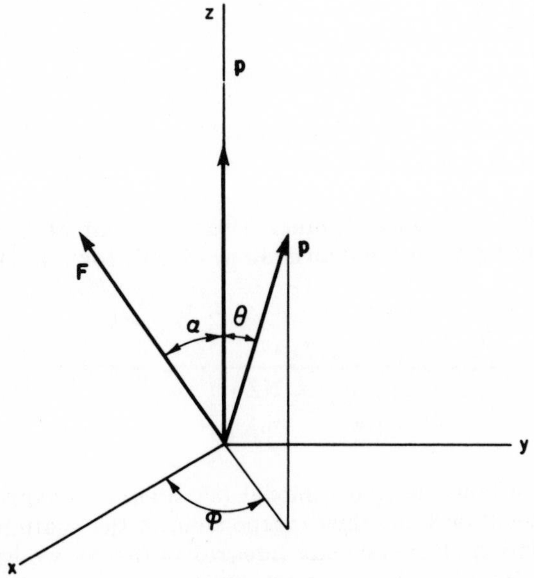

Fig. 5-4

The second term integrates to zero. (Of course α is held constant in the integration.) We then arrive at our final formula for the relaxation time:

$$\frac{1}{\tau} = \frac{k_o^2}{\pi\hbar}\left(\frac{dp}{dE}\right)_{E_o} \int_0^{\pi} |M(p', p)|^2 (1 - \cos\theta) \sin\theta \, d\theta \tag{5-78}$$

Let us now make a rough estimate of our general formula for the relaxation time by using plane waves rather than Bloch functions and by applying the Fermi-Thomas approximation. With the aid of (5-68), $|M(p', p)|^2$, as defined in (5-77), becomes

$$|M(p', p)|^2 = \frac{N}{M}\frac{\hbar}{2\omega_k}\left[\frac{4\pi Ze^2}{k\varepsilon(k, 0)}\right]^2 \frac{\kappa T}{\hbar\omega_k} = NA_k^2\left[\frac{4\pi Ze^2}{k\varepsilon(k, 0)}\right]^2 \tag{5-79}$$

where A_k represents the phonon "oscillator amplitude" and is defined in this case by

$$A_k^2 = \frac{\kappa T}{2M\omega_k^2} \tag{5-80}$$

The maximum wave number k_m for a phonon is

$$k_m = \left(\frac{2}{Z}\right)^{1/3} k_o$$

so that

$$(k_m/k_{FT})^2 \cong 2.4/r_s$$

We conclude that it is not altogether a bad approximation to neglect k^2 compared with k_{FT}^2 in the expression, (5-69), for $\varepsilon(k, 0)$. We then obtain

$$|M(p', p)|^2 \cong Nk^2A_k^2\left\{\frac{4\pi Ze^2}{\dfrac{3}{v_o^2}\dfrac{4\pi NZe^2}{m^*}}\right\}^2 = \frac{4}{9}k^2A_k^2\frac{\varepsilon_F^2}{N} \tag{5-81}$$

Notice that if we take the Debye model ($\omega_k = sk$) this expression becomes independent of k and thus independent of the scattering angle θ.

In the evaluation of the angular integral in (5-78), we have to take note of the maximum scattering angle in the absence of U processes, θ_{max}, which we find easily on recalling that all transitions occur between momentum states at the top of the Fermi distribution (corresponding to k_o). We let $\mathbf{k} = \mathbf{p} - \mathbf{p}'$ and write (see Fig. 5-5):

$$k_m^2 = 2k_o^2 - 2k_o^2 \cos\theta_{max} = 4k_o^2 \sin^2 \frac{1}{2}\theta_{max}$$

$$\sin\frac{1}{2}\theta_{max} = \frac{1}{2}\left(\frac{2}{Z}\right)^{1/3} \qquad (5\text{-}82)$$

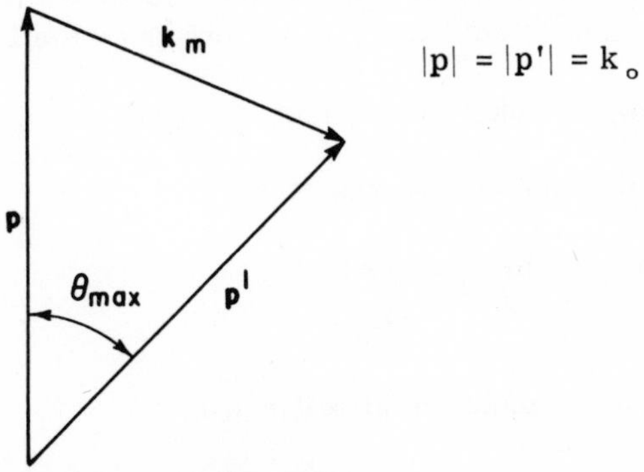

Fig. 5-5. Maximum scattering angle.

For $Z = 1$, $\theta_{max} \cong 79°$. On changing variables to $\mu = \sin(\theta/2)$, we get for the angular integral:

$$\int_0^{\theta_{max}} (1-\cos\theta)\sin\theta \; d\theta = 8\int_0^{\frac{1}{2}\left(\frac{2}{Z}\right)^{1/3}} \mu^3 \, d\mu = Z^{-4/3}2^{-5/3} \qquad (5\text{-}83)$$

We can now collect factors and obtain the relaxation time for $Z = 1$. From (5-76), (5-78), (5-81), and (5-83), we obtain

$$\frac{1}{\tau} = \left(\frac{k_o^2}{\pi\hbar}\right)\left(\frac{m^*}{\hbar^2 k_o}\right)\left(\frac{4}{9}\, k^2 A_k^2 \,\frac{\mathcal{E}_F^2}{N}\right) 2^{-5/3} \qquad (5\text{-}84)$$

In the Debye model we have the following relations:

$$k^2 A_k^2 = \kappa T/2Ms^2$$

$$Ms^2 = \frac{1}{3} m^* v_o^2 = \frac{2}{3} E_o = \frac{1}{3} \frac{\hbar^2 k_o^2}{m^*}$$

and thus we obtain

$$\frac{\hbar}{\tau} = \frac{\pi}{2^{8/3}} \kappa T \cong \kappa T/2 \tag{5-85a}$$

It is customary to express the relaxation time in terms of an "interaction constant" C.[18] If we introduce the Debye temperature θ_D,

$$\kappa\theta_D = \hbar s k_m = 2^{1/3} \hbar s k_o$$

we get the well-known result[18]

$$\frac{\hbar}{\tau} = \frac{\pi}{3} \frac{m^*}{M} C^2 \frac{\kappa T}{(\kappa\theta_D)^2} \tag{5-85b}$$

provided we make the identification

$$C = \varepsilon_F$$

5-7 MORE DETAILED CALCULATIONS OF THE RELAXATION TIME

In our simple calculation above, we found that $|M|^2$ was independent of angle and had the value

$$|M|^2 = \frac{4}{9} k^2 A_k^2 \frac{C^2}{N}$$

When we use better wave functions and potentials, we find a dependence on angle and take this into account by letting

$$|M(p', p)|^2 = \frac{4}{9} k^2 A_k^2 \frac{|G(\mu)|^2}{N} \qquad \mu = \sin\frac{\theta}{2} \tag{5-86a}$$

The formula we get for the relaxation time is then just the "classical" one above, with the interaction constant

$$C^2 = 2^{14/3} \int_0^1 |G(\mu)|^2 \mu^3 \, d\mu \tag{5-86b}$$

as is easily verified.

How can we improve on our order-of-magnitude calculation?

1. We assumed that the wave functions were plane waves. A better approximation would be to use Bloch waves.

2. We assumed Coulombic interactions and took account of the screening by inserting an exponential factor in the ion-electron potential. This method of treating the screening (Fermi-Thomas approximation) is perhaps not too bad, but the "bare" ion-core potentials must be improved.

These improvements were effected by Bardeen in his classic self-consistent field calculation[6]; we sketch his derivation here. More detailed calculations may be found in Ziman.[19] Bardeen's starting point is the calculation of the matrix element, using the *unshielded* potential:

$$\begin{aligned}\mathcal{V}^{I}_{k+K_n} &= \int \psi^*_{p+k+K_n} [\varepsilon_k \cdot \nabla V(r)]\, \psi_p \, d^3r \\ &= \int e^{-i(k+K_n)\cdot r} u^*_{p+k+K_n} u_p \varepsilon_k \cdot \nabla V(r)\, d^3r\end{aligned} \tag{5-87}$$

Now, it is possible to evaluate the above integral by splitting the region of integration into the interior and exterior of the Wigner-Seitz cell (replaced by the customary sphere).[17] In the exterior region ($r > r_o$), we take V to be a simple Coulomb interaction,

$$V_{ext.} = e^2/r$$

and use the plane-wave approximation ($u_k = 1$). Since, in general, the fluctuations in the wave function occur within a small distance of the core, this approximation is not at all bad. In the interior of the Wigner-Seitz sphere we change the volume integral to a surface integral and include the potential of a uniform distribution of negative charge [compare (3-55)]:

$$V_{int.} = V_o + \frac{3}{2}\frac{e^2}{r_o} - \frac{1}{2}\frac{e^2 r^2}{r_o^3}$$

Furthermore, assume that the periodic part of the Bloch function, u_p, can be approximated by the solution for $p = o$, u_o.

For further details on the above calculation, we refer the reader to Bardeen's 1937 paper.[6] We quote the result here:

$$\begin{aligned}v^{I}_{k+K_n} &= -i\,\frac{|k+K_n|}{N}\left\{\frac{4\pi N e^2}{|k+K_n|^2} + V_{int}(r_o) - E_{min}\right\} \\ &\quad\times \cos(\varepsilon_k, k+K_n)\left[\frac{3(\sin x - x\cos x)}{x^3}\right]\end{aligned} \tag{5-88}$$

E_{min} is the lowest eigenvalue for the problem defined by

$$\left[-\frac{\hbar^2}{2m}\nabla^2 + V_{int}\right]u(\mathbf{r}) = Eu(\mathbf{r})$$

subject to $u'(r_o) = 0$; and $x \equiv r_o|\mathbf{k} + \mathbf{K}_n|$.

Bardeen then used first-order perturbation theory to compute the change in the wave functions due to the ionic motion, thereby obtaining the screened interaction with the lattice. His final result was the familiar result

$$M(p',p) = -N^{1/2}A_k \frac{V^I_{k+K_n}}{\varepsilon(k,0)} \tag{5-89}$$

where $\varepsilon(k,0)$ is the RPA dielectric constant.

In the calculation to obtain the relaxation time, we now face the difficulty of a complicated angle dependence in $M(p', p)$; for those terms with $\mathbf{K}_n \neq 0$, all factors contain only $|\mathbf{k}+\mathbf{K}_n| = 2k_o\mu$, except for the oscillator amplitude A_k. Bardeen's suggestion was that we replace A_k by $A(k_{max})$ for the U processes—the whole integrand then depends only on $\mu = \sin\theta/2$, for all values of $\mathbf{p} - \mathbf{p}'$. This serves to underestimate the effectiveness of the U processes, but the neglect of exchange effects in the treatment of the screening tends to cancel this; the results are quite good for the light alkalis. Table 5-1 gives the ratio of the interaction constant to the Fermi energy for various monatomic metals. (The experimental values are obtained simply by solving the standard expressions

$$\sigma = \frac{ne^2\tau}{m^*}; \qquad \frac{\hbar}{\tau} = \frac{\pi}{3}\frac{m^*}{M}C^2\frac{\kappa T}{(\kappa\theta_D)^2}$$

for C.)

Table 5-1
Interaction Constant for Monovalent Metals

	Na	K	Rb	Cs	Cu	Ag	Au
$\left(\frac{C}{E_o}\right)$ theory	0.72	0.77	0.80	0.82	0.61	0.64	0.64
$\left(\frac{C}{E_o}\right)$ expt.	0.82	0.87	1.09	1.27	1.30	1.23	1.55

It was also assumed that $V_{int}(r_o) = E_{min}$ in the calculation of these quantities.

Jones has given a more accurate treatment of the U processes in his review article.[1] He assumes that the change in potential due to the displacement of an ion is effective only within the polyhedron containing the ion. The results are excellent for sodium—about 1 per cent from the experimental value for the conductivity. Indeed this result is almost "too" good, in view of the many approximations which go into it.

5-8 LOW-TEMPERATURE CONDUCTIVITY

Let us list some of the major differences in the situations at low temperatures ($T \ll \theta_D$) and at high temperatures ($T \gg \theta_D$).

For high-temperature electron-phonon scattering, we have essentially elastic scattering ($\hbar\omega \ll \kappa T$); all phonon states are excited; those with highest momenta are most important (since we have a phase-space factor of k^2); and we do not have to distinguish between absorption and creation processes, for $\overline{N}_{k\mu} \gg 1$.

On the other hand, at low temperatures the quantum nature of the phonon processes becomes very important. This manifests itself in the greatly reduced matrix elements; the occupation numbers

$$N_{k\mu}^{o} = \frac{1}{e^{\beta\hbar\omega} - 1}$$

are very small except for those phonons for which $\hbar\omega \lesssim \kappa T$; again, the phase-space factor, k^2, means that the most important phonons are those for which $\hbar\omega \cong \kappa T$. In the Boltzmann equations for the distributions, one must be careful to distinguish between emission and absorption processes, since one no longer can assume $N \gg 1$. Finally, the inelastic nature of the collision processes has to be accounted for ($\delta E \cong \kappa T$).

Nonetheless, one can give a simple "plausibility" argument for the temperature dependence low-temperature conductivity. In some ways, the more-elegant Bloch theory is not much more accurate than a treatment of this type.[20] We begin by assuming that one can define a relaxation time at low temperatures, even though this may not actually prove possible. We therefore write the conductivity as

$$\sigma = \frac{ne^2\tau}{m}$$

so that τ contains the temperature dependence of the conductivity. We want to demonstrate that the resistivity obeys a T^5 law ($\sigma \sim T^{-5}$).

According to our previous calculation,

$$\frac{1}{\tau} = \text{(number of collisions/time) (effectiveness of these collisions)} = \sum_k |M_k|^2 \, \delta(E_p - E_{p'} - \hbar\omega_k)\,(1 - \cos\theta)$$

We have changed to a summation over phonon wave vectors—a consistent procedure since the initial and final momenta are connected in a unique fashion.

Now

$$|M_k|^2 = \frac{4}{9}\,\frac{C^2}{N}\,k^2 A_k^2 \tag{5-90}$$

and, for phonon emission,

$$A_k^2 = \frac{\hbar}{2M\omega_k}\,(N_k + 1)$$

If we neglect the difference between emission and absorption, we may take

$$A_k^2 \cong \frac{\hbar}{2M\omega_k}\,N_k \tag{5-91}$$

On combining (5-90) and (5-91) we find that $|M_k|^2 \sim kN_k$. On changing from a summation to an integral, we get an extra factor k^2 in the integrand. The "collision effectiveness," measured by the factor $(1 - \cos\theta)$, brings in another factor k^2, since

$$1 - \cos\theta = k^2/2k_0^2$$

Finally, the δ function brings in a factor $1/k$. The rapid decrease of the factor N_k beyond $\hbar\omega \cong \kappa T$ leads us to set $N_k = 1$ for $\hbar\omega \leq \kappa T$ and $N_k = 0$ for $\hbar\omega > \kappa T$, whence we find:

$$1/\tau \sim (k_{eff})^5 \sim T^5$$

This T^5 law is well confirmed by experiment.[21]

This brings us to the so-called "Peierls dilemma" concerning the scattering mechanism at low temperatures.[22] The dilemma arises because the processes by which the phonons maintain equilibrium seem to be rapidly damped out at low temperatures. We have assumed above that they are in equilibrium, and obtained a result in agreement with experiment. The picture which we can form is quite simple:

Since the phonons effectively collide only with electrons through N processes, they cannot return the electron distribution to equilibrium, but will be "carried along" with the electrons when a field is applied; the conductivity will be infinite. Actually, both electron-electron collisions and scattering by impurities yield a finite conductivity, but the temperature dependence of σ arising from these processes is wrong. So if the U processes and phonon-phonon scattering are both "frozen out," we cannot see how the phonons contribute to the resistance.

Before indicating how the paradox has been resolved, we will sharpen it by showing (1) that U processes are frozen out, and (2) that the phonon-phonon collision time becomes long compared with other collision times at low temperatures.

1. The U processes involve an exchange of momentum between the lattice and the electron-phonon distribution and hence can serve to return it to equilibrium. But for the monovalent metals, the Fermi distribution lies well within the first Brillouin zone; this means that there is a *smallest* phonon momentum which can participate in U processes (we have to add two vectors of length k_o with a vector of length k to obtain one of length $(2)^{4/3}k_o$; $2k_o(2^{1/3} - 1)$. (See Fig. 5-6, and recall the discussion of Sec. 2-6.) When the temperature gets so low that these phonons are frozen out, the conductivity should take on an exponential behavior (if it is limited by electron-phonon collisions only). For sodium, this temperature is around 20°K. But the T^5 law is valid experimentally much below 20°K.

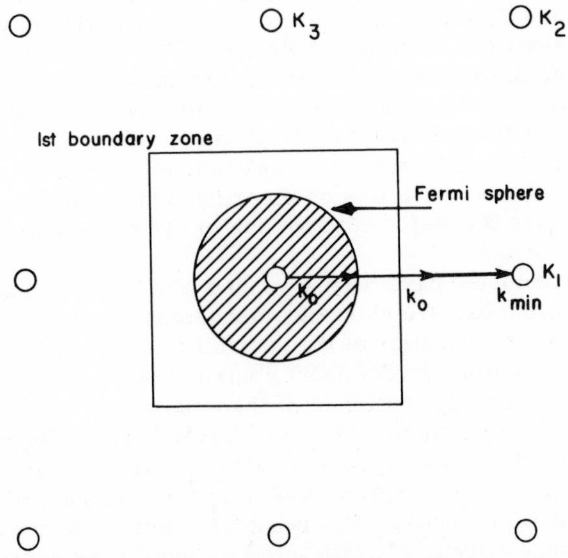

Fig. 5-6. Minimum phonon momentum for U process.

2. Let us estimate the collision times for the phonons. At room temperature,

$$\frac{\hbar}{\tau_{\text{electron-phonon}}} \sim \kappa T \qquad \tau_{e\text{-}p} \cong 2.5 \times 10^{-14} \text{ sec}$$

$$\frac{1}{\tau_{\text{phonon-electron}}} \sim \frac{\hbar\omega}{E_o} \frac{1}{\tau_{e\text{-}p}} \qquad \tau_{p\text{-}e} \cong 10^3 \tau_{e\text{-}p} \cong 10^{-11} \text{ sec}$$

So at room temperatures the phonons certainly do not come to equilibrium as a result of collisions with electrons. (The verification of this estimate in a little more detail is an excellent exercise for the interested reader.)

At low temperatures the situation will be even more pronounced; we must therefore consider the phonon-phonon collision time in sure detail. We can find the temperature dependence of $\tau_{p\text{-}p}$ by the following argument: The thermal conductivity is proportional to the product of the specific heat and the collision time (mean free path). We can obtain an estimate of the effectiveness of phonon-phonon interactions by considering the situation in ionic crystals where the phonons represent the only mechanism of conduction. The thermal conductivity there varies as $1/T$ for low temperatures, and the specific heat obeys the usual T^3 law. Therefore one finds that $\tau_{p\text{-}p} \sim T^{-4}$. For low-enough temperatures this will be long compared to the collision time with the electrons ($\sim T^{-1}$); hence phonon-phonon scattering is also frozen out of the picture. How do we explain the T^5 law, then?

Bailyn and Brooks[23] have given the most satisfactory explanation to date—the alkalis are highly anisotropic, in such a way that the velocity of one of the transverse phonons is at least 0.4 smaller than the longitudinal velocity. Therefore, at really low temperatures one will deal mostly with these transverse phonons. Brooks and Bailyn have carried out a calculation which takes into account in detail the dependence of the phonon velocities on direction and obtain the result that U processes give the major contribution to the resistance down to $T \sim 2°K$.

Other arguments have been advanced which depend on electron-electron collisions. We close our discussion of the theory of conductivity with a consideration of the possibility of electron-electron collisions representing the dominant contribution to the resistivity. We give here only a rough estimate of the importance of such collisions; more careful calculations have been carried out by Abrahams.[24]

We first remark that collisions between electrons contribute to the resistivity only if the conduction band is nonisotropic, or if one takes into account U processes. The reason is simple: In the absence of either of these effects, electron-electron collisions conserve momentum and so cannot serve to disrupt a directed current of the electrons. We may estimate the collision time for electron-electron scattering by assuming that only s-wave collisions are of importance, and that further, the effective interaction is of the screened Coulomb variety, $\exp(-k_{FT} r/r)$. In this case, one finds a collision cross section which is, approximately,

$$\sigma_{eff} = \frac{4\pi}{k_{FT}^2}\left(\frac{\kappa T}{\varepsilon_F}\right)^2 = \frac{4\pi}{3}\left(\frac{mv_o^2}{4\pi Ne^2}\right)\left(\frac{\kappa T}{\varepsilon_F}\right)^2 \qquad (5\text{-}92)$$

The factors of $(\kappa T/\varepsilon_F)$ take account of the Pauli principle restrictions on both the initial and final states in the scattering process. The collision time is then

$$\left(\frac{1}{\tau}\right)_{e^- - e^-} = v_o N \sigma_{eff} \cong \frac{80}{r_s^3}\left(\frac{\kappa T}{\varepsilon_F}\right)^2 \times 10^{15}\,\text{sec}^{-1} \qquad (5\text{-}93)$$

Let us compare this result with the collision time for electron-electron collisions and electron-impurity collisions at low temperatures. As we have seen, $1/\tau_{e^- - ph}$ varies as T^5, so that at sufficiently low temperatures electron-electron scattering will prove more important than electron-phonon scattering. On the other hand, the collision time for impurity scattering is temperature-independent and is inversely proportional to the impurity concentration. For sodium at 4°K one finds

$$\left(\frac{1}{\tau}\right)_{e^- - ph} = 4 \times 10^7/\text{sec}^{-1} \cong \frac{1}{\tau_{e^- - e^-}} \qquad (5\text{-}94)$$

On the other hand, the collision time for impurity scattering is given by

$$\left(\frac{1}{\tau}\right)_{e^- - imp} = \frac{80}{r_s^3}\left(\frac{N_i}{N}\right) \times 10^{15} \qquad (5\text{-}95)$$

if we assume a screened Coulomb interaction between the electrons and impurities of charge 1 and density N_i which has the same form as that between electrons. (This assumption is sufficient for our present purposes.) On comparing (5-93) and (5-95) we see that the electron-impurity collision time is comparable to that for electron-electron collisions at 4°K only if one has an impurity concentration of 10^{-8}, a purity unobtainable for sodium at present. In general, observation of electron-electron scattering in simple metals will require impurity concentrations of this order of magnitude.

5-9 QUASI-PARTICLE PROPERTIES

The calculation of the quasi-particle properties for electrons which interact with one another and with phonons has not yet been carried out in detail for either the free-electron gas or for the properties of simple metals. In general, field-theoretic techniques are required; it is furthermore clear from the preceding sections that if one wants to get anything like a quantitative result, it is necessary to take into account the influence of periodicity upon v_k^i and Ω_k. Thus far, the most detailed investigations which have been carried out are due to Simkin.[25]

Simkin has calculated the influence of the electron-phonon interactions on both the spin susceptibility and specific heat of the electron gas. He finds that the spin susceptibility is unaffected by electron-phonon interactions to order m/M. This result is not difficult to understand. If we recall that the spin susceptibility depends on the change in the Fermi energy in the presence of the magnetic field, and, further recognize that the Fermi energy (like the cohesive energy and the compressibility) is unaffected by electron-phonon interactions to order m/M, we see that the spin susceptibility is unaffected to this order. (Note that the interaction of the electrons with the periodic field of the *fixed* ions is, of course, of considerable importance.) On the other hand, the specific heat is affected by the electron-phonon interaction. Simkin has carried out detailed calculations for sodium; he finds that the electron-phonon interaction acts to enhance the specific heat by some 10 per cent, a result in good accord with the results of Silverstein, and with experiment, as discussed in Sec. 3-6.

References

1. For further details see, for example, H. Jones, "Handbuch der Physik," Springer, Berlin, 1956, Vol. XIX, pp. 245-249; J. M. Ziman, "Electrons and Phonons," Clarendon Press, Oxford, 1960.
2. H. Fröhlich, *Proc. Roy. Soc. (London)*, **A215**, 291 (1952).
3. J. Bardeen and D. Pines, *Phys. Rev.*, **99**, 1140 (1955).
4. C. B. Clark, *Phys. Rev.*, 109, 1133 (1958).
5. R. A. Coldwell-Horsfall and A. A. Maradudin, *J. Math. Phys.*, 1, 395 (1960).
6. J. Bardeen, *Phys. Rev.*, **52**, 688 (1937).
7. D. Bohm and T. Staver, *Phys. Rev.*, **84**, 836 (1952).
8. T. Staver, Ph.D. thesis, Princeton University, 1952, unpublished.
9. D. Pines, "The Many-Body Problem," Benjamin, New York, 1962, pp. 82-91.
10. P. Nozières, "Theory of Interacting Fermion Systems," Dunod-Benjamin, Paris-New York, 1963.

10a. P. Nozières and D. Pines (to be published).

11. W. Kohn, *Phys. Rev. Letters*, 2, 393 (1959); E. J. Woll, Jr., and W. Kohn, *Phys. Rev.*, 126, 1693 (1962).
12. B. N. Brockhouse, K. R. Rao, and A. D. B. Woods, *Phys. Rev. Letters*, 7, 93 (1961); B. N. Brockhouse, T. Arase, G. Caglioti, K. R. Ras, and A. D. B. Woods, *Phys. Rev.*, 128, 1099 (1962).
12a. In a field-theoretic calculation, it turns out that the effective electron interaction involves the *propagating* dielectric constant in place of the *retarded* dielectric constant considered here. The difference is of some importance in detailed calculations of the integral equation for the energy gap in the BCS theory of superconductivity. The relationship between propagating and retarded dielectric constants is considered in Problem 3-5.
13. J. Bardeen, L. N. Cooper, and J. R. Schrieffer, *Phys. Rev.*, 108, 1175 (1957).
13a. D. Pines, *Phys. Rev.*, 109, 280 (1958); P. Morel, *Phys. Chem. Solids*, 10, 277 (1959).
14. For a recent detailed discussion of this and related questions, see M. Dresden, *Rev. Mod. Phys.*, 33, 265 (1961).
14a. J. S. van Wieringen, *Proc. Phys. Soc. (London)*, A67, 206 (1954); G. V. Chester and A. Thellung, *Proc. Phys. Soc. (London)*, 73, 745 (1959).
15. R. E. Peierls, "Quantum Theory of Solids," Clarendon Press, Oxford, 1955, Chap. VI.
16. D. Pines and J. R. Schrieffer, *Phys. Rev.*, 125, 804 (1962).
16a. The development here follows closely that of Ref. 15.
17. N. F. Mott and H. Jones, "Theory of the Properties of Metals and Alloys," Clarendon Press, Oxford, 1936, Chap. VII.
18. A. Sommerfeld and H. A. Bethe, "Handbuch der Physik," Springer, Berlin, 1933, Vol. XXIV-II.
19. J. M. Ziman, "Electrons and Phonons," Clarendon Press, Oxford, 1960.
20. A. H. Wilson, "The Theory of Metals," Cambridge University Press, Cambridge, 1953, 2nd ed., pp. 277-279; 300-325.
21. G. K. White, *Can. J. Phys.*, 34, 1328 (1956).
22. R. E. Peierls, *Ann. Physik*, 4, 121 (1930).
23. M. Bailyn and H. Brooks, *Bull. Am. Phys. Soc.*, [II] 1, 300 (1956); M. Bailyn, *Phys. Rev.*, 112, 1587 (1958).
24. E. Abrahams, *Phys. Rev.*, 95, 839 (1954).
25. D. Simkin, Ph.D. thesis, Univ. Illinois, 1963, unpublished.

Problems

5-1 Show that in the RPA, $\varepsilon_{eff}(k\omega)$ is given by (5-36), if U processes are neglected; show that with U processes one finds (5-56), where the phonon frequencies ω_k are determined by (5-46b).

5-2 Show, for the "jellium" model, that the term representing spontaneous emission of phonons, which appears in (5-64), may be obtained directly from an expression for the energy loss by an electron in the metal. [*Hint*: Recall that $W(k, \omega_1) = (d/dt)(N_k \hbar\omega_1)$, and use (3-112).]

5-3 Calculate, for the "jellium" model, the lifetime against phonon emission for an electron near the Fermi surface.

5-4 Discuss the approach to equilibrium of the coupled systems of electrons and plasma oscillations in a finite-temperature plasma, along the lines of Sec. 5-5. [The matrix element for electron-plasmon coupling is $M_1(k, p) = (2\pi e^2 \hbar\omega_q/q^2)^{1/2}$, where ω_q is the frequency of the plasmon.] Show that the plasmons come to equilibrium as a result of the competition between Landau damping and Ĉerenkov emission of plasma waves.

5-5 Assume the electrons in a metal possess a drift velocity $\mathbf{v}_d$, and that their distribution function is then a displaced Fermi-Dirac distribution

$$f(p, v_d) = \frac{1}{e^{\beta(\epsilon_{p-mv_d} - \epsilon_F)} + 1}$$

Determine, in the "jellium" model, the drift velocity for which a long-wavelength phonon mode becomes unstable, for a metal at $T = 0$.

Appendix A

SECOND QUANTIZATION

For the investigation of a quantum mechanical system composed of identical particles, the formal device known as the second quantization frequently proves useful in the mathematical description of the system. In this appendix, the formalism is briefly described. The interested reader is referred to the relevant texts[1] for further details.

Let us consider a set of interacting particles. The wave function for the system must be either symmetric or antisymmetric. If the wave function is symmetric, the particles are bosons, obeying the Bose-Einstein statistics; if antisymmetric, they are fermions, governed by the Fermi-Dirac statistics.

Let us choose a complete set of orthonormal single-particle wave functions, $\phi_i(r)$ $(i = 1, 2, \ldots)$. We assume that the single-particle states are arranged in a certain order. The state of the many-particle system can be specified if we specify the occupation number n_i of each single-particle state. Accordingly, we write the state vector of the system as

$$|n_1, n_2, \ldots, n_i, \ldots\rangle = \Phi(n_1, n_2, \ldots, n_i, \ldots)$$

This wave function is identical in physical content to one written as the symmetrized or antisymmetrized sum of the products of the single-particle wave functions. One can take the state vectors to form an orthonormal set,

$$\langle n_1', n_2', \ldots, n_i', \ldots | n_1, n_2, \ldots, n_i, \ldots\rangle = \delta_{n_1 n_1'} \delta_{n_2 n_2'} \cdots \delta_{n_i n_i'} \cdots \quad \text{(A-1)}$$

We now introduce the creation and destruction operators which relate different state vectors. For bosons,

$$a_i \Phi(\ldots, n_i, \ldots) = \sqrt{n_i}\ \Phi(\ldots, n_i - 1, \ldots) \tag{A-2a}$$

$$a_i^+ \Phi(\ldots, n_i, \ldots) = \sqrt{n_i + 1}\ \Phi(\ldots, n_i + 1, \ldots) \tag{A-2b}$$

and for fermions,

$$c_i \Phi(\ldots, n_i, \ldots) = \sqrt{n_i}\ (-1)^{\sum_{j<i} n_j}\ \Phi(\ldots, n_i - 1, \ldots) \tag{A-3a}$$

$$c_i^+ \Phi(\ldots, n_i, \ldots) = \sqrt{1 - n_i}\ (-1)^{\sum_{j<i} n_j}\ \Phi(\ldots, n_i + 1, \ldots) \tag{A-3b}$$

The factor $(-1)^{\sum_{j<i} n_j}$ appearing in (A-3) stems from the requirement that the wave function be antisymmetric for fermions. It is thus necessary that the ordering of the state is fixed in some way.

The commutation rules for the operators follow directly from the relations (A-2) and (A-3) and vice versa. They are

$$\left[a_i, a_j\right] = \left[a_i^+, a_j^+\right] = 0 \tag{A-4a}$$

$$\left[a_i, a_j^+\right] = \delta_{ij} \tag{A-4b}$$

and

$$\left\{c_i, c_j\right\} = \left\{c_i^+, c_j^+\right\} = 0 \tag{A-5a}$$

$$\left\{c_i, c_j^+\right\} = \delta_{ij} \tag{A-5b}$$

We use the bracket [,] for the commutator,

$$[a, b] = ab - ba$$

and the brace { , } for the anticommutator,

$$\{a, b\} = ab + ba$$

We remark that all the physical properties of the system associated with the symmetry property of its wave function are naturally built in the commutation relations, as we shall see.

The operators for the occupation numbers, n_i, are given by $a_i^+ a_i$ or $c_i^+ c_i$ according to the statistics, i.e.,

$$a_i^+ a_i\ \Phi(\ldots, n_i, \ldots) = n_i\ \Phi(\ldots, n_i, \ldots) \tag{A-6}$$

$$c_i^+ c_i\ \Phi(\ldots, n_i, \ldots) = n_i\ \Phi(\ldots, n_i, \ldots) \tag{A-7}$$

It is straightforward to obtain (A-6) from (A-2). The derivation of (A-7) from (A-3) is slightly more involved. First, by letting i = j in (A-5a), we see that

$$c_i^+ c_i^+ = \left(c_i^+\right)^2 = 0 \tag{A-8}$$

In other words, it is impossible for two fermions to occupy a single state; thus the Pauli exclusion principle is seen to be contained in the commutation rules, (A-5). For the proof of (A-7), it is therefore sufficient to show that (A-7) follows from (A-3) for $n_i = 0$ and $n_i = 1$; the calculations go as follows:

$$c_i^+ c_i \Phi(\ldots, n_i, \ldots) = \begin{cases} 0 & n_i = 0 \\ \Phi(\ldots, n_i, \ldots) & n_i = 1 \end{cases}$$

and (A-7) is proved.

One can build up a state vector from the vacuum state $|0\rangle$ with no particles present. A state with one boson present is described as $a_i^+ |0\rangle$; a two-particle state is either $a_i^+ a_j^+ |0\rangle$ $(i \neq j)$, or $(1/\sqrt{2})$ $(a_i^+)^2 |0\rangle$. We see that state vectors are symmetric under the interchange of i and j. For fermions additional care must be taken for the ordering of the creation operators, since an interchange of two particles brings a factor of (- 1) because the wave function for the fermion system is antisymmetric.

Let us now consider a many-body sum of single-particle operators,

$$F_1 = \sum_i f_i(r_i) \tag{A-9}$$

An example of such a single-particle operator is the kinetic energy of a particle, $p_i^2/2m = -(\hbar^2/2m)\nabla_i^2$. Another example is the Bloch operator, $-(\hbar^2/2m)\nabla_i^2 + V(r_i)$, where $V(r_i)$ is a periodic potential. One can then show by comparing the matrix elements that (A-9) is expressed in terms of the creation and annihilation operators as

$$F_1 = \sum_{ij} \langle i|f_1|j\rangle \, a_i^+ a_j \tag{A-10}$$

for bosons, where

$$\langle i|f_1|j\rangle = \int \phi_i^*(r) f_1(r) \phi_j(r) \, dr \tag{A-11}$$

Identical formulas apply for fermions.

Let us now consider a sum of two-particle operators

$$F_2 = \sum_{i \neq j} f_2(r_i, r_j) \tag{A-12}$$

An important example of such a two-particle operator is the Coulomb interaction, $e^2/|r_i - r_j|$. It is then straightforward to show that the sum (A-12), in terms of the creation and annihilation operators, takes the form

$$F_2 = \frac{1}{2} \sum_{\substack{ij\\km}} \langle ij|f_2|km\rangle\, a_i^+ a_j^+ a_m a_k \tag{A-13}$$

where

$$\langle ij|f_2|km\rangle = \iint \phi_i^*(r_1)\phi_j^*(r_2) f_2(r_1, r_2)\phi_k(r_1)\phi_m(r_2)\,dr_1\, dr_2 \tag{A-14}$$

Again these formulas are applicable to fermions as well.

Before going into a discussion of the electron gas, let us introduce field operators, $\psi^+(r)$ and $\psi(r)$, which prove very useful. These are constructed as a coherent sum of the creation and annihilation operators. For bosons,

$$\psi_B(r) = \sum_i \phi_i(r)\, a_i \tag{A-15a}$$

$$\psi_B^+(r) = \sum_i \phi_i^*(r)\, a_i^+ \tag{A-15b}$$

and for fermions,

$$\psi_F(r) = \sum_i \phi_i(r)\, c_i \tag{A-16a}$$

$$\psi_F^+(r) = \sum_i \phi_i^*(r)\, c_i^+ \tag{A-16b}$$

It is clear that $\psi^+(r)$ [representing $\psi_B^+(r)$ and $\psi_F^+(r)$] creates a particle at r and $\psi(r)$ destroys a particle at r. If one recalls that the $\phi_i(r)$ form a complete set of orthonormal wave functions, it is easy to prove the following commutation rules from (A-4) and (A-5):

$$\left[\psi_B(r), \psi_B(r')\right] = \left[\psi_B^+(r), \psi_B^+(r')\right] = 0 \tag{A-17a}$$

$$\left[\psi_B(r), \psi_B^+(r')\right] = \delta(r - r') \tag{A-17b}$$

and

$$\left\{\psi_F(r), \psi_F(r')\right\} = \left\{\psi_F^+(r), \psi_F^+(r')\right\} = 0 \tag{A-18a}$$

$$\left\{\psi_F(r), \psi_F^+(r')\right\} = \delta(r - r') \tag{A-18b}$$

The density of particles at r is expressed as

$$\rho(r) = \psi^+(r)\psi(r) \tag{A-19}$$

and the sum of single- and two-particle operators defined by (A-9) and (A-12) is

$$F_1 = \int \psi^+(r) f_1 \psi(r)\, dr \tag{A-20}$$

$$F_2 = \frac{1}{2} \int\int \left[\psi^+(r_1)\psi(r_1) f_2 \psi^+(r_2)\psi(r_2) - n_0 f_2 \delta(r_1 - r_2)\right] dr_1\, dr_2$$

$$= \frac{1}{2} \int\int \psi^+(r_1)\psi^+(r_2) f_2 \psi(r_2)\psi(r_1)\, dr_1\, dr_2 \tag{A-21}$$

The second term in the first expression of F_2 corresponds to the subtraction of those terms with i = j which are contained in the integral of the first term. The equivalence of these formulas and those of (A-10) and (A-13) is clearly seen through (A-15) or (A-16).

Let us now focus our attention on the description of a many-electron system. If the system is invariant under spatial translation, the most convenient single-particle states, $\phi_i(r)$ are the plane-wave states of momentum p. Assuming the system is confined in a box of volume L^3, one has

$$\phi_p(r) = \frac{1}{\sqrt{L^3}} e^{i p \cdot r}$$

This wave function must be multiplied by the appropriate spin wave function, determined by the spin projection σ along a certain direction (say the Z axis). On the other hand, if we consider the electrons moving in a periodic lattice field, the convenient single-particle states are the Bloch waves,

$$\psi_{kn}(r) = \frac{e^{i k \cdot r}}{\sqrt{L^3}} u_{kn}(r)$$

In the reduced zone scheme the wave vectors **k** are restricted to the first Brillouin zone and the subscript n serves to label the different energy bands.

In dealing with the interacting electron gas it is often convenient to redefine the "vacuum" state as the ground-state wave function $|0\rangle = \Psi_o$, appropriate to a filled Fermi sphere (of radius k_o) at T = 0. Then, as a direct consequence of the Pauli principle we have

$$c^+_{p\sigma}|0\rangle = 0 \qquad |p| < k_o \tag{A-22a}$$

$$c_{p\sigma}|0\rangle = 0 \qquad |p| > k_o \tag{A-22b}$$

The expectation value of the occupation number operator in the ground state, of course, gives the Fermi distribution at T = 0.

$$n_{p\sigma} = \langle 0|c^+_{p\sigma}c_{p\sigma}|0\rangle = \begin{cases} 0 & |p| > k_o \\ 1 & |p| < k_o \end{cases} \tag{A-23}$$

The Fourier components of electron density fluctuations,

$$\rho_{\mathbf{k}} = \sum_i e^{-i\mathbf{k}\cdot\mathbf{r}_i} \tag{A-24}$$

can be expressed in terms of $c^+_{p\sigma}$ and $c_{p\sigma}$ by means of formulas (A-9) to (A-11). Alternatively, one can directly Fourier-transform the expression (A-19). Either way, one obtains

$$\rho_{\mathbf{k}} = \sum_{p\sigma} c^+_{p-k\,\sigma}c_{p\sigma} \tag{A-25}$$

Finally we express the Hamiltonian for an interacting electron system in terms of the creation and annihilation operators. We consider the translational invariant case; a similar formalism applies for the Bloch wave states. In the light of the above discussion one can easily obtain the following expressions:

$$H = \sum_i p_i^2/2m + (1/2)\sum_{i\neq j} \mathcal{V}(|r_i - r_j|)$$

$$= \int \frac{\hbar^2}{2m} \nabla\psi^+(r)\,\nabla\psi(r)\,dr$$

$$+ \frac{1}{2}\iint \psi^+(r)\psi^+(r')\,\mathcal{V}(|r - r'|)\,\psi(r')\,\psi(r)\,dr\;dr'$$

$$= \sum_{p\sigma} \varepsilon(p)\,c^+_{p\sigma}c_{p\sigma} + \frac{1}{2}\sum_{\substack{pp'k\\ \sigma\sigma'}} \mathcal{V}_k\,c^+_{p-k\sigma}c^+_{p'+k\sigma'}c_{p'\sigma'}c_{p\sigma} \tag{A-26}$$

where

$$\varepsilon(p) = \hbar^2 p^2/2m \tag{A-27}$$

$$\mathcal{V}_k = \int \mathcal{V}(r) e^{-i\mathbf{k}\cdot\mathbf{r}}\, dr$$

$$= 4\pi e^2/k^2 L^3 \quad \text{(for a Coulomb interaction)} \tag{A-28}$$

A comment follows on the k summation of the potential-energy term in (A-26). As is clearly seen from (A-26), the terms with $k = 0$ give the self-energy of the "smeared-out" negative charge in that expression. However, we always consider these electrons moving in a smeared-out background of positive charge to cancel that self-energy of the negative charge. Therefore we understand that in the summation of the second term of (A-26) the terms with $k = 0$ are excluded because of the presence of the smeared-out background of positive charge.

References

1. F. Mandl, "Introduction to Quantum Field Theory," Interscience, New York, 1960; L. I. Schiff, "Quantum Mechanics," 2nd ed., McGraw-Hill, New York, 1955; S. S. Schweber, "An Introduction To Relativistic Quantum Field Theory," Row, Peterson, Evanston, Ill., 1961.

Appendix B

LINEAR RESPONSE FUNCTIONS; KRAMERS-KRONIG RELATIONS

In defining and calculating $1/\varepsilon(\mathbf{k}\omega)$, we have been dealing with a particular case of a linear response function for the electron gas. It is of interest to examine our approach from a somewhat more general point of view. Suppose we regard the test charge, $z\rho_{ext}(\mathbf{r}'t')$, as being applied in a volume $d\mathbf{r}'$ during a time dt'; the test charge will then introduce a disturbance in the expectation value of the electron density at $\mathbf{r}$ and t, $\langle \rho(\mathbf{r}t) \rangle$. We can, in general, relate this disturbance to the test charge by means of a kernel, $K(\mathbf{r}-\mathbf{r}', t-t')$,

$$\langle \rho(\mathbf{r}t) \rangle = K(\mathbf{r}-\mathbf{r}', t-t')\, z\rho_{ext}(\mathbf{r}'t')\, d\mathbf{r}'\, dt' \qquad \text{(A-29)}$$

In general, the kernel K should be regarded as $K(\mathbf{r}, \mathbf{r}'; t-t')$; for a system with spatial translational invariance, it takes the form (A-29). (Time translational invariance is always assumed.)

The response of the system must be causal; this imposes the following requirement on $K(\mathbf{r}-\mathbf{r}', t-t')$:

$$K(\mathbf{r}-\mathbf{r}', t-t') = 0 \qquad \text{for } t < t' \qquad \text{(A-30)}$$

since, as is obvious, no effect at $\mathbf{r}, t$ can be observed prior to the introduction of the disturbance at a time t'. The assumption of linearity manifests itself in two ways. First, the kernel must be a function which depends only on the properties of the system in the absence of the test charge. Second, the principle of superposition applies, i.e., the total influence of the entire test-charge field $z\rho_{ext}(\mathbf{r}'t')$ upon $\langle \rho(\mathbf{r}\,t) \rangle$ can be calculated by integrating (A-29) over space and time, according to

$$< \rho(\mathbf{r}t) > = \int d\mathbf{r}' \int_{-\infty}^{t} dt' \, K(\mathbf{r} - \mathbf{r}', t - t') \, z\rho_{ext}(\mathbf{r}'t') \qquad \text{(A-31)}$$

where we have made use of the causality condition, (A-30). Equation (A-31) can be transformed directly into a relation between the Fourier components:

$$< \rho(\mathbf{k}\omega) > = K(\mathbf{k}\omega) \, z\rho_{ext}(\mathbf{k}\omega) \qquad \text{(A-32)}$$

where $K(\mathbf{k}\omega)$ is given by

$$K(\mathbf{k}\omega) = \int d\mathbf{r} \int_{0}^{\infty} dt \, K(\mathbf{r}t) \, e^{-i(\mathbf{k}\cdot\mathbf{r} - \omega t)} \qquad \text{(A-33)}$$

Remark that $K(\mathbf{k}\omega)$ is defined by a one-sided Fourier transform with respect to time.

$K(\mathbf{k}\omega)$ is the linear response function of the system. On comparing (A-33) with (3-105a), we obtain

$$K(\mathbf{k}\omega) = 1 - \frac{1}{\varepsilon(\mathbf{k}\omega)} \qquad \text{(A-34)}$$

In the limit $\omega \to \infty$, the function $K(\mathbf{k}\omega)$ may tend to a finite limit. For the case of the electron gas, the limit is zero; electrons cannot follow a disturbance with infinite frequency. We shall in the following assume that $K(\mathbf{k}\omega) \to 0$ as $\omega \to \infty$.*

From (A-33), and from the fact that $K(\mathbf{r}t)$ is finite for all positive t, one can show directly that $K(\mathbf{k}\omega)$ has no singularities in the whole of the upper half complex ω plane. Indeed, for a complex frequency, $\omega = \omega_1 + i\omega_2$, such that $\omega_2 > 0$, $K(\mathbf{k}, \omega_1 + i\omega_2)$ calculated according to (A-33) must converge because of the presence of the exponentially decreasing factor $e^{-\omega_2 t}$. The integral (A-33) is, in fact, well defined only in the upper half of the complex ω plane; it may then be continued analytically into the lower half-plane.

The content of the foregoing statements may be compactly expressed by

$$\lim_{\delta \to 0} \int_{-\infty}^{\infty} \frac{K(\mathbf{k}\omega') \, d\omega'}{\omega' - \omega + i|\delta|} = 0 \qquad \text{(A-35)}$$

*When $K(\mathbf{k}\omega)$ tends to a nonzero limit, $K(\mathbf{k}\infty)$, the relations to be derived in the following are to be modified by taking $K(\mathbf{k}\omega) - K(\mathbf{k}\infty)$.

That (A-35) holds is seen by closing the contour with the aid of the infinite semicircle c_∞ in the upper half-plane, as shown in Fig. A-1.

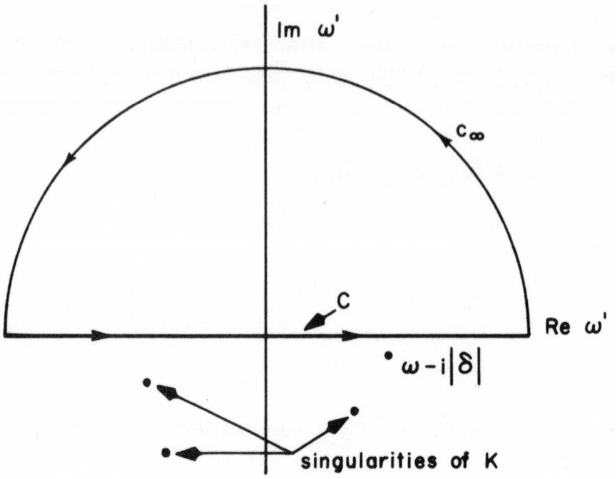

Fig. A-1

Since there are no singularities of $K(k\omega')$ or $1/(\omega' - \omega + i\,\delta)$ encircled by the contour c and c_∞, we have from Cauchy's theorem,

$$\int_c + \int_{c_\infty} = 0$$

However, we see that the integration $\int_{c_\infty}$ itself vanishes because for large $|\omega'|$, $1/(\omega' - \omega + i|\delta|)$ behaves like $1/\omega'$ and $K(k\omega')$ approaches zero (as we have assumed). Hence we are left with the integration along the contour c, and the result is (A-35).

We now obtain the set of Kramers-Kronig relations on picking up the real and imaginary parts of (A-35) separately:

$$\text{Re } K(k\omega) = \frac{1}{\pi} \text{ P} \int_{-\infty}^{\infty} \frac{\text{Im } K(k\omega')}{\omega' - \omega} d\omega' \qquad \text{(A-36a)}$$

$$\text{Im } K(k\omega) = -\frac{1}{\pi} \text{ P} \int_{-\infty}^{\infty} \frac{\text{Re } K(k\omega')}{\omega' - \omega} d\omega' \qquad \text{(A-36b)}$$

where P indicates taking the principal-part integral. It is therefore said that the Kramers-Kronig relations are a direct consequence of the physical principle of causality.

In particular, combining (A-34) with (A-36), one has

$$\mathrm{Re}\,\frac{1}{\varepsilon(k\omega)} - 1 = \frac{1}{\pi}\, P \int_{-\infty}^{\infty} \mathrm{Im}\,[1/\varepsilon(k\omega')]\, \frac{d\omega'}{\omega' - \omega} \tag{A-37a}$$

$$\mathrm{Im}\,\frac{1}{\varepsilon(k\omega)} = \frac{1}{\pi}\, P \int_{-\infty}^{\infty} \{1 - \mathrm{Re}\,[1/\varepsilon(k\omega')]\}\, \frac{d\omega'}{\omega' - \omega} \tag{A-37b}$$

One can likewise show that $K^{-1}(k\omega)$ is analytic in the upper half-plane. To show this one must show that $K(k\omega)$ can never be zero there. We have, on making use of (4-117), the expression

$$K(k\omega) = \frac{4\pi e^2}{\hbar k^2} \int_0^{\infty} d\omega'\; S(k\omega')\, \frac{2\omega'}{\omega^2 - \omega'^2}$$

where ω is taken to possess always a positive imaginary part. Let $\omega = \omega_1 + i\omega_2$, and take the imaginary parts of the above equation. One finds directly that $\mathrm{Im}\,K(k\omega) = 0$ only if $\omega_1 = 0$, that is, only along the imaginary axis. We consider then, the real quantity,

$$K(k, i\alpha) = -\frac{4\pi e^2}{\hbar k^2} \int_0^{\infty} d\omega'\; S(k\omega')\, \frac{2\omega'}{\alpha^2 + \omega'^2}$$

which is nonvanishing, since all quantities in the integrand are positive. Since $K^{-1}(k\omega)$ is analytic in the upper half of the complex plane, it satisfies a set of Kramers-Kronig relations directly analogous to (A-36a) and (A-36b).

We next consider the analytic properties of $\varepsilon(k\omega)$. We have

$$\frac{1}{\varepsilon(k\omega)} - 1 = \frac{4\pi e^2}{\hbar k^2} \int_0^{\infty} d\omega'\; S(k\omega')\, \frac{2\omega'}{\omega^2 - \omega'^2}$$

$\varepsilon(k\omega)$ will be analytic in the upper half-plane provided $1/\varepsilon(k\omega)$ has no zeros there. Again taking the imaginary parts of the above equation, one sees that $1/\varepsilon(k\omega)$ can be zero only if $\omega = i\alpha$. We further have

$$\frac{1}{\varepsilon(k, i\alpha)} = 1 - \frac{8\pi e^2}{\hbar k^2} \int_0^{\infty} d\omega'\, \frac{S(k\omega')\omega'}{\omega'^2 + \alpha^2}$$

The integral on the right-hand side is a maximum at $\alpha = 0$. We conclude, then, that $\varepsilon(k\omega)$ will be analytic in the upper half of the complex plane provided

$$1 > \frac{8\pi e^2}{\hbar k^2} \int_0^\infty d\omega' \, \frac{S(k\omega')}{\omega'}$$

or, what is equivalent, provided

$$\varepsilon(k, 0) \geq 0$$

For an electron gas in the long-wavelength limit, it is possible to prove that $\varepsilon(k, 0) \geq 0$, so that in this limit $\varepsilon(k\omega)$ is indeed analytic in the upper half of the complex plane. Where this condition is satisfied, one has also a set of Kramers-Kronig relations for $\varepsilon(k\omega)$ which take the form

$$\text{Re } \varepsilon(k\omega) - 1 = \frac{1}{\pi} P \int_{-\infty}^{\infty} \text{Im } \varepsilon(k\omega') \, \frac{d\omega'}{\omega' - \omega} \tag{A-38a}$$

$$\text{Im } \varepsilon(k\omega) = \frac{1}{\pi} P \int_{-\infty}^{\infty} [1 - \text{Re } \varepsilon(k\omega')] \, \frac{d\omega'}{\omega' - \omega} \tag{A-38b}$$

A few fundamental assumptions have been interwoven in the scheme of discussions cited above. The physical principle of causality may be something one must rely upon; the energy-conservation principle will guarantee the finiteness of $K(\mathbf{r}, t)$ for all positive t; and the translational invariance holds true for a large class of physical systems. Nonetheless we may encounter physical examples for which linear response functions violate the causal requirement, or dynamical instabilities are indicated. Here we see a breakdown of the linearity assumption; the linear response function can no longer describe the behavior of the system correctly. The onset of such an instability may be regarded as indicating a possible phase transition; such problems have recently attracted the interest of many physicists.[1]

References

1. For example, L. P. Kadanoff and P. C. Martin, *Phys. Rev.*, 124, 670 (1961); N. D. Mermin, *Ann. Phys. (N. Y.)*, 18, 421, 454 (1962).

Appendix C

THE RPA CALCULATION OF THE GROUND-STATE ENERGY

When we summed the lowest-order polarization diagrams in Fig. 3-15 to obtain the RPA dielectric constant, we indicated the equivalence of the RPA calculation and the Gell-Mann and Brueckner[1] selected summation of the ring diagrams. We now demonstrate the equivalence of the two approaches by calculating the ground-state energy in the random phase approximation.

The ground-state energy in the RPA is readily obtained with the aid of (3-129) and (3-130):

$$E_{RPA} = E^{(0)} - \sum_{k} \int_{0}^{e^2} \frac{d\alpha}{\alpha} \left\{ \int_{0}^{\infty} \hbar (d\omega/2\pi) \operatorname{Im} \left[\frac{1}{\varepsilon_{RPA}(k\omega)} \right] + \frac{2\pi N\alpha}{k^2} \right\} \tag{A-39}$$

In order to get the correlation energy per electron, let us subtract from (A-39) the ground-state energy in the Hartree-Fock approximation,

$$E_{HF} = E^{(0)} - \sum_{k} \int_{0}^{e^2} \frac{d\alpha}{\alpha} \left\{ \int_{0}^{\infty} \hbar (d\omega/2\pi) \operatorname{Im} \left[\frac{1}{\varepsilon_{HF}(k\omega)} \right] + \frac{2\pi N\alpha}{k^2} \right\}$$

and divide by the number of the electrons N, to obtain

$$E^{RPA}_{corr} \equiv (E_{RPA} - E_{HF})/N$$

$$= - \frac{\hbar}{2\pi N} \sum_{k} \int_{0}^{e^2} \frac{d\alpha}{\alpha} \int_{0}^{\infty} d\omega \operatorname{Im} \left[\frac{1}{\varepsilon_{RPA}(k\omega)} - \frac{1}{\varepsilon_{HF}(k\omega)} \right]$$

$$E_{corr}^{RPA} = -\frac{\hbar}{2\pi N}\sum_k \int_0^{e^2}\frac{d\alpha}{\alpha}\int_0^{\infty} d\omega \, \mathrm{Im}\left[\frac{1}{1+4\pi\alpha_o(k\omega)} - 1 + 4\pi\alpha_o(k\omega)\right]$$

$$= -\frac{\hbar}{2\pi N}\sum_k \int_0^{e^2}\frac{d\alpha}{\alpha}\int_0^{\infty} d\omega \, \mathrm{Im}\, A(k\omega)$$

$$= \sum_k E(k) \qquad \text{(A-40)}$$

where

$$A(k\omega) = \frac{1}{1+4\pi\alpha_o(k\omega)} - 1 + 4\pi\alpha_o(k\omega) \qquad \text{(A-41)}$$

and

$$E(k) = -\frac{\hbar}{2\pi N}\int_0^{e^2}\frac{d\alpha}{\alpha}\int_0^{\infty} d\omega \, \mathrm{Im}\left[\frac{1}{1+4\pi\alpha_o(k\omega)} - 1 + 4\pi\alpha_o(k\omega)\right]$$

$$= -\frac{\hbar}{2\pi N}\int_0^{e^2}\frac{d\alpha}{\alpha}\int_0^{\infty} d\omega \, \mathrm{Im}\, A(k\omega) \qquad \text{(A-42)}$$

As is clear from our previous discussions, for small k the function $A(k\omega)$ possesses two kinds of singularities in the complex ω plane; one, a cut from $\omega = 0$ to $\omega_{max} \cong kv_o$ associated with the continuum of the electron-hole pair excitations; the other, the plasmon pole located above the pair continuum at $\omega = \omega_k$ (see Fig. A-2). We also recall that $A(k\omega)$ has been calculated with retarded boundary conditions, so that the frequencies ω in (3-144) have been assumed to contain a small positive imaginary part $i\delta$. To make this point explicit, we write $A^+(k\omega)$ for the retarded $A(k\omega)$. In particular, $A^+(k\omega)$ is analytic in the upper half of the complex ω plane, as we have argued for $K(k\omega)$ and $1/\varepsilon(k\omega)$.

Formally it is equally possible to consider a response function with *advanced* boundary conditions. Such an $A(k\omega)$ deserves the symbol $A^-(k\omega)$, and for this, $4\pi\alpha_o^-(k\omega)$ must be given by

$$4\pi\alpha_o^-(k\omega) = \frac{4\pi e^2}{\hbar k^2}\sum_{p\sigma} n_{p\sigma}(1 - n_{p+k\sigma})\left\{\frac{1}{\omega + \omega(p,k) - i\delta} - \frac{1}{\omega - \omega(p,k) - i\delta}\right\}$$

(A-43)

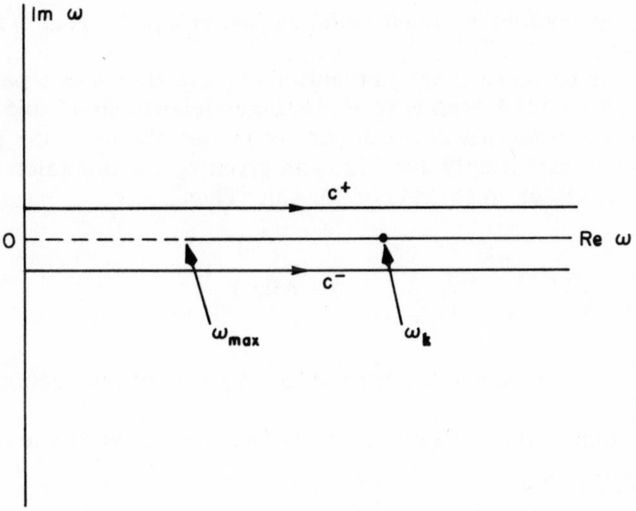

Fig. A-2

It is clear that $A^-(k\omega)$ is analytic in the lower half of the complex ω plane, and we also see from (3-144) and (A-43) that $A^-(k\omega)$ is just the complex conjugate of $A^+(k\omega)$. In other words, the imaginary part of $A^+(k\omega)$ can be expressed in terms of $A^+(k\omega)$ and $A^-(k\omega)$ as

$$\text{Im } A^+(k\omega) = \frac{1}{2i}\left[A^+(k\omega) - A^-(k\omega)\right] \qquad \text{(A-44)}$$

Equation (A-42) becomes

$$E(k) = -\frac{\hbar}{4\pi i N}\int_0^{e^2}\frac{d\alpha}{\alpha}\int_0^{\infty} d\omega \left[A^+(k\omega) - A^-(k\omega)\right]$$

$$= -\frac{\hbar}{4\pi i N}\int_0^{e^2}\frac{d\alpha}{\alpha}\int_{c^+} d\omega\, A^+(k\omega)$$

$$+\frac{\hbar}{4\pi i N}\int_0^{e^2}\frac{d\alpha}{\alpha}\int_{c^-} d\omega\, A^-(k\omega) \qquad \text{(A-45)}$$

The paths of ω integration in (A-45) are clear. The contour c^+ must be taken from 0 to ∞ just above the real ω axis, in such a way that all the singularities of $A^+(k\omega)$ lie below the path of integration; in the same way, the contour c^- must be taken just below the real ω axis [cf. Fig. A-2].

In fact, having taken these precautions on the choice of a path of integration, we do not even have to distinguish between A^+ and A^-; the distinction is automatically taken care of by our choice of the integration paths; we may simply use $A(\mathbf{k}\omega)$ as given by the omission of the δ's appearing either in (3-144) or (A-43). Then

$$E(k) = \frac{\hbar}{4\pi i N} \int_0^{e^2} \frac{d\alpha}{\alpha} \int_{c^- - c^+} d\omega \; A(k\omega) \tag{A-46}$$

The path $c^- - c^+$ means going from 0 to ∞ by c^- and then returning by c^+.

We now distort the contour in the following way. We first remark that

$$\int_{c^- - c^+} = \int_{c_1} + \int_{c_2} \tag{A-47}$$

where c_1 and c_2 are given in Fig. A-3. The physical meaning of the separate contributions from c_1 and c_2 is clear. For long wavelengths,

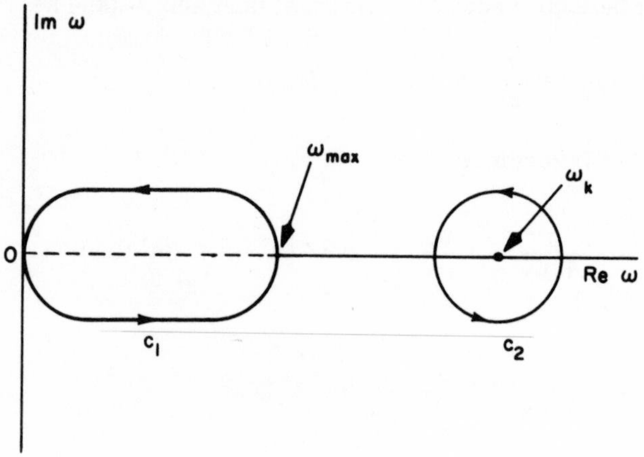

Fig. A-3

c_2 gives the plasmon contribution (indeed, the plasmon zero-point energy) and c_1 is the contribution of the pair continuum to the correlation energy; the latter may be directly identified with the contribution made by the residual particle interaction, H_{rp}, in the BP approach. Detailed calculation (Nozieres and Pines[2]) then shows that the long-wavelength contributions are just those given by $E_c^{l.r.}(\beta)$, Eq. (3-94).

Another fruitful distortion of the contour is illustrated in Fig. A-4. As is clear, we have

$$\int_{c^- - c^+} + \int_{c_3} + \int_{c_\infty^+} + \int_{c_\infty^-} = 0$$

As $\omega \to \infty$, $4\pi\alpha_0(k\omega)$ approaches zero faster than $1/\omega$. So, as (A-41) shows, $A(k\omega)$ approaches zero faster than $1/\omega^2$, which is sufficient to guarantee

$$\int_{c_\infty^+} = \int_{c_\infty^-} = 0$$

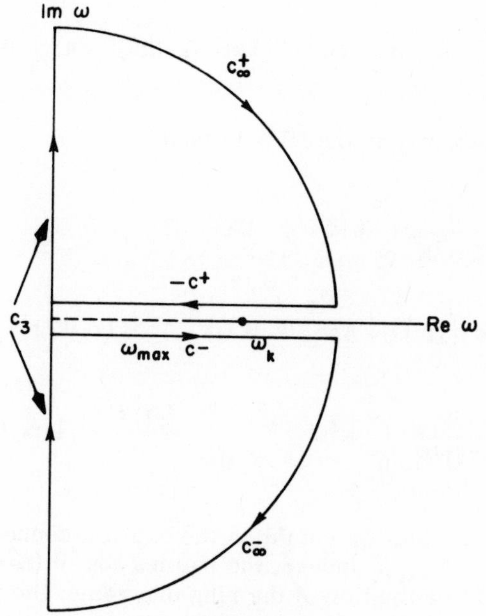

Fig. A-4

Hence we have

$$E(k) = -\frac{\hbar}{4\pi i N}\int_0^{e^2}\frac{d\alpha}{\alpha}\int_{c_3} d\omega\, A(k\omega)$$

or writing

$$\omega = i\lambda k$$

we obtain

$$E(k) = -\frac{\hbar}{4\pi N}\int_0^{e^2}\frac{d\alpha}{\alpha}\int_{-\infty}^{\infty} kd\lambda\, A(k, ik\lambda)$$

$$= -\frac{\hbar k}{4\pi N}\int_0^{e^2}\frac{d\alpha}{\alpha}\int_{-\infty}^{\infty} d\lambda\left[\frac{1}{1+4\pi\alpha_o(k, ik\lambda)} - 1 + 4\pi\alpha_o(k, ik\lambda)\right]$$

We perform the α integration first; since $4\pi\alpha_o(k, ik\lambda)$ is proportional to the coupling constant α, we obtain

$$E(k) = \frac{\hbar k}{4\pi N}\int_{-\infty}^{\infty} d\lambda\,\left\{\ln\left[1 + 4\pi\alpha_o(k, ik\lambda)\right] - 4\pi\alpha_o(k, ik\lambda)\right\} \qquad \text{(A-48)}$$

The correlation energy in the RPA is then

$$E_{corr}^{RPA} = \frac{\hbar}{(2\pi)^3 N}\int_0^{\infty} k^3 dk \int_{-\infty}^{\infty} d\lambda$$

$$\times \left\{\ln\left[1 + 4\pi\alpha_o(k, ik\lambda)\right] - 4\pi\alpha_o(k, ik\lambda)\right\} \qquad \text{(A-49a)}$$

$$= \frac{\hbar}{(2\pi)^3 N}\int_0^{\infty} k^3 dk \int_{-\infty}^{\infty}\sum_{n=2}^{\infty}\frac{(-1)^{n-1}}{n}\left[4\pi\alpha_o(k, ik\lambda)\right]^n \qquad \text{(A-49b)}$$

It is in this fashion that we establish the explicit connection with the GB calculation of E_{corr}. Indeed, the summation in (A-49b) just corresponds to the GB summation of the ring diagrams; the term involving $[4\pi\alpha_o(k, ik\lambda)]^2$, for instance, comes from the second-order polarization diagram, Fig. 3-10b. In fact, one can make the identification

$$4\pi\alpha_o(k, ik\lambda) = \left(\frac{4}{9\pi}\right)^{1/3}\frac{r_s}{\pi^2 q}\, Q_q(\lambda/v_o)$$

where $Q_q(u)$ has been defined by GB as

$$Q_q(u) = \int dp \int_{-\infty}^{\infty} dt\; e^{ituq} \exp\left\{-|t|\left(\frac{1}{2}q^2 + q\cdot p\right)\right\}$$

and

$$q = k/k_o$$

The result of the calculation (A-49) is once again

$$E_{corr}^{RPA} = 0.062 \ln r_s - 0.142 \quad \text{rydberg} \tag{A-50}$$

in the high-density limit.

References

1. M. Gell-Mann and K. A. Brueckner, *Phys. Rev.*, 106, 364 (1957).
2. P. Nozieres and D. Pines, *Phys. Rev.*, 111, 442 (1958).